VOL 2

Experience
Chemistry

SAVVAS
LEARNING COMPANY

FLINN SCIENTIFIC

We are excited and proud to partner with Flinn Scientific in the development of this highly innovative program. Flinn Scientific supports science educators in opening young minds to the challenges and joys of scientific discovery.

The cover shows bismuth, a commonly used, naturally occurring metal that has some unique properties. The layered, hollowed-out shape of crystallized bismuth is typical of "hopper crystals." The multiple colors of a bismuth crystal are caused by differences in the oxide layer that forms on its surface. Sebastian Janicki/Shutterstock; Bkgd: Sylverarts Vectors/Shutterstock

Christopher Moore, Ph.D. is the Dr. George F. Haddix Community Chair in Physical Science at the University of Nebraska Omaha, where he directs programs for pre- and in-service secondary chemistry and physics teachers. Holding an M.S. in applied physics and a Ph.D. in chemistry from Virginia Commonwealth University, Dr. Moore has worked as a physical science teacher at several secondary schools in Virginia, as a professional materials scientist, and as a scholar of and consultant on science education. His education research focuses on the development of scientific reasoning and expert-like science practice abilities, and his materials science research focuses on electronic materials for devices. He is the author of the books *Teaching Science Thinking: Using Scientific Reasoning in the Classroom* and *Creating Scientists: Teaching and Assessing Science Practice for the NGSS.*

Michael Wysession, Ph.D. is a Professor of Earth and Planetary Sciences at Washington University in St. Louis and Executive Director of The Teaching Center. Author of more than 100 science and science education publications, Dr. Wysession was awarded the prestigious National Science Foundation Presidential Faculty Fellowship and Packard Foundation Fellowship for his research in geophysics, primarily focused on using seismic tomography to determine the forces driving plate tectonics. Dr. Wysession is also a leader in geoscience literacy and education; he is the chair of the Earth Science Literacy Initiative, author of several popular video lectures on geoscience in The Great Courses series, and a lead writer of the Next Generation Science Standards.

Consulting Author

Bryn Lutes, Ph.D. is a chemist, technology translator, and educator. Holding a Ph.D. in organometallic chemistry, Dr. Lutes has worked both in and out of the classroom to help faculty incorporate active-learning techniques and technology to support student learning. She currently teaches General Chemistry for post-baccalaureate premedical students, Quantitative Reasoning, and Inorganic Chemistry Laboratory, where she continues to explore and incorporate active-learning and technology-assisted pedagogies.

CONSULTANT AND REVIEWERS

Program Consultant

Tanya Katovich is a chemistry educator and consultant. In 2015, she received the Davidson Award, presented annually by the Chemical Industry Council of Illinois to an outstanding chemistry teacher in Illinois. In 2017, Tanya became an Illinois finalist for the Presidential Award for Excellence in Mathematics and Science Teaching (PAEMST). She currently serves as the Vice-President and a member of the board of directors for the nonprofit organization Northern Illinois Science Educators (NISE).

Academic Reviewers

Aida Awad
Adjunct Instructor
American Intercontinental University
Buckeye, AZ

Nicole Bouvier-Brown, Ph.D.
Associate Professor of Chemistry & Biochemistry
Loyola Marymount University
Los Angeles, CA

Drew Budner, Ph.D.
Assistant Professor of Chemistry
Coastal Carolina University
Conway, SC

Thomas Bussey, Ph.D.
Assistant Teaching Professor
Department of Chemistry & Biochemistry
University of California, San Diego
La Jolla, CA

Stephen Contakes, Ph.D.
Associate Professor of Chemistry
Westmont College
Santa Barbara, CA

Michael Everest, Ph.D.
Professor of Chemistry
Westmont College
Santa Barbara, CA

Alison J. Frontier, Ph.D.
Professor of Chemistry
University of Rochester
Rochester, NY

Tiffany Hayden, Ph.D.
Associate Professor of Chemistry
Erskine College
Due West, SC

Hasan Palandoken, Ph.D.
Associate Professor
Department of Chemistry & Biochemistry
California Polytechnic State University
San Luis Obispo, CA

Robert Senter, Ph.D.
Instructor and Lab Coordinator
Department of Chemistry & Biochemistry
Loyola Marymount University
Los Angeles, CA

Amanda Silberstein, Ph.D.
Assistant Professor of Chemistry
Westmont College
Santa Barbara, CA

Harry A. Stern, Ph.D.
Center for Integrated Research Computing
University of Rochester
Rochester, NY

Shanju Zhang, Ph.D.
Associate Professor
Department of Chemistry & Biochemistry
California Polytechnic State University
San Luis Obispo, CA

Teacher Reviewers

Scot Abel
Science Curriculum Coordinator
DC Everest Area School District
Weston, WI

Gregory Aniol
Chemistry Teacher
Riverside Unified School District
Riverside, CA

Ed Bolton
Chemistry Teacher
Marquette High School
Chesterfield, MO

Manny Colon
Science Department Chair/
 Science and Engineering
 Teacher
University Preparatory School
Victorville, CA

Jenn M. Corcoran
Chemistry Teacher
Naugatuck High School
Naugatuck, CT

Karl Craddock
Science Department Chair
William Fremd High School
Palatine, IL

Stephanie Farmer
Chemistry Teacher
Dougherty Valley High School
San Ramon, CA

Jodi Fertoli
Chemistry Teacher
Staten Island Technical High
 School
Staten Island, NY

Rhonda Frohn
Chemistry Teacher
Conejo Valley Unified School
 District
Thousand Oaks, CA

Sean Gilbert
Chemistry Teacher
Leuzinger High School
Lawndale, CA

Martin Goldman
Chemistry Teacher
Edison High School
Edison, NJ

Rodger Golgart
Chemistry Teacher
Grand Terrace High School
Grand Terrace, CA

Ricardo Gutierrez
Biology/Earth Science Teacher
Temescal Canyon High School
Lake Elsinore, CA

Ava Hughes
Chemistry Teacher
Northwest High School
Cedar Hill, MO

Jessica Johnson
Chemistry Teacher
Jackson Public Schools
Jackson, MS

Brittney Kang
Science Teacher
Portola High School
Irvine, CA

Katie Keeler
Chemistry Teacher
Newbury Park High School
Newbury Park, CA

Kathryn Nelson, MEd, NBCT
Science Department Chair
Sylvania Northview High School
Sylvania, OH

Natalie Nevi
Chemistry Teacher
Norwin High School
North Huntingdon, PA

Ayanna Pantallion
Chemistry Teacher
Santa Monica-Malibu Unified
 School District
Santa Monica, CA

Kurt Rogers
Chemistry Teacher
Northern Highlands High
 School
Allendale, NJ

Michelle Tindall
K–12 Curriculum Coordinator
Birmingham Public Schools
Birmingham, MI

Susan Todd
Chemistry Teacher
Claxton High School
Claxton, Georgia

Dawn Toth
Chemistry Teacher
Redlands Unified School District
Redlands, CA

Amanda Waterfield
Chemistry Teacher
Victor Valley Unified School
 District
Victorville, CA

Lab Review
All labs in the program
were developed and
tested by **FLINN**
SCIENTIFIC

PROGRAM CONTENTS

STORYLINE 3

The Chemistry of Climate Change   2

ANCHORING PHENOMENON Why are we seeing more extreme weather?

GO ONLINE to find hands-on and virtual labs, CER and Modeling activities, and other resources — authentic readings, videos, and animations — that complete the Experiences.

GO ONLINE to find hands-on and virtual labs, CER and Modeling activities, and other resources — authentic readings, videos, and animations — that complete the Experiences.

ASSESSMENTS

- Pre/Post-Test
- End-of-Course Test
- Experience Notebook Problem Bank

STORYLINE 3
- Quizzes
- 3-D Assessments
- Online Problem Bank

STORYLINE 4
- Quizzes
- 3-D Assessments
- Online Problem Bank
- Benchmark 3-D Assessment

STORYLINE 5
- Quizzes
- 3-D Assessments
- Online Problem Bank
- Benchmark 3-D Assessment

FLINN SCIENTIFIC
PERFORMANCE-BASED ASSESSMENTS

STORYLINE 3
- Cartesian Divers
- Microhabitat in a Bottle
- Climate Change and the Carbon Cycle

STORYLINE 4
- Reaction Rates and Equilibrium
- Quantitative Analysis of Acid Rain
- Calcium Carbonate and Shell Production

STORYLINE 5
- Battery Challenge
- Prepare and Characterize Biodiesel
- Natural Radiation
- Make the Chemistry Lab Greener

FLINN SCIENTIFIC
INQUIRY LABS

STORYLINE 3
- Compressibility
- Relationships Between Gas Variables
- The Ideal Gas Law
- Gas Diffusion
- Feedback and Climate Change
- Energy in the Atmosphere
- Albedo and Composition of Earth's Surface

- How Melting Ice Affects Sea Level
- Observe Air Pollution
- Carbon Dioxide and Its Role in Climate
- How Nature Records Changes in Climate
- Human Activity and Carbon Emissions
- Model Climate Change with Melting Ice
- Climate Change and Keeping Cool
- Solar Cell Technology

STORYLINE 4
- Reaction Rates: Iodine Clock
- Collision Theory
- Explore Chemical Equilibrium
- Supersaturation and Thermodynamics
- Measure pH with Indicators
- Measure Acid Strength
- Titrations—The Study of Acid-Base Chemistry
- Analysis of Buffer Solutions and Ranges
- The pH of Seawater
- Carbon Dioxide Levels in Water
- Ocean Currents
- The Fate of Carbonate in Acidifying Oceans

STORYLINE 5
- Explore Iron Corrosion
- Metal Activity
- Build a Micro Battery
- Investigate Different Hydrocarbons
- Ester Synthesis
- Protein and Amino Acid Tests
- Radioactive Decay
- Nuclear Energy
- Nuclear Radiation and Shielding
- Toxicity of Road Deicers
- Green Chemistry Analysis of a Reaction
- How to Recycle Polylactic Acid Plastics

FLINN SCIENTIFIC
ENGINEERING DESIGN CHALLENGES

STORYLINE 3
- What's in a Container?
- Design a Green Roof

STORYLINE 4
- Use Equilibrium for a Commercial Application
- Design a Natural pH Indicator
- Design a Model of Ocean Acidification

STORYLINE 5
- Polymers: Bouncy Balls
- Uses and Production of Ash Water
- Plastic from Biowaste

ANIMATIONS

STORYLINE 3
- What Causes Pressure Changes in a Gas
- Why Are There No Ideal Gases?
- Patterns in the Wind
- The Carbon Cycle
- Energy to Earth
- Cold and White: A Reinforcing Feedback Loop
- Bad Vibes From Greenhouse Gases
- Can Volcanoes Change the Climate?
- Renewable Energy and Energy Storage

STORYLINE 4
- Reaction Rate and Molecular Collisions
- Looking Closely at Collisions and Activation Energy
- Conductivity of Strong and Weak Acids
- Buffer Systems
- El Niño, La Niña, and Heat Storage
- Carbon Dioxide, Ocean Acidification, and Shell Formation

STORYLINE 5
- Oxidation and Reduction at the Atomic Scale
- Energy Conversion in a Voltaic Cell
- Polymerization
- Sugar, Starch, and Glycogen
- Uranium Enrichment
- From Feedstocks to Medicine
- How Catalysts Promote Greener Chemistry

INTERACTIVITIES

STORYLINE 3
- Going for a Hike
- Wetlands and the Carbon Cycle
- Flow of Energy and Greenhouse Gases
- Climate Change and Fire

STORYLINE 4
- Reaction Rates and Activation Energy
- Exploring Acid Strength and Concentration
- Ocean pH

STORYLINE 5
- Identifying Types of Organic Compounds
- Comparing Nuclear and Chemical Reactions
- Paper Mill Wastewater Treatment

VIRTUAL LABS

STORYLINE 3
- Gas Behavior in Popping Candy
- Sampling the Past
- Glaciers on Rainier

STORYLINE 4
- Equilibrium Shifting
- Explore Buffer Systems
- The Effect of Ocean Acidification on Shells

STORYLINE 5
- Modeling Gemstone Color Formation
- Protein Structure and Food Design
- Energy-Efficient Ammonia Production

VIDEOS
- Anchoring Phenomenon
- Investigative Phenomenon
- Lab Demo
- Lab Summary
- Virtual Nerd Math Support

ADDITIONAL RESOURCES
- Authentic Reading
- Claim-Evidence-Reasoning
- Modeling
- Analyzing Data
- Discussion Rubric
- Peer Review Rubric
- Writing About Science
- Problem-Based Learning
- Virtual Reality
- Practice Problems
- PhET Simulations

End-of-Book Resources

The Chemistry of Climate Change

Why are we seeing more extreme weather?

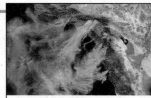

Investigation 9
The Behavior of Gases

Investigation 10
Weather and Climate

Investigation 11
Global Climate Change

ANCHORING PHENOMENON

Inquiry Launch Look at the image of a pedestrian trying to make her way across a street during a blizzard. How do you think extreme weather events like this blizzard will be different in the future? Why?

A common misconception about climate change is that cold weather events will decrease in frequency or severity. Propose an explanation for why the frequency and severity of future extreme weather events are likely to only increase and become more extreme. ✏

....

....

....

....

....

....

🖥 **GO ONLINE** to engage with real-world phenomena. Watch the anchoring phenomenon video and preview the optional **problem-based learning experience**.

INVESTIGATIVE PHENOMENON

GO ONLINE to Engage with real-world phenomena by watching a video and to complete a modeling interactive worksheet.

What causes the Santa Ana winds?

The Behavior of Gases

The Santa Ana winds are strong, dry winds that originate inland in the Great Basin and blow across southern California out toward the ocean. Often called "devil winds," they result in dangerous gusts that are hot and dry, contributing to increased wildfires during early autumn. Once you have viewed the Investigative Phenomenon video and completed a modeling exercise to draft an explanation for the cause of wind, answer these reflection questions.

1) **CCC Energy and Matter** Wind consists of matter in motion. Where do you think the energy comes from that produces wind, putting matter in motion? ✏️

....

....

....

2) **SEP Develop a Model** On the map, sketch a model for the Santa Ana winds, starting with where they originate and in which direction they blow. ✏️

Properties of Gases

 GO ONLINE to Explore and Explain the properties of gases and how the kinetic theory is used to explain them.

Compressibility

Unlike a solid or a liquid, a gas can expand to fill its container, leaving significant volumes of empty space between gas particles. The volume of this empty space is significantly larger than the volume of all the gas particles put together. All of this empty space also means that gases can easily be compressed or squeezed into a smaller volume. **Compressibility** is a measure of how much the volume of matter decreases under a certain amount of pressure.

◼ Because the molecules are far apart, gases are easily compressed as compared to solids and liquids.

Compressing a Gas Gases can be easily compressed because of the spaces between gas particles. As a result, the same amount of gas can fit into containers of many different sizes.

In a smaller container, the same number of particles are compressed in less volume. However, the volume is still mostly empty space.

(3) **SEP Plan an Investigation** Choosing the clothes that you will pack for a trip involves making choices based on the expected weather and the amount of volume available in your bag or suitcase. Design an experiment that would allow you to determine the relative compressibility of different types of clothing that range from bulky to compact. 🖊

....

....

Gas Pressure and Amount of Gas

You can use the kinetic theory to predict how a gas will respond to a change in conditions. Adding more gas particles to a rigid container does not change the volume, but it does affect the pressure. Because gas particles are in constant motion, adding more particles increases the gas pressure. With more particles, there are more collisions. This increase in collisions results in an increase in pressure.

The higher pressure leads to more collisions of particles with the walls of the container and with one another. If the pressure gets high enough, the container may rupture.

Adding Gas to a Container As you pump gas into a closed container (fixed volume), pressure increases as more particles are added.

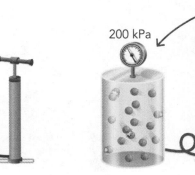

100 kPa 200 kPa 600 kPa

Pumping Air Into a Tire Air pumps increase tire pressure by moving outside air (gas particles) into the tire.

When you pull up on the handle, a one-way valve opens and allows outside air to flow into the chamber.

When pressing down on the handle, the top one-way valve closes while the bottom valve opens. The piston pushes the air in the chamber into the tire.

(4) SEP Design a Solution How could you change the design of the pump so that it increases the pressure in the tire with fewer strokes? ✏️

....

....

Gas Pressure and Volume

You can also increase gas pressure by decreasing its volume. When you compress the gas into a smaller amount of space, the particles are forced closer together. This closeness increases the likelihood of collisions and, therefore, the pressure goes up. The more compressed a gas is, the higher its pressure will be.

Pressing down on a piston requires someone or something to push. This push is equivalent to the pressure inside the cylinder. You have to push down harder to make the volume smaller.

Decreasing Volume As you push down on the handle, you decrease the volume of a cylinder containing gas, resulting in an increase of gas pressure. This higher pressure makes it harder to keep reducing the volume.

When the piston top is not moving, the pressure of the gas pushing up on the top is equal to the pressure from the piston top pushing down on the gas.

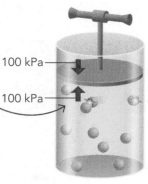

100 kPa

100 kPa

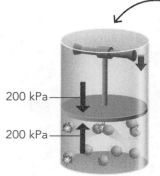

200 kPa

200 kPa

Pushing down and decreasing the volume of a fixed amount of gas leads to more collisions between gas particles as well as between gas particles and the inside walls of the container.

(5) **SEP Develop a Model** Bicycle tires will often burst when hitting a rock too fast. Sketch a model that can explain why the tire is likely to burst in this situation. ✏️

Gas Pressure and Temperature

Temperature is the average kinetic energy of the particles of a gas. Therefore, increasing the temperature causes the particles to move faster. Faster-moving particles increase the likelihood and force of a collision, and, therefore, the pressure goes up.

Increasing Temperature At constant volume, pressure and temperature are directly proportional. When temperature increases, pressure also increases due to the faster-moving particles.

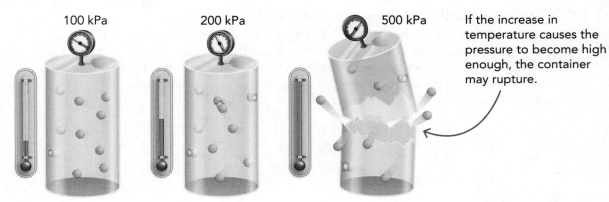

100 kPa   200 kPa   500 kPa

If the increase in temperature causes the pressure to become high enough, the container may rupture.

SEP Interpret Data The graph shows the pressure in a certain car tire as a function of temperature. Use the graph to determine how much a car's tire pressure could change in your region between January and July. ✎

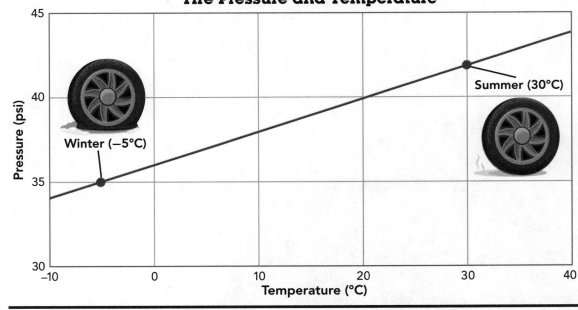

Tire Pressure and Temperature

Winter (−5°C)

Summer (30°C)

GO ONLINE to Elaborate on and Evaluate your knowledge of the properties of gases by completing the class discussion and data analysis activities.

In the modeling worksheet, you developed a model to explain how winds manifest as a result of the behavior of gases in the atmosphere. With a partner, complete the prompt below and then reevaluate your model.

⑦ **SEP Obtain and Evaluate Information** Look up data for the average January air temperatures in the Great Basin and Los Angeles. By comparing temperatures, what would this information alone suggest about the difference in air pressure between these two regions? If air moves from high pressure to low pressure, is this consistent with the direction of the Santa Ana winds? ✎

....

....

....

....

....

....

The Gas Laws

GO ONLINE to Explore and Explain the mathematical relationships among variables such as gas pressure, temperature, and volume of a gas.

Boyle's Law

Robert Boyle was the first person to systematically describe the relationship between the pressure and volume of a gas. **Boyle's law** states that when the temperature and number of particles in a gas are held constant, the volume (V) varies inversely with the pressure (P). In 1662, Boyle developed a mathematical model of this relationship as follows:

$$P_1 \times V_1 = P_2 \times V_2$$

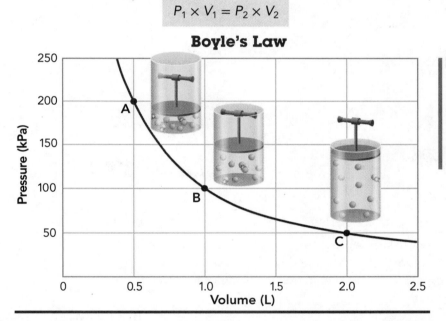

Pressure and Volume
As the volume increases, pressure decreases. Pressure is inversely proportional to volume. Inversely proportional means that as one increases the other decreases.

8 **SEP Analyze and Interpret Data** Use the graph to complete the table for points A, B, and C. Discuss with a partner the pattern you observe in this last column. Then, complete the row for point D (not shown on graph). ✏️

Using Boyle's Law			
Point	**V (L)**	**P (kPa)**	**$P \times V$ (kPa·L)**
A			
B			
C			
D	4.0		

Using Boyle's Law

A balloon contains 30.0 L of helium gas at 103 kPa. What is the volume of the helium when the balloon rises to an altitude where the pressure is only 25.0 kPa? (Assume that the temperature remains constant.)

ANALYZE List the knowns and the unknown.

Knowns	Unknown
$P_1 = 103$ kPa	$V_2 = ?$ L
$V_1 = 30.0$ L	
$P_2 = 25.0$ kPa	

CALCULATE Solve for the unknown.

Start with Boyle's Law.	$P_1 \times V_1 = P_2 \times V_2$
Isolate V_2 by dividing both sides by P_2.	$\dfrac{P_1 \times V_1}{P_2} = \dfrac{P_2 \times V_2}{P_2}$
Simplify the equation to isolate V_2.	$V_2 = \dfrac{P_1 \times V_1}{P_2}$
Substitute the known values into the equation and solve.	$V_2 = \dfrac{103 \text{ kPa} \times 30.0 \text{ L}}{25.0 \text{ kPa}} = 124 \text{ L}$

EVALUATE Does the result make sense?

A decrease in pressure at constant temperature must correspond to a proportional increase in volume. The calculated result agrees with both kinetic theory and the pressure-volume relationship. Additionally, the units have canceled correctly.

9 **SEP Use Mathematics** A gas with a volume of 4.00 L at a pressure of 205 kPa is allowed to expand to a volume of 12.0 L. What is the pressure in the container if the temperature remains constant? ✏️

GO ONLINE for more practice problems.

Cooling Balloons The photos show four balloons being dipped in a beaker of liquid nitrogen. As the air inside cools, the volume of each balloon shrinks so much that all four balloons fit inside the beaker.

Charles's Law

In 1787, French physicist Jacques Charles studied the effect of temperature on the volume of a gas at constant pressure. This relationship is called **Charles's law,** and it states that the volume (V) of a fixed mass of gas is directly proportional to its temperature (T) if the pressure is held constant. The mathematical expression of Charles's law is as follows:

$$\frac{V_1}{T_1} = \frac{V_2}{T_2}$$

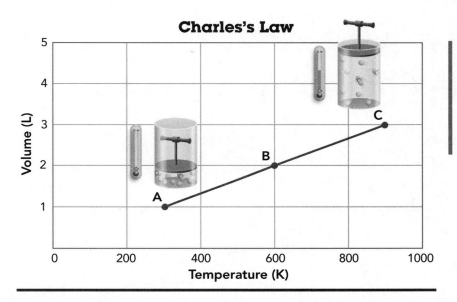

Charles's Law

Volume and Temperature If pressure and number of particles are held constant, expanding the volume increases the temperature, and compressing the volume decreases the temperature.

10 **SEP Interpret Data** Use the graph to complete the table for points A, B, and C. Discuss the pattern you observe in this column with a partner. ✏️

Using Charle's Law			
Point	*T* (K)	*V* (L)	*V/T* (L/K)
A	300		
B	600		
C	900		

Using Charles's Law

A balloon inflated in a room at 24°C has a volume of 4.00 L. The balloon is then heated to a temperature of 58°C. What is the new volume if the pressure remains constant?

ANALYZE List the knowns and the unknown.

Knowns	Unknown
$V_1 = 4.00$ L	$V_2 = ?$ L
$T_1 = 24$°C	
$T_2 = 58$°C	

CALCULATE Solve for the unknown.

Because you will use a gas law, start by expressing the temperatures in kelvins.

$T_1 = 24$°C $+ 273 = 297$ K
$T_2 = 58$°C $+ 273 = 331$ K

Write the equation for Charles's law.

$$\frac{V_1}{T_1} = \frac{V_2}{T_2}$$

Isolate V_2 by multiplying both sides by T_2 and simplifying the equation.

$$\frac{V_1}{T_1} \times T_2 = \frac{V_2}{\cancel{T_2}} \times \cancel{T_2} \qquad V_2 = \frac{V_1 \times T_2}{T_1}$$

Substitute the known values into the equation and solve.

$$V_2 = \frac{4.00 \text{ L} \times 331 \cancel{K}}{297 \cancel{K}} = 4.46 \text{ L}$$

EVALUATE Does the result make sense?

The volume increases as the temperature increases. This result agrees with both the kinetic theory and Charles's law. Additionally, the units have cancelled correctly.

11 **SEP Use Mathematics** If a sample of gas occupies 6.80 L at 325°C, what will its volume be at 25°C if the pressure does not change? ✏

GO ONLINE for more practice problems.

Absolute Zero

Charles made another interesting observation when he analyzed his data. When he extrapolated, or extended, the line formed in a graph of his data, he noticed that the line always intersects the temperature axis at −273.15°C. This happened no matter which gas he was investigating.

▶ Recognizing a pattern in the graphs, Charles discovered the coldest temperature possible.

In 1848, Scottish physicist Lord Kelvin devised an absolute temperature scale based on the intersection point Charles had observed. This scale is now known as the Kelvin scale. The intersection point (−273.15°C) was defined as absolute zero temperature (0 K) on the Kelvin scale. Using the kinetic theory of gases, scientists expect the motion of particles to decrease as the temperature is lowered. **Absolute zero** is the temperature at which all such motion stops.

(12) **SEP Interpret Data** A point shown on the graph represents the volume of 0.014 mol of CO_2 at 1 atm pressure and 0°C. Using this point and absolute zero, sketch a line on the graph that represents the volume versus temperature curve for CO_2. Make a prediction for the volume of CO_2 at 100°C and discuss your prediction with a classmate. ✏

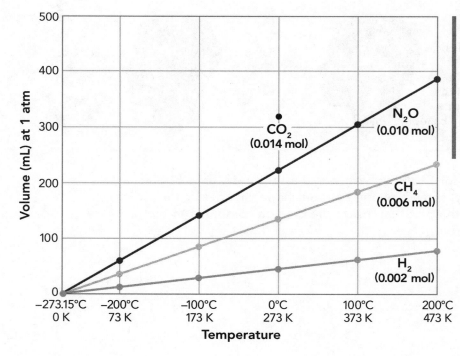

Volume and Temperature
The graphs show the volume as a function of temperature for different amounts of three gases at 1 atm pressure. All of the lines extrapolate to −273.15°C at V = 0 L, regardless of the type or amount of gas.

Understanding Constant Pressure

Why is a balloon a **constant pressure system?**

Pressure Balance A balloon is not a rigid container. The skin of the balloon is flexible, so the size of the balloon adjusts until **the pressure inside the balloon is exactly equal to the pressure outside the balloon.**

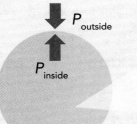

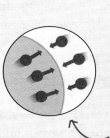

Pressure is a result of collisions. The **collisions of the air particles on the outside of the balloon must balance the collisions on the inside.** Otherwise, the balloon would collapse or expand.

Increasing Temperature Air particles move faster when heated. To keep the number of collisions constant, the particles must be farther apart. Therefore, **the volume expands, but the pressure inside remains the same as outside the balloon.**

Increasing Particles When you blow into a balloon, you add more air particles. **To keep the number of collisions the same, the volume expands, but the pressure inside remains the same** as outside the balloon.

(13) **SEP Develop a Model** Sketch a before-and-after model for a hot-air balloon. Specifically, show how the balloon shape changes as the air inside is heated and how the pressure inside the balloon compares to the pressure outside of the balloon. ✏️

Gay-Lussac's Law

Relationship Between Pressure and Temperature In 1802, French chemist Joseph Gay-Lussac discovered the relationship between the pressure and temperature of a gas. This relationship is called **Gay-Lussac's law,** which states that the pressure (*P*) of a fixed mass of gas is proportional to its temperature (*T*) if the volume is held constant. The mathematical expression of Gay-Lussac's law is as follows:

$$\frac{P_1}{T_1} = \frac{P_2}{T_2}$$

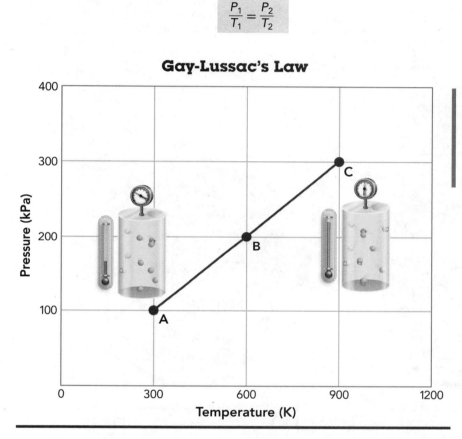

Gay-Lussac's Law

Pressure and Temperature For a gas at constant volume, the pressure is directly proportional to its temperature in Kelvin. If the temperature increases, the pressure increases.

(14) **SEP Analyze and Interpret Data** Using the graph, complete the table for points A, B, and C. Discuss with a partner the pattern you observe in the last column of the table. Then, complete the row for point D (not shown on graph). ✏️

Using Gay-Lussac's Law			
Point	P (kPa)	T (K)	P/T (kPa/K)
A	100		
B	200		
C	300		
D		1200	

Applying Gay-Lussac's Law Gay-Lussac's law can be applied to reduce the time it takes to cook food by using a pressure cooker. In an open container, the volume is not fixed, and steam (gaseous water) can easily expand. As a result, the pressure above the boiling liquid does not change. In a pressure cooker, the volume is constant, allowing an increase in pressure. The increase in pressure above the liquid leads to an increase in the boiling point of the liquid. The food can now be cooked at a hotter temperature, cooking it faster.

As the air is warmed by the steam, it expands. The pressure stays the same.

As the air is warmed by the steam, it cannot expand because the volume is fixed. The pressure increases.

Boiling Water in an Open Container If you heat water in a pot without a lid (an open system), the volume is not fixed, and steam (gaseous water) can easily expand and leave the system.

Boiling Water in a Closed Container In a pressure cooker, steam generated from heated water is trapped inside the constant-volume container.

(15) **SEP Obtain and Evaluate Information** Using an online resource, find the average pressure inside a pressure cooker. Based on that pressure, estimate the average temperature inside a pressure cooker. ✎

....

....

....

....

Combined Gas Law

When only the amount of gas is held constant, the **combined gas law** describes the relationship among pressure, volume, and temperature. This single expression combines Boyle's law, Charles's law, and Gay-Lussac's law.

The Relationship Between Pressure, Volume, and Temperature
Boyle's law, Charles's law, and Gay-Lussac's law can be mathematically combined to form a single equation called the combined gas law.

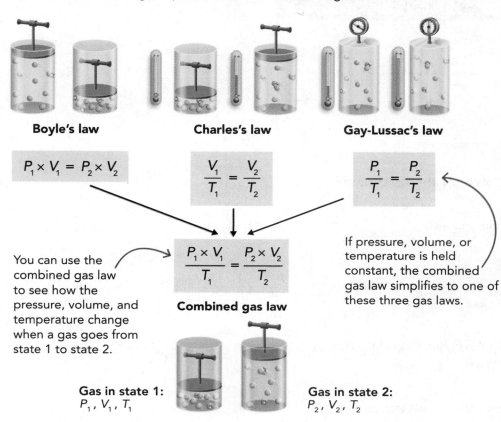

Boyle's law

$$P_1 \times V_1 = P_2 \times V_2$$

Charles's law

$$\frac{V_1}{T_1} = \frac{V_2}{T_2}$$

Gay-Lussac's law

$$\frac{P_1}{T_1} = \frac{P_2}{T_2}$$

You can use the combined gas law to see how the pressure, volume, and temperature change when a gas goes from state 1 to state 2.

$$\frac{P_1 \times V_1}{T_1} = \frac{P_2 \times V_2}{T_2}$$

Combined gas law

If pressure, volume, or temperature is held constant, the combined gas law simplifies to one of these three gas laws.

Gas in state 1:
P_1, V_1, T_1

Gas in state 2:
P_2, V_2, T_2

(16) **SEP Use Computational Thinking** A weather balloon rises high into the atmosphere. As the balloon ascends, the pressure on the balloon decreases as atmospheric pressure decreases. The temperature also drops. These two variables compete to either increase or decrease the volume of the balloon. Using the data in the table, determine whether pressure or temperature "wins." Explain if the balloon expands or contracts.

Altitude (m)	P (kPa)	T (K)
0	101.3	288
1000	89.88	282
2000	79.50	275
3000	70.12	277
4000	61.66	262
5000	54.05	256

Using the Combined Gas Law

The volume of a gas-filled balloon is 30.0 L at 313 K and 153 kPa pressure. What would the volume be at standard temperature and pressure (STP)?

ANALYZE List the knowns and the unknown.

Knowns	Unknown
$V_1 = 30.0$ L	$V_2 = ?$ L
$T_1 = 313$ K	
$P_1 = 153$ kPa	
$T_2 = 273$ K (standard temperature)	
$P_2 = 100$ kPa (standard pressure)	

CALCULATE Solve for the unknown.

State the combined gas law.

$$\frac{P_1 V_1}{T_1} = \frac{P_2 V_2}{T_2}$$

Rearrange the equation to isolate V_2 by multiplying both sides by T_2 and dividing both sides by P_2.

$$\frac{P_1 V_1}{T_1} \times \frac{T_2}{P_2} = \frac{P_2 V_2}{T_2} \times \frac{T_2}{P_2} \qquad V_2 = \frac{(P_1 \times V_1 \times T_2)}{(P_2 \times T_1)}$$

Substitute the known quantities into the equation and solve.

$$V_2 = \frac{(153 \text{ kPa} \times 30.0 \text{ L} \times 273 \text{ K})}{(100 \text{ kPa} \times 313 \text{ K})} = 40.0 \text{ L}$$

EVALUATE Does the result make sense?

A decrease in temperature and a decrease in pressure have opposite effects on the volume. To evaluate the increase in volume, multiply V_2 (30.0 L) by the ratio of P_1 to P_2 (1.51) and the ratio of T_1 to T_2 (0.872). The result is 40.0 L.

(17) **SEP Use Mathematics** A 5.00-L air sample has a pressure of 107 kPa at a temperature of −50.0°C. If the temperature is raised to 102°C and the volume expands to 7.00 L, what will the new pressure be? ✎

GO ONLINE for more practice problems.

Avogadro's Law

In 1811, Italian scientist Amedeo Avogadro hypothesized that any two samples of gas, even if the gases are different, will have the same volume when they are held at the same pressure and temperature. The relationship between the volume (*V*) of a gas and the number of moles of gas (*n*) is called **Avogadro's law** and is expressed as follows:

$$\frac{n_1}{V_1} = \frac{n_2}{V_2}$$

Exploring Avogadro's Law

What is the relationship **between moles, mass, and volume?**

Avogadro's Hypothesis
Avogadro hypothesized that any two **samples of gas containing the same number of particles (atoms or molecules) will have the same volume** when held at the same pressure and temperature. The size and mass of the particles does not matter.

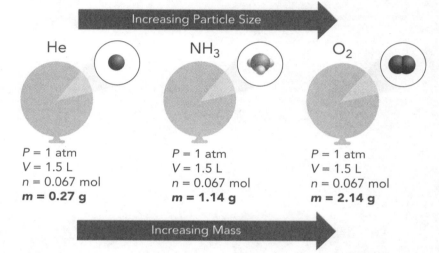

Increasing Particle Size

He   NH₃   O₂

$P = 1$ atm	$P = 1$ atm	$P = 1$ atm
$V = 1.5$ L	$V = 1.5$ L	$V = 1.5$ L
$n = 0.067$ mol	$n = 0.067$ mol	$n = 0.067$ mol
$m = 0.27$ g	**$m = 1.14$ g**	**$m = 2.14$ g**

Increasing Mass

A basketball contains approximately 7.5 L of gas. Three basketballs combined contain about one mole of gas particles. **The volume of one mole of gas (22.4 L) is called the molar volume (V_m).**

Even though the mass is very different, each gas has the same volume. Avogadro's hypothesis makes sense when you consider that the size of the gas particles is extremely small when compared to the distances between them.

Gas	V_m (L/mol)
He	22.434
O₂	22.97
NH₃	22.079

Avogadro's law is a good approximation, but it does not accurately model some gases. The actual molar volumes for He, O₂, and NH₃ are shown in the table.

---

(18) CCC Cause and Effect As the Avogadro's law infographic indicates, the molar volume of various gases at STP is defined as having a volume of 22.4 L. This is for ideal situations and mostly applies to gas particles that are very small. Would you expect to see a difference in actual molar volumes for different-sized gas particles? Explain your answer. ✏️

....

....

INVESTIGATIVE PHENOMENON

GO ONLINE to Elaborate on and Evaluate your knowledge of the gas laws by completing the peer review and engineering design activities.

In the modeling worksheet, you developed a model to explain how winds manifest as a result of the behavior of gases in the atmosphere. With a partner, complete the prompt below and then reevaluate your model.

19 **SEP Use Mathematical Thinking** Use Gay-Lussac's law to estimate the temperature change for a column of air moving from high altitude up in the Santa Ana Mountains to low altitude by the Pacific Ocean. Use authoritative online resources to obtain the data you need to use in your calculation. ✎

....

....

....

....

....

....

Ideal Gases

GO ONLINE to Explore and Explain how the behaviors of real gases differ from that of the hypothetical ideal gas.

Ideal Gas Law

Combining All Four Gas Laws A hypothetical gas that exactly obeys the kinetic model of gases is called an **ideal gas.** An ideal gas has particles of infinitesimal and insignificant size and no intermolecular attractive forces between the particles.

The **ideal gas law** describes the relationship among number of moles (n), pressure (P), volume (V), and temperature (T). The quantity $(P \times V)/(T \times n)$ is a constant for any ideal gas. This constant is called the ideal gas constant (R) and has a value of 8.31 (L·kPa)/(K·mol). The mathematical expression for the ideal gas law can be written in terms of the gas constant as follows:

$$\frac{PV}{Tn} = R, \text{ or } PV = nRT$$

Combining the Four Gas Laws The ideal gas law provides a relationship between the pressure, volume, number of moles, and temperature of any gas that obeys the kinetic model.

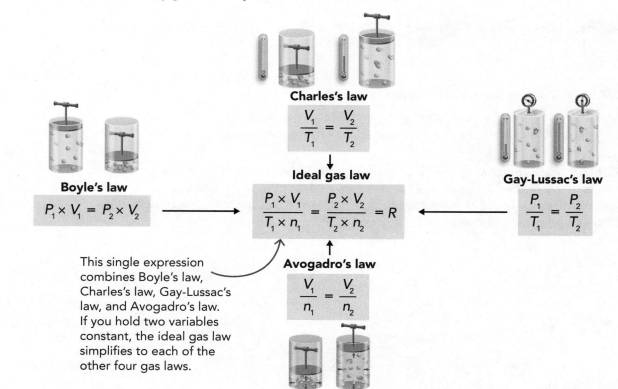

Charles's law
$$\frac{V_1}{T_1} = \frac{V_2}{T_2}$$

Ideal gas law

Boyle's law
$$P_1 \times V_1 = P_2 \times V_2$$

$$\frac{P_1 \times V_1}{T_1 \times n_1} = \frac{P_2 \times V_2}{T_2 \times n_2} = R$$

Gay-Lussac's law
$$\frac{P_1}{T_1} = \frac{P_2}{T_2}$$

Avogadro's law
$$\frac{V_1}{n_1} = \frac{V_2}{n_2}$$

This single expression combines Boyle's law, Charles's law, Gay-Lussac's law, and Avogadro's law. If you hold two variables constant, the ideal gas law simplifies to each of the other four gas laws.

Using the Ideal Gas Law

A deep underground cavern contains 2.24×10^6 L of methane gas (CH_4) at a pressure of 1.50×10^3 kPa and a temperature of 315 K. How many kilograms of CH_4 does the cavern contain?

ANALYZE List the knowns and the unknown.

Knowns		Unknown
$P = 1.50 \times 10^3$ kPa	$V = 2.24 \times 10^6$ L	$m = ?$ kg
$T = 315$ K	$R = 8.31$ (L•kPa)/(K•mol)	
molar mass$_{CH_4} = 16.0$ g		

CALCULATE Solve for the unknown.

State the ideal gas law. Rearrange the equation to isolate n.

$$P \times V = n \times R \times T \qquad n = \frac{(P \times V)}{(R \times T)}$$

Substitute the known quantities into the equation to find the number of moles of methane.

$$n = \frac{(1.50 \times 10^3 \text{ kPa}) \times (2.24 \times 10^6 \text{ L})}{(8.31 \text{ (L•kPa)/(K•mol)}) \times 315 \text{ K}} = 1.28 \times 10^6 \text{ mol } CH_4$$

Convert from moles to grams.

$$1.28 \times 10^6 \text{ mol } CH_4 \times \frac{(16.0 \text{ g } CH_4)}{1 \text{ mol } CH_4} = 2.05 \times 10^7 \text{ g } CH_4$$

Convert from grams to kilograms.

$$2.05 \times 10^7 \text{ g } CH_4 \times \frac{(1 \text{ kg})}{10^3 \text{ g}} = 2.05 \times 10^4 \text{ kg } CH_4$$

EVALUATE Does the result make sense?

Although the methane is compressed, its volume is still very large. Therefore, it is reasonable that the cavern contains a large mass of methane.

(20) **SEP Use Mathematics** A child's lungs can hold 2.20 L of air. How many grams of air do her lungs hold at a pressure of 102 kPa and a body temperature of 37°C? Use a molar mass of 29 g/mol for air, which is about 20% O_2 (32 g/mol) and 80% N_2 (28 g/mol). ✏️

GO ONLINE for more practice problems.

Applications of the Ideal Gas Law The ideal gas law can be used to find the molar volume and density of a gas if certain properties are known. When dealing with large amounts of gas, such as in the atmosphere, it's easier to work with gas densities and molar volumes, since the absolute volumes are very large. It's very difficult to know the volume and number of moles of the escaping gas, but the pressure and temperature are relatively easy to measure.

Rewriting the ideal gas law in terms of the molar volume (V_m) results in an expression with variables that are not dependent on the size of the system:

$$V_m = \frac{RT}{P}$$

Rewriting the ideal gas law in terms of the density (ρ) and molar mass (M) also results in an expression with variables that are not dependent on the size of the system:

$$\rho = \frac{PM}{RT}$$

(21) **SEP Use Mathematics** The CO_2 gas inside the rigid container of a fire extinguisher is held at a high pressure (5,700 kPa). Determine the molar volume and the density of the contained CO_2 gas if the fire extinguisher has been sitting at room temperature (298 K). ✎

Fire Extinguishers and the Ideal Gas Law Some fire extinguishers are filled with CO_2 gas. The dense CO_2 sinks in the less dense air, settling on top of the fire and smothering it.

Measuring the volume of gas escaping from a fire extinguisher is impossible, so we instead write the ideal gas law in terms of density.

Isobaric, Isovolumetric, and Isothermal Processes

The ideal gas law contains four variables that can vary independently, depending on the circumstances. When dealing with gases, it is important to isolate two of the variables to study the dependent relationship between the other two variables. For closed systems, the moles of gas are always constant. A closed-system process for which the pressure is held constant is called an **isobaric process.** A closed-system process for which the volume is held constant is an **isovolumetric process** (or isochoric process). A closed-system process that is held at constant temperature is an **isothermal process.**

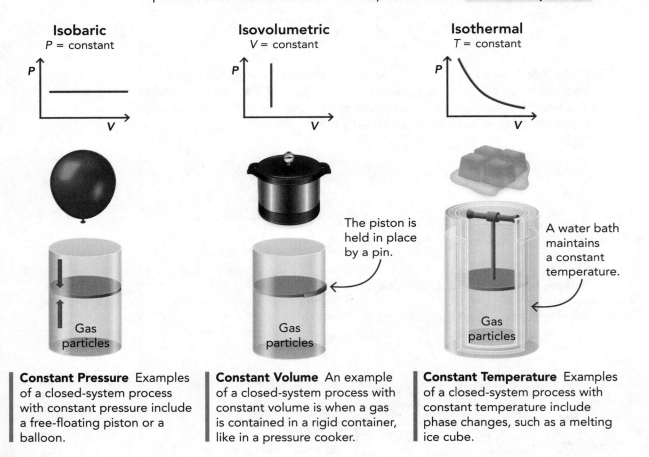

Isobaric	Isovolumetric	Isothermal
P = constant	V = constant	T = constant

The piston is held in place by a pin.

A water bath maintains a constant temperature.

Constant Pressure Examples of a closed-system process with constant pressure include a free-floating piston or a balloon.

Constant Volume An example of a closed-system process with constant volume is when a gas is contained in a rigid container, like in a pressure cooker.

Constant Temperature Examples of a closed-system process with constant temperature include phase changes, such as a melting ice cube.

(22) **SEP Plan an Investigation** You are asked to determine the number of moles in an unknown sample of gas housed in a cylinder with a movable piston. You look around the lab, but you cannot find a thermometer. Describe the experiment you could perform to answer the research question without measuring temperature. Which type of process would you use? ✏

....

....

....

Real Gases

Intermolecular Forces and the Size of Gas Particles The kinetic theory ignores the sizes of gas particles and their intermolecular forces. In the kinetic theory, the container's entire volume is available for molecular motion. However, the molecules of actual gases, referred to as real gases, have small but measurable volumes. Similarly, molecules of real gases also experience small but measurable intermolecular attractive forces.

Underestimated Volume As the volume of a gas is decreased or the pressure increased, more and more of the total volume becomes unavailable for molecular motion. Therefore, the ideal gas law underestimates the volume.

Overestimated Pressure Similarly, a decrease in the gas volume or an increase in the pressure causes the intermolecular distances to shorten. Because the molecules are closer together, the intermolecular forces become more significant. This reduces the number of collisions between molecules and the container walls, decreasing the gas pressure. Therefore, the ideal gas law overestimates the pressure.

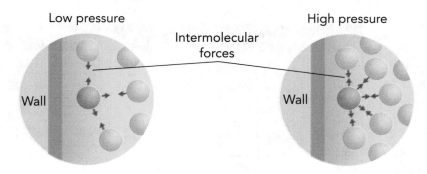

Low pressure

High pressure

Intermolecular forces

Wall

Wall

23 **SEP Use Models** Imagine you have a sample of 10 tennis balls and a sample of 10 marbles, each sitting in a chamber at constant pressure and temperature. If you modeled each sample as an ideal gas, how would the volumes of the two samples compare? In reality, how would the volumes compare?

....

....

The van der Waals Equation Dutch physicist Johannes van der Waals modified the ideal gas law to take into account both the gas particle size and the intermolecular forces. The mathematical expression is called the **van der Waals equation** and is as follows:

$$\left(P + \frac{an^2}{V^2}\right)(V - nb) = nRT$$

The constants *a* and *b* are empirical constants that correct for the intermolecular attraction and the gas particle volume, respectively. The values of *a* and *b* are different for each gas. For example, gaseous H_2O has a very large value for *a* because it is a very polar molecule, and therefore the molecules experience strong intermolecular forces.

Real Gases at Low Pressures At low pressure, the ideal gas law is a good approximation for most gases.

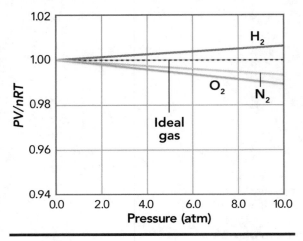

Real Gases at High Pressures At high pressure, actual gas behavior begins to significantly deviate from the ideal gas law.

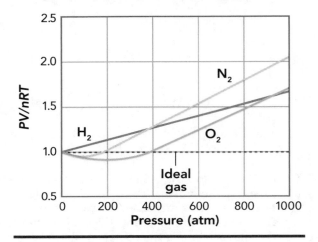

(24) **CCC Patterns** The table shows several gases, the primary intermolecular forces between their particles, and their empirical van der Waals constants *a* and *b*. What pattern do you recognize between the intermolecular forces and *a*? Now, looking only at the noble gases, why might *a* get bigger going from He to Ne to Ar?

Gas	Intermolecular Forces	a (L²·atm)/mol²	b (L/mol)
He	dispersion	0.03410	0.0238
Ne	dispersion	0.205	0.0167
Ar	dispersion	1.337	0.032
CH_4	dipole-dipole	2.273	0.0430
NH_3	hydrogen bond	4.170	0.0371
H_2O	hydrogen bond	5.536	0.0305

....

....

....

Intensive and Extensive Properties of Gases

Pressure and temperature are called **intensive** properties because they do not change based on the scale, or size, of the gas being considered. The volume and number of moles of gas do change with scale, so they are considered **extensive** properties. When dealing with large open systems, such as the atmosphere, the extensive properties are difficult to define. It is often convenient to write the ideal gas law completely in terms of intensive properties.

We have already seen that the ideal gas law can be written in terms of intensive properties such as density (ρ), pressure (P), temperature (T), and molar mass (M). The ideal gas law can also be written to simplify the ideal gas constant and molar mass. $R_{specific}$ is the gas constant divided by the molar mass and is called the **specific gas constant.**

$$P = \rho\left(\frac{R}{M}\right)T = \rho R_{specific} T$$

Measuring Properties Pressure and temperature in a region of atmosphere can be measured with a barometer and a thermometer, respectively. There is no way to measure the volume and number of particles.

(25) **SEP Use a Model** On the landscape image, sketch where you would place a barometer and thermometer to measure the average pressure and temperature in the cloud region. Discuss with a classmate why the volume and number of particles would be difficult to measure. ✏️

GO ONLINE to Elaborate on and Evaluate your knowledge of ideal gas behavior by completing the class discussion and writing activities.

In the modeling worksheet, you developed a model to explain how winds manifest as a result of the behavior of gases in the atmosphere. With a partner, complete the prompt below and then discuss how the fast-moving, hot, dry Santa Ana winds spread forest fires.

26 **SEP Develop a Model** Based on the ideal gas law, sketch what happens to the air over a small fire. Make sure you consider both the density and the pressure of the air immediately over the fire and the air in the surrounding vicinity.

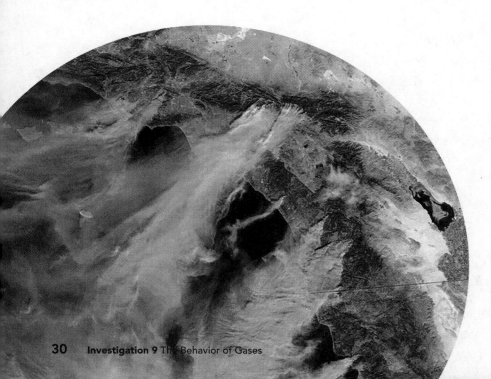

Gases in Earth's Atmosphere

 GO ONLINE to Explore and Explain atmospheric gases in familiar scenarios.

Composition of the Atmosphere

Earth's atmosphere is made up of many different gases. The atmosphere is primarily made up of nitrogen and oxygen, with small amounts of trace gases. The contribution each gas makes to the total atmospheric pressure is called the partial pressure.

Composition of Dry Air The table and charts show the composition of dry air, or air that does not contain any water vapor. The table shows both the volume by percentage and the partial pressure of each gas.

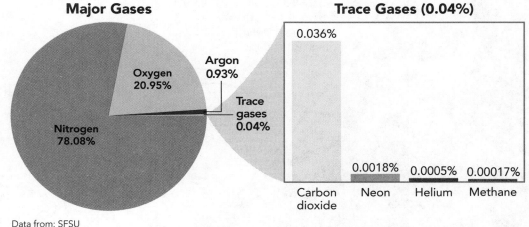

Data from: SFSU

Compostion of Dry Air		
Component	**Percentage of Total Volume**	**Partial Pressure (kPa)**
Nitrogen	78.08	79.11
Oxygen	20.95	21.22
Argon	0.93	0.95
Carbon dioxide and others	0.04	0.04
Total	**100.00**	**101.32**

The contribution of each gas to the total pressure of the atmosphere is due to its percent volume. For example, nitrogen contributes (78.08 ÷ 100%) × 101.32 = 79.11.

Dalton's Law

In 1801, chemist John Dalton recognized that at constant volume and temperature, the total pressure exerted by a mixture of gases is equal to the sum of the partial pressures of the component gases. This is called **Dalton's law,** and it is expressed mathematically as follows:

$$P_{total} = P_1 + P_2 + P_3 + ...$$

For example, dry air is a mixture of a number of gases, (N_2, O_2, CO_2, Ar, etc.). The individual partial pressures of each gas can be added together to get a total atmospheric pressure, which at sea level equals 101.32 kPa.

Air at High Altitude As you ascend a high mountain, you will notice that the air is thinner at high altitudes, making it more difficult to breathe. This is due to less oxygen being taken in for each breath.

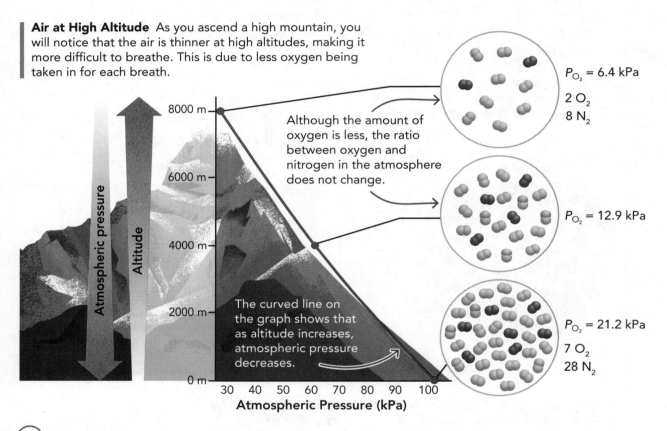

Although the amount of oxygen is less, the ratio between oxygen and nitrogen in the atmosphere does not change.

P_{O_2} = 6.4 kPa

2 O_2
8 N_2

P_{O_2} = 12.9 kPa

The curved line on the graph shows that as altitude increases, atmospheric pressure decreases.

P_{O_2} = 21.2 kPa

7 O_2
28 N_2

Atmospheric pressure

Altitude

8000 m
6000 m
4000 m
2000 m
0 m

30 40 50 60 70 80 90 100

Atmospheric Pressure (kPa)

(27) **SEP Analyze and Interpret Data** The table shows the pressure in a SCUBA diver's lungs at various depths. Nitrogen narcosis is a problem for divers when the N_2 partial pressure in their lungs exceeds 700 kPa. Complete the table and discuss with a classmate at what depth narcosis becomes an issue.

Lung Air Pressure at Various Depths Underwater			
N_2 Volume (%)	Depth (m)	Pressure (kPa)	P_{N_2} (kPa)
	0	101.32	
	30.48	404.32	
	91.44	1010.32	

Using Dalton's Law

Air contains oxygen, nitrogen, argon, and trace amounts of other gases. What is the partial pressure of oxygen (P_{O_2}) at 101.30 kPa of total pressure if the partial pressures of nitrogen, argon, and other gases are 79.10 kPa, 0.94 kPa, and 0.040 kPa, respectively?

ANALYZE List the knowns and the unknown.

Knowns	Unknown
P_{N_2} = 79.10 kPa	P_{O_2} = ? kPa
P_{Ar} = 0.94 kPa	
P_{others} = 0.040 kPa	
P_{total} = 101.30 kPa	

CALCULATE Solve for the unknown.

State Dalton's law.

$$P_{total} = P_{O_2} + P_{N_2} + P_{Ar} + P_{others}$$

Rearrange the equation to isolate P_{O_2}.

$$P_{O_2} = P_{total} - P_{N_2} - P_{Ar} - P_{others}$$

Substitute the known quantities into the equation to find the partial pressure of oxygen.

$$P_{O_2} = 101.30 \text{ kPa} - 79.10 \text{ kPa} - 0.94 \text{ kPa} - 0.040 \text{ kPa}$$

$$P_{O_2} = 21.22 \text{ kPa}$$

EVALUATE Does the result make sense?

The partial pressure of oxygen must be smaller than that of nitrogen. The other partial pressures are smaller, so the calculated answer of 21.22 kPa seems reasonable.

(28) **SEP Use Mathematics** A gas mixture containing oxygen, nitrogen, and carbon dioxide has a total pressure of 32.9 kPa. If P_{O_2} = 6.6 kPa and P_{N_2} = 23.0 kPa, what is P_{CO_2}? 🖊

GO ONLINE for more practice problems.

Diffusion

Diffusion is the tendency of molecules to move toward areas of lower concentration until the concentration is uniform. Suppose you open a bottle of perfume in one corner of a room. At some point, a person standing at the opposite corner will be able to smell the perfume.

Diffusion of Gas Molecules
When a perfume bottle is opened, volatile, or odorant, molecules in perfume change to gas through evaporation and mix with the surrounding air.

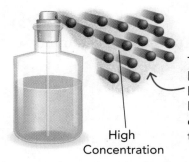

Low Concentration

High Concentration

The gas molecules have a higher concentration and higher pressure when they leave the perfume bottle compared to the rest of the room.

Since there is a high concentration of odorant gas molecules in one corner of the room, **the odorant molecules begin to diffuse and spread out** through the air in the room to regions of low or no odorant concentration.

Diffusion

Eventually, the odorant gas molecules will be evenly dispersed throughout the room, such that the **concentration of odorant molecules is at equilibrium** and constant everywhere.

Diffusion and Particle Speed
For two gases at the same temperature, the average kinetic energy (*KE*) is the same. If the mass (*m*) of one of the particles is larger, then the velocity (*v*) of the particle must be smaller. Kinetic energy is related to mass and velocity by the equation $KE = \frac{1}{2}mv^2$.

Small particles move faster. A larger velocity results in a faster rate of diffusion.

29 **SEP Develop a Model** The ideal gas law and the concept of diffusion are demonstrated many ways in everyday life. For example, an air pump draws in air during the upstroke. Describe what happens to the pressure and volume inside the pump. ✏️

....

....

....

Graham's Law

Another process that involves the movement of molecules in a gas is called effusion. During **effusion,** a gas escapes through a tiny hole in its container. Scottish chemist Thomas Graham studied rates of effusion during the 1840s. From his observations, he proposed an explanation, now called **Graham's law of effusion,** which states that the rate of effusion of a gas is inversely proportional to the square root of the gas's molar mass (*M*). This law can also be applied to the diffusion of gases. Graham's law can be written as follows for two gases, A and B:

$$\frac{\text{Rate}_A}{\text{Rate}_B} = \sqrt{\frac{M_B}{M_A}}$$

Effusion and Molecule Size
A larger quantity of small molecules can move through a hole during a given amount of time than larger molecules can. This means small molecules will effuse faster than large molecules.

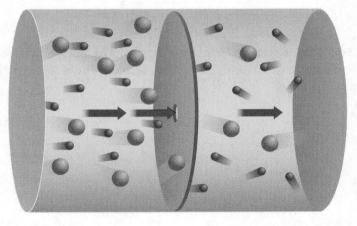

30 **SEP Develop Models** Sketch two balloons of equal volume, one filled with helium and one filled with oxygen. Then, sketch the balloons after one week, modeling which balloon has deflated more. ✏️

Comparing Effusion Rates

How much faster does helium (He) effuse than nitrogen (N_2) at the same temperature?

ANALYZE List the knowns and the unknown.

Knowns	Unknown
molar mass of He = 4.0 g/mol	Ratio of effusion rates = ?
molar mass of N_2 = 28.0 g/mol	

CALCULATE Solve for the unknown.

Start with the equation for Graham's law of effusion.

$$\frac{Rate_{He}}{Rate_{N_2}} = \frac{\sqrt{M_{N_2}}}{\sqrt{M_{He}}}$$

Substitute the molar masses of nitrogen and helium into the equation to find the ratio of effusion rates.

$$\frac{Rate_{He}}{Rate_{N_2}} = \frac{\sqrt{28.0 \text{ g/mol}}}{\sqrt{4.0 \text{ g/mol}}} = \sqrt{7.0} = 2.7$$

EVALUATE Does the result make sense?

Helium atoms are less massive than nitrogen molecules, so it makes sense that helium effuses faster than nitrogen.

(31) **SEP Use Mathematics** Calculate the ratio of the velocity of hydrogen molecules to the velocity of carbon dioxide molecules at the same temperature. ✏️

(32) **SEP Use Mathematics** Your friend says that argon gas effuses faster than oxygen gas because argon gas is monatomic and oxygen gas is diatomic. Do you agree? Explain your reasoning. ✏️

GO ONLINE for more practice problems.

Wind

Wind Is the Diffusion of Air Wind is caused by the movement of air particles and can be explained using the ideal gas law and the concept of diffusion. For an open system like the atmosphere, the air will move from regions of high pressure to regions of low pressure.

Air Heated From Below The sun's rays shine on the surface of Earth, warming the air directly above the surface through radiation. The air heats in an isobaric process, resulting in the expansion of the air directly above the ground.

Warmed Air Rises The density of the gas decreases as the temperature increases at constant pressure. This results in the expansion of the air directly above the ground. Since the air above the ground is now less dense than the air surrounding it, this section of air begins to rise.

Wind Is Diffusing Air Relatively warm temperatures cause air to rise, reducing the pressure and air concentration near the ground. Relatively cold temperatures cause air to fall toward the ground, increasing pressure and air concentration. As a result, air diffuses from the high-pressure, cold region to the low-pressure, warm region. This movement of air is wind.

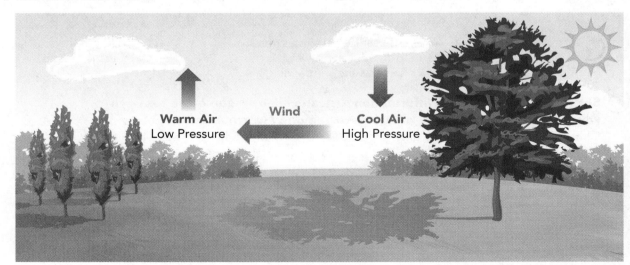

Using a Mathematical Model to Explain Wind The intensive form of the ideal gas law is useful for mathematically modeling the behavior of air. Recall that density is related to pressure, temperature, the gas constant, and the molar mass of gas:

$$P = \rho R_{specific} T$$

Looking at this equation, you may think that high temperature should result in high pressure. In reality, the pressure of a sample of air will actually stay constant; it is the density that changes according to the equation. The air behaves in a way similar to an isobaric system, such as the inside of a balloon. When the temperature of an air sample increases, density decreases. The warmer, less dense air will rise, leaving behind a low-pressure void. The pressure of the warmed air doesn't change; the pressure of the void left behind is what is actually different. Air that was not heated will rush in to fill the void through diffusion, resulting in wind.

Pressure and Temperature The pressure of a heated sample of air actually stays constant, consistent with the ideal gas law. It's the empty space left behind by the rising gas that results in a low-pressure region.

Pressure is constant for heated gas, like a balloon. Density decreases and the air rises.

This sample of air has pressure P and density ρ, which is the same as the surrounding air.

Pressure is low in the area left behind by the rising gas.

(33) SEP Obtain and Evaluate Information Use an online resource and research why the Great Plains area is the windiest region in North America. From Chinook winds to blizzards and tornadoes, strong winds have always had a major role as part of the Great Plains story. Include the topography of the Great Plains as part of your explanation as to how these powerful winds are generated in this region. ✏️

....

....

....

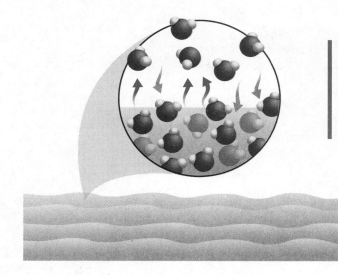

Saturated Water Vapor Evaporation of water can happen until equilibrium is achieved between molecules going back and forth between the liquid and gas phases. Saturated vapor pressure is the partial pressure of water in the air at this equilibrium point.

Humidity

So far, air has been modeled as being dry. However, air almost always contains a varying amount of water vapor, which results from the evaporation of liquid water on Earth's surface. The maximum pressure of water vapor in air is called **saturated vapor pressure.** The temperature at which the air is saturated with water vapor is called the **dewpoint.** If the air is cooled further than the dewpoint, then some of the water vapor will condense back into the liquid phase, resulting in cloud formation or rain. **Relative humidity** (*RH*) is the percent ratio of actual water vapor partial pressure to the saturated vapor pressure. It can be expressed mathematically as follows:

$$RH = \frac{\text{actual water vapor partial pressure}}{\text{saturated vapor pressure}} \times 100$$

Relative Humidity Saturated vapor pressure varies with temperature. Therefore, the relative humidity also varies with temperature. The diagram shows the amount of actual water vapor as a fraction of the amount possible. The actual amount of water vapor in the air stays constant, going from 10°C to 30°C. However, the relative humidity decreases.

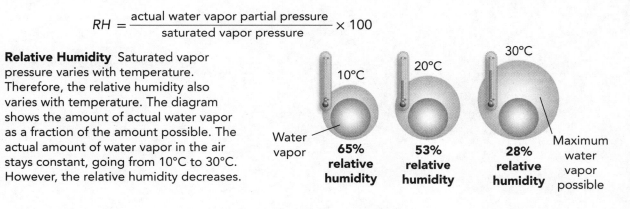

Water vapor — **65% relative humidity** — **53% relative humidity** — **28% relative humidity** — Maximum water vapor possible (10°C, 20°C, 30°C)

(34) **Predict** As you descend a mountain, the total atmospheric pressure increases, while the partial pressure of water vapor remains constant. Use Dalton's law to infer how the relative humidity would change. How would the relative humidity change if the air also got warmer? ✏️

....

....

....

(35) Predict Would you expect saturated vapor pressure to change more drastically from winter to summer over the equator or in the northern Pacific Ocean? Explain your answer. ✏️

....

....

....

Revisit

INVESTIGATIVE PHENOMENON

GO ONLINE to Elaborate on and Evaluate your knowledge of gases in Earth's atmosphere by completing the class discussion and writing activities.

In the modeling worksheet, you developed a model to explain how winds manifest as a result of the behavior of gases in the atmosphere. With a partner, complete the prompt below and then reevaluate your model.

(36) SEP Construct an Explanation As air moves rapidly from high altitude up in the Santa Ana Mountains to low altitude by the Pacific Ocean, the relative humidity of the air dramatically decreases. Explain why. ✏️

....

....

....

....

GO ONLINE to Evaluate what you learned about the behavior of gases and the ideal gas laws by using the available assessment resources.

In the Performance Task, you constructed Cartesian divers that descend through a bottle of water in a particular order. Wrap up your engineering project with the following questions.

(37) **Design an Experiment** How could you modify the performance task so that the behavior of the Cartesian divers demonstrate Gay-Lussac's law? ✎

....

....

....

....

....

(38) **Construct an Explanation** Buoyancy is the measure of the ability of an object to float in a fluid. How does the buoyancy of the Cartesian diver change when the bottle it is inside is squeezed? ✎

....

....

....

(39) **Revisit the Anchoring Phenomenon** How does what you learned about the gas laws and wind help explain how to predict the movement of severe weather events? ✎

....

....

....

....

INVESTIGATIVE PHENOMENON

GO ONLINE to Engage with real-world phenomena by watching a video and to complete a CER interactive worksheet.

What is causing drought in California?

Weather and Climate

Some parts of California regularly experience droughts. However, these droughts have become more frequent and more severe in recent decades. Once you have viewed the Investigative Phenomenon video and used the Claim-Evidence-Reasoning worksheet to craft an explanation, answer the following reflection questions about things that might increase the chance of a drought.

1) **CCC Stability and Change** Feedbacks can stabilize or destabilize the climate, causing or preventing extreme weather events such as floods and droughts. List two factors that can affect the stability of California's climate. Identify if the factors stabilize or destabilize the climate. 🖋

Factor	Effect

2) **SEP Develop and Use Models** Using a factor you identified in question 1, develop a simple model to explain how it stabilizes or destabilizes California's climate. 🖋

....

....

....

....

....

EXPERIENCE 1

Earth's Surface Systems

GO ONLINE to Explore and Explain activities to detect carbon dioxide and how carbon from familiar objects moves through the carbon cycle.

Flow of Energy in Earth Systems

Earth's surface geologic system processes are largely driven by the flow of electromagnetic radiation from the sun. Earth's interior geologic system processes are driven by something else: the flow of heat out of Earth. Earth's internal heat is primarily generated by the gradual radioactive decay of four isotopes: potassium-40, thorium-232, uranium-235, and uranium-238.

Over time, Earth's surface temperature goes up or down depending on whether the net energy flow at Earth's surface is positive or negative.

Solar Radiation The sun's energy powers the water cycle and the erosion of land, and it creates Earth's weather. It also moves the slow undersea currents that circle the planet.

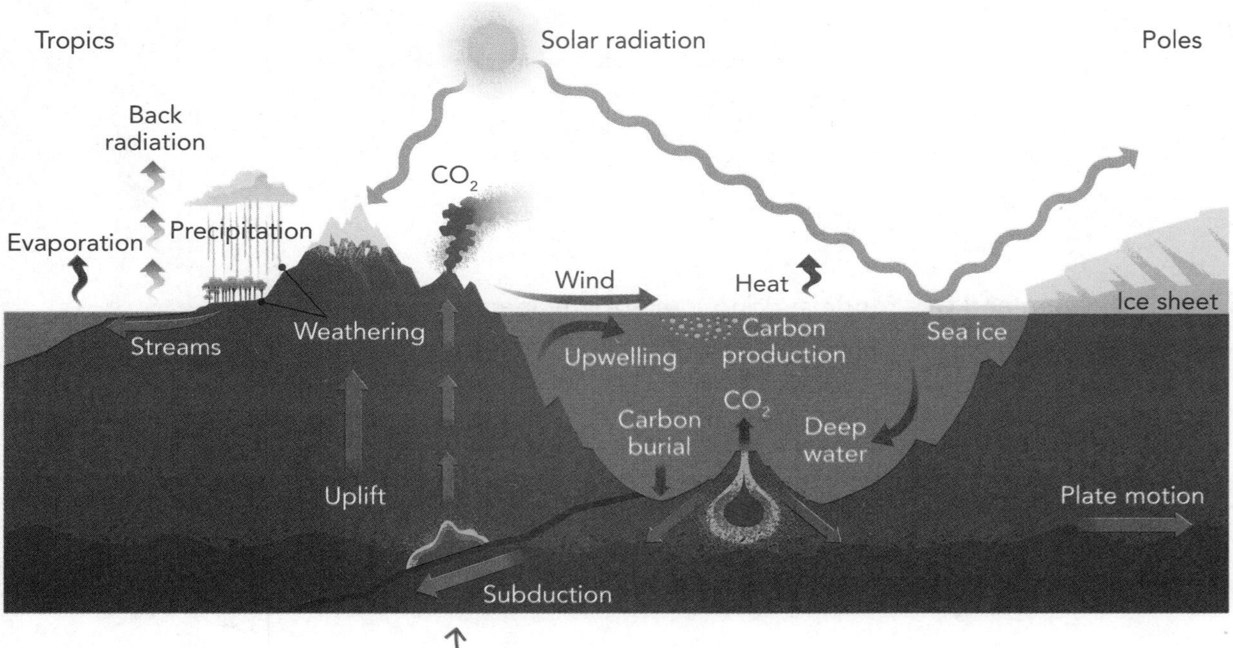

The flow of heat out of Earth moves the tectonic plates, causing earthquakes and creating volcanoes and other types of mountains.

Biogeochemical Cycles

Residence Time The energy arriving from the sun and escaping from Earth's interior drives the cycling of many types of matter through Earth's different systems (the geosphere, atmosphere, hydrosphere, and biosphere).

Those materials have different pathways and residence times in each system. Some, such as carbon, oxygen, nitrogen, phosphorus, sulfur, and water, are vital to life.

■ Biogeochemistry is an interdisciplinary field that studies the cycling of certain elements and compounds that are vital to life.

Water Reservoirs Fresh water is essential to human life, yet, as the table shows, it is only a small fraction of the water on Earth's surface, and most of it is frozen in glaciers and ice caps.

Water in the Hydrosphere		
Reservoir	**Volume (thousands of km³)**	**Residence Time**
Ocean	1,370,000	3100 years
Glaciers	29,000	16,000 years
Groundwater	4,000	300 years
Freshwater Lakes	125	1–100 years
Saline lakes	104	10–1000 years
Soil moisture	67	280 days
Atmosphere	14	9 days
Rivers	1.2	12–20 days

Residence time refers to the average amount of time a molecule spends in any of Earth's reservoirs. For instance, a raindrop that falls into a river might spend weeks in the river before it reaches a lake or the ocean.

3 **CCC Systems and System Models** Explain how residence time is related to the relative size of a reservoir, and why. 🖉

....

....

....

The Sun-Driven Water Cycle Unlike geologic processes that occur deep inside Earth, processes that happen at Earth's surface are driven mostly by energy from the sun. The water cycle is a sun-driven system. As water on Earth's surface absorbs energy from sunlight, the water begins a series of changes that carry it into the atmosphere, back to Earth's surface, and back into the atmosphere again. Sunlight is also responsible for driving the large-scale atmospheric currents that carry water vapor all around the planet.

Although the cycling of matter within the hydrologic system is powered by energy from the sun, the force of gravity also plays a role in the cycle as it pulls water toward Earth's center, causing rain to fall and water to flow downhill across Earth's surface.

④ **CCC Energy and Matter** Examine the diagram of the water cycle. Draw a circle around each process that requires energy input from the sun. Draw a square around each process where gravity plays a role. ✎

As water vapor cools, it condenses to form water droplets or ice particles. These particles eventually fall back to Earth's surface as precipitation.

Energy from sunlight causes evaporation of water and warms the air near the surface, forming air currents that carry water vapor to higher altitudes.

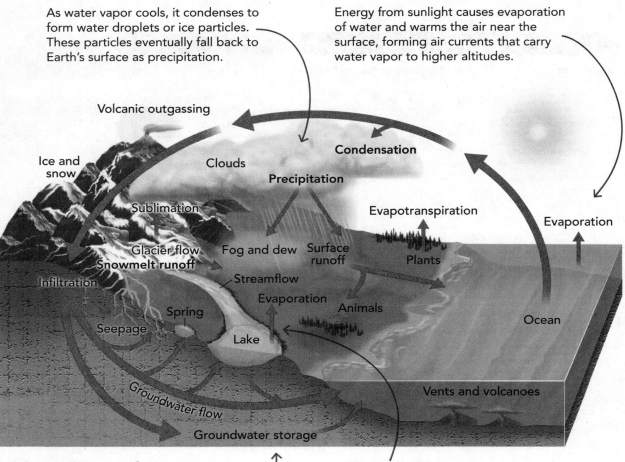

Only a small amount of precipitation makes it into rivers and glaciers. This surface water, along with groundwater, eventually flows back to the ocean or evaporates back into the atmosphere.

Most precipitation re-evaporates or is absorbed by plants and then is transpired back into the atmosphere. The rest infiltrates the ground to form groundwater.

Energy and Life Without photosynthesis, carbon dioxide would still dissolve in seawater, and weathering of rocks would still occur, but the carbon cycle would be very different.

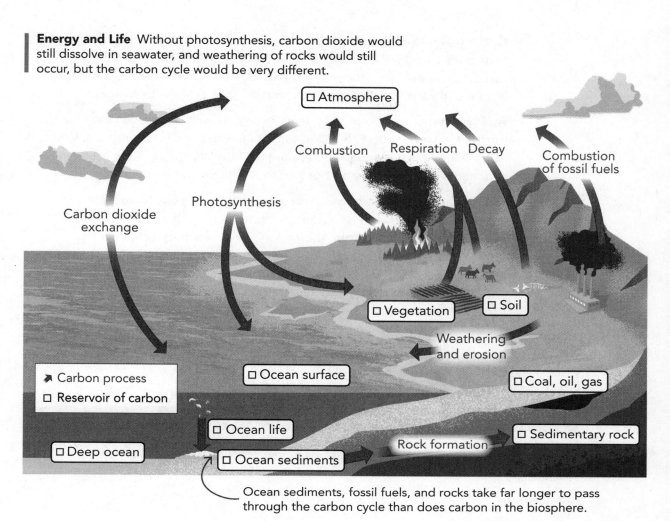

Ocean sediments, fossil fuels, and rocks take far longer to pass through the carbon cycle than does carbon in the biosphere.

Energy and the Carbon Cycle

Solar Energy to Carbon Photosynthesis is the vital process that plants use to create and store energy from the light of the sun. The energy needed for photosynthesis comes daily from the sun, but not the carbon used for storing it, which cycles continually through Earth's systems. About 550 billion tons of carbon is stored in the biosphere.

Photosynthesis is not very efficient; it typically captures and stores only 0.1–0.2% of the energy of sunlight. However, because fossil fuels such as coal and oil are the remains of millions of years of ancient organisms, they are, in a sense, millions of years of fossil sunbeams.

(5) **SEP Obtain, Evaluate, and Communicate Information** Go online to investigate the range of ages of the coal that is used for generating electric power in the United States. Describe the differences between the residence time for carbon in coal and in other parts of the carbon cycle. ✎

....

....

Carbon Cycle One of the most important materials cycling through Earth's systems is carbon, the foundation for life on Earth. Understanding the carbon cycle involves studying not only the reservoirs where carbon resides, but its pathways among them and its residence times within them.

At any given time, about 550 billion tons of carbon is stored in the biosphere, with most (475 billion tons) as a result of photosynthesis. When living things die, most of the carbon goes into the soil or ocean bottom sediments and becomes part of the geosphere.

Nearly all of Earth's carbon is locked away in Earth's crustal rocks, most as calcium carbonate in limestone, a common rock that forms from the sedimentation of shells from millions of years' worth of dead marine organisms. Limestone returns to the surface very slowly, through geologic processes such as mountain building, uplift, and erosion. Vast amounts of carbon also exist in the geosphere in the soil and in fossil fuels such as coal, oil, and natural gas.

Carbon Reservoirs Earth's many carbon reservoirs differ vastly in the amount and form of carbon that they hold. The element also cycles at different rates through each reservoir.

Carbon in Earth's Systems		
Reservoir	**Mass (Billions of metric tons)**	**Estimated Residence Time**
Marine Life	6	20 days
Atmosphere	865	4 years
Surface Ocean	900	4 years
Land Vegetation	450	4–6 years
Dissolved Ocean Organic Carbon	700	350 years
Intermediate and Deep Ocean	37,300	370 years
Soil	1500–2400	1000s of years
Ocean Floor Surface Sediments	1750	10,000s of years
Ocean Methane Gas Hydrates	1500–6000	10,000s of years
Permafrost	1700	100,000s of years
Fossil Fuels	570–1500	Millions of years
Carbonate Rocks	48,000,000	10s of millions of years
Other Rocks in Earth's Crust	42,000,000	100s of millions of years

(6) **CCC Patterns** Use the table to compare surface carbon reservoirs, such as land vegetation and the atmosphere, with those in the rocks of Earth's crust. What pattern do you observe? 🖉

....

....

New Rock Igneous rock forms at Earth's surface during volcanic eruptions, such as this eruption of Volcán de Fuego in Guatemala in November of 2018. Other processes of erosion and deposition will alter this rock as it moves through the rock cycle.

Rock Cycle

Rock Cycle Forces The surface of Earth is constantly changing. Earth's systems interact in countless ways, and these interactions form the geologic processes that shape and reshape our planet's surface.

Geology occurs at time scales that range from milliseconds to millions of years and at spatial scales from atoms to tectonic plates. Nearly all geologic processes occur along a spectrum, from small-scale and continuous to large-scale and catastrophic. For example, volcanoes usually bubble out lava, creating new land, but the occasional supervolcano eruption can cover Earth's surface with ash and drive species to extinction.

Earth's surface is a battleground between two powerful dueling engines: the internal engine powered by heat from radioactive decay, which drives plate tectonics, and the external sun-powered water cycle, which drives precipitation, erosion, and sedimentation. These two combine to form the many pathways that Earth materials take, which is often summarized as the **rock cycle**. As fast as internal forces push up mountains or add surface rock through volcanism, the erosion from rain, ice, and wind tears them down. It is a constant battle, won sometimes by the internal engine when mountain ranges are thrust up into the sky, and other times by erosion, as those mountains are torn away, sometimes atom by atom, and carried to the sea.

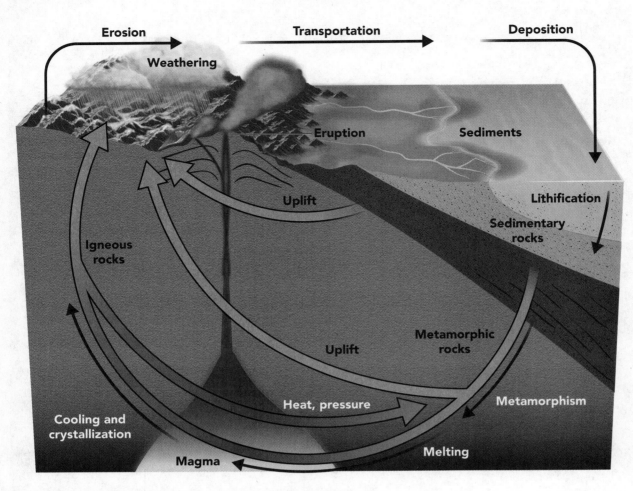

Erosion → **Transportation** → **Deposition** →

Weathering

Eruption   **Sediments**

Uplift

Lithification

Sedimentary rocks

Igneous rocks

Uplift   **Metamorphic rocks**

Heat, pressure   **Metamorphism**

Cooling and crystallization

Melting

Magma

Constant Transformation Rock can be igneous, sedimentary, or metamorphic, but powerful processes, some driven by external energy from the sun and others by Earth's internal heat, constantly change one kind of rock into another.

The Cycling of Material An important part of the rock cycle is the melting of rock. Magma forms at Earth's surface for several reasons, including high temperatures, decreases in pressure, and the presence of water. Volcanoes form where magma reaches the surface and erupts, but magma can also cool and harden to form igneous rocks underground.

At the surface, rock is broken down into small pieces (sediments) through the processes of weathering, which can be both chemical and physical. Sediments are then removed and carried downhill by the processes of erosion, often as part of the water cycle through floods, streams, and glaciers. Sediments are primarily chemically dissolved ions, but also include solid pieces of gravel, sand, and silt, and they almost always end up in the ocean.

Sediments become rock again through the process of sedimentation, where sediments are compacted and squeezed and then cemented together by the chemical precipitation of new minerals out of aqueous solutions. If burial continues, with more rock piled on top, the increasing pressure and temperature will change existing minerals in a sedimentary rock into new minerals, forming a metamorphic rock. **Metamorphism** is primarily a chemical process where increasing temperature and pressure alter the shape and composition of minerals. If metamorphism goes too far, the rock will melt to form new magma and the rock cycle will begin again.

Reinforcing and Counterbalancing Feedbacks

Change to one Earth system almost always causes change to other systems. In certain cases, the affected system will respond and apply a change back on the first system. This process is called a **feedback**. Feedbacks that amplify a change are called **reinforcing feedbacks**, or "positive" feedbacks. Feedbacks that resist or reduce a change are called **counterbalancing feedbacks**, or "negative" feedbacks. Earth systems operate within set parameters that maintain a state of equilibrium. Therefore, most feedbacks are counterbalancing, which means they act in a way that keeps the system in balance.

Reinforcing Feedback Water flows faster on the outside of a river curve, eroding the outside of the bend and making the meander grow.

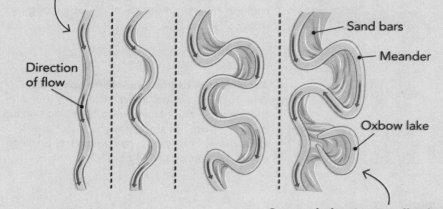

Direction of flow

Sand bars

Meander

Oxbow lake

Counterbalancing Feedback Eventually, the meanders get so large that they cut themselves off and the system returns to the starting state of a straight river.

⑦ **SEP Develop and Use Models** Use examples from your own experience to complete the diagrams by writing related processes that reinforce or counterbalance each other in the proper boxes. ✏

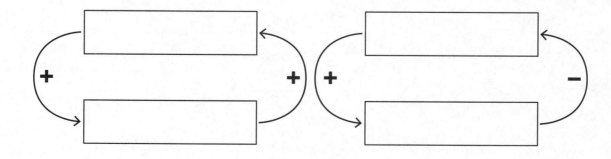

Feedback Tipping Points

When an old equilibrium cannot be restored by the usual feedback mechanisms, the system can reach a **tipping point.** These thresholds can cause sudden and irreversible changes to the system, which must then find a new equilibrium. These cycles are also called "non-linear" feedbacks, because the changes do not happen steadily, like the slope of a straight line.

Scientists worry that more natural systems will reach their tipping points as global temperatures rise. For example, following a century of gradual warming, some West Antarctic ice sheets that had existed for thousands of years recently disintegrated in a single day or a few weeks.

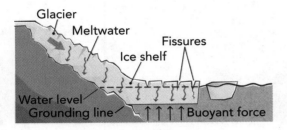

Warmer temperatures destabilize ice shelf
Meltwater from the glacier surface speeds up the melting and downhill flow of the glacier. It causes fractures in the ice shelf, which begins to break up.

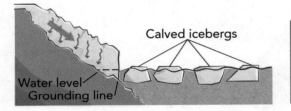

Acceleration of glacial melting and flow
Without the buoyant support of the water on the ice shelf, the glacier flows faster downhill due to gravity. Its surface melts faster and loses mass. The system has passed its tipping point and cannot rebuild the ice shelf.

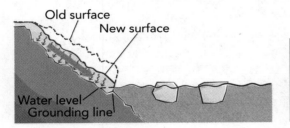

Unstable glacier after ice shelf collapses
Rapid fracturing and calving of sea ice breaks up the ice shelf. The glacier flows faster. The shelf reaches a tipping point when it retreats past the grounding line, because it has less support from seawater.

(8) **SEP Constructing Explanations Based on Evidence** Explain why the complete disappearance of a glacier is an example of a non-linear tipping point. ✏️

....

....

....

....

....

Land Use in the United States

How do we **use our land** in the United States?

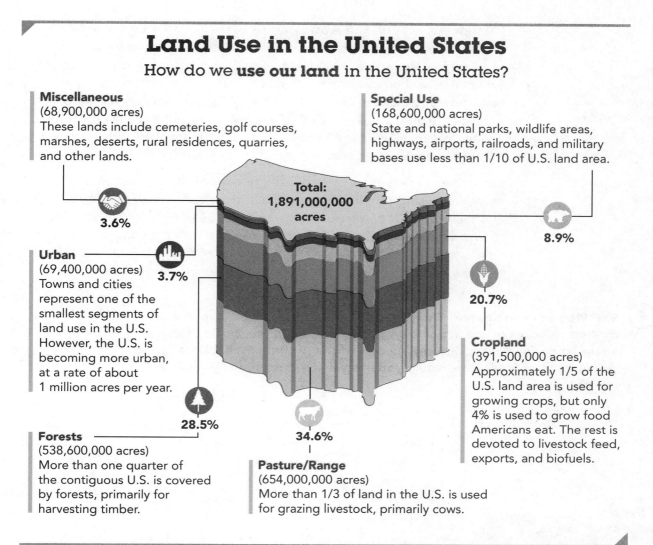

Miscellaneous
(68,900,000 acres)
These lands include cemeteries, golf courses, marshes, deserts, rural residences, quarries, and other lands.

3.6%

Special Use
(168,600,000 acres)
State and national parks, wildlife areas, highways, airports, railroads, and military bases use less than 1/10 of U.S. land area.

8.9%

Urban
(69,400,000 acres)
Towns and cities represent one of the smallest segments of land use in the U.S. However, the U.S. is becoming more urban, at a rate of about 1 million acres per year.

3.7%

Total: 1,891,000,000 acres

20.7%

Cropland
(391,500,000 acres)
Approximately 1/5 of the U.S. land area is used for growing crops, but only 4% is used to grow food Americans eat. The rest is devoted to livestock feed, exports, and biofuels.

28.5%

Forests
(538,600,000 acres)
More than one quarter of the contiguous U.S. is covered by forests, primarily for harvesting timber.

34.6%

Pasture/Range
(654,000,000 acres)
More than 1/3 of land in the U.S. is used for grazing livestock, primarily cows.

Human Impacts on the Earth System

Human Impacts on Earth's Surface Humans are now the main agent of geologic change at Earth's surface, controlling more than 50% of its land. We use 40% of land just to raise crops and graze animals to feed ourselves. Humans and the livestock we eat account for 96% of the total biomass of all land mammals—all wild mammals are now just 4%. In forty years, human activities have reduced the total number of Earth's vertebrates by more than half, and nearly all insects are gone in areas where people live. Human-released carbon dioxide has made the ocean 30% more acidic. In the U.S., the total area of developed land is now larger than the state of California, requiring the extraction of 8 billion tons of rock and minerals each year. Human activities such as mining, farming, and road-building now erode Earth's surface six times faster than all natural causes combined.

Human Impacts on the Atmosphere Many human activities put pollutants into the atmosphere. For example, the burning of fossil fuels releases greenhouse gases and large amounts of sulfur dioxide and nitrous oxides. These chemicals react with naturally occurring molecules in the atmosphere to become sulfuric and nitric acids, which acidify rainwater and damage organisms and property. These pollutants enter the hydrosphere and biosphere, where they harm living things. Greenhouse gases have led to a significant increase in atmospheric temperatures.

Fortunately, humans can monitor the release of these pollutants (especially using satellites), assess their impacts on Earth's systems, and take action to mitigate them. The U.S. Clean Air Acts have greatly reduced national air pollution levels. Global bans on chlorofluorocarbons have halted the destruction of the ozone layer. And international efforts are now underway to reduce the level of greenhouse gas emissions.

9 **SEP Plan an Investigation** Do research to find out what an "ozone action day" is. How are ozone action days designed around feedbacks? Design an investigation to measure the success of the program. What data would you need to collect? How would you analyze it? Are there any tipping points? ✏️

....

....

Revisit

INVESTIGATIVE PHENOMENON

📶 **GO ONLINE** to Elaborate on and Evaluate your knowledge of the carbon cycle by completing the class discussion and writing activities.

In the CER worksheet, you drafted a scientific argument about the possible causes of droughts. With a partner, reevaluate the evidence cited in your arguments.

10 **SEP Engage in Argument** Construct and defend an argument that the human use of lands in California has increased the severity of droughts. ✏️

....

....

....

Water and Energy in the Atmosphere

🛜 **GO ONLINE** to Explore and Explain specific heat and its effects on climate.

Earth's Radiative Energy Budget

Energy Budget Earth's surface **energy budget** describes where energy comes from and where it goes. It is driven by incoming solar radiation, mostly in the form of visible light. This incoming sunlight is about 340 watts of power for each square meter (340 W/m^2), but nearly a third of the energy is immediately reflected back out into space by clouds and Earth's surface. The energy that is absorbed by Earth's surface is reradiated upward as infrared energy, some of which is absorbed by gases in the atmosphere and then reradiated back toward the surface, creating a cycle known as the **greenhouse effect.**

Earth's Surface Energy Budget Most pathways of energy to and from Earth's surface take the form of electromagnetic radiation, primarily in the form of incoming sunlight or outgoing infrared light.

Components of Earth's Energy Budget Earth's energy budget is a complex system fueled by energy incoming from the sun, and the transfer of energy back and forth between Earth's surface and its atmosphere.

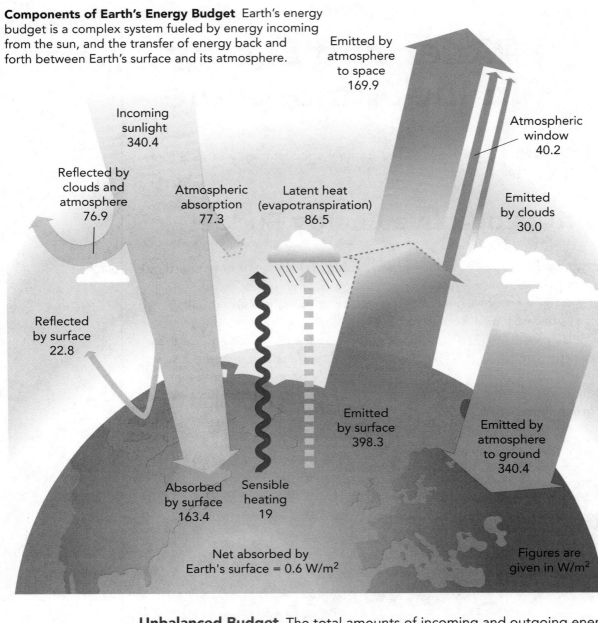

Emitted by atmosphere to space
169.9

Incoming sunlight
340.4

Atmospheric window
40.2

Reflected by clouds and atmosphere
76.9

Atmospheric absorption
77.3

Latent heat (evapotranspiration)
86.5

Emitted by clouds
30.0

Reflected by surface
22.8

Emitted by surface
398.3

Emitted by atmosphere to ground
340.4

Absorbed by surface
163.4

Sensible heating
19

Net absorbed by Earth's surface = 0.6 W/m²

Figures are given in W/m²

Unbalanced Budget The total amounts of incoming and outgoing energy are not the same. Due to human increases in greenhouse gases, more is entering than is currently leaving, causing Earth's surface to warm.

11 **SEP Develop and Use Models** Using this model of Earth's surface energy budget, explain why more than twice as much energy reaching Earth's surface is in the form of long-wave infrared radiation than short-wave visible radiation, despite the fact that sunlight is mostly visible radiation. ✏️

....

....

....

Temperature and Pressure in the Atmosphere

Earth's atmosphere extends for hundreds of kilometers into space, but because its gases are compressible, most of the atmosphere can be found within 5.5 km of the surface. The atmosphere is divided into several layers based on composition and temperature. Clouds and weather exist in the dense troposphere. Temperatures increase through the stratosphere because ozone in this layer absorbs ultraviolet radiation from the sun. Aurorae (such as the northern lights) occur within the thermosphere and exosphere.

Earth's Atmosphere

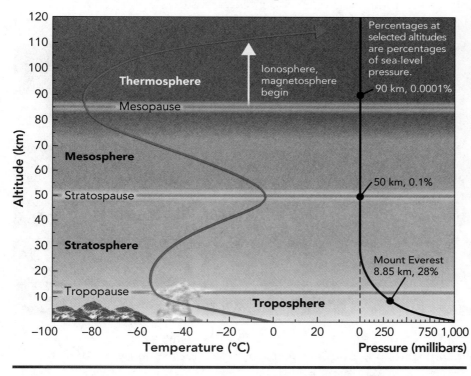

Layers and properties of Earth's Atmosphere
The temperatures at the stratopause and in the thermosphere are high, but this is misleading. Due to the near-vacuum conditions at these high altitudes, only a few gas molecules interact with sunlight, but they are very energetic.

(12) **CCC Cause and Effect** Most passenger airplanes fly at the top of the troposphere, about 10.5 km high, but don't go much higher than that. This height allows planes to combust the least amount of fuel. Construct an explanation for why passenger planes don't fly much below that and why they don't fly much above that. ✏️

....

....

....

Evaporation and Transpiration

The water cycle starts with **evapotranspiration,** a combination of evaporation from bodies of water and transpiration from the leaves of plants. These are both driven by the energy of sunlight. The absorption of the sun's electromagnetic radiation by liquid water can change it into water vapor. Water vapor molecules are at a higher energy state than liquid water molecules, and sunlight provides this energy. Each year the equivalent of about 400,000 cubic kilometers of water evaporates from the ocean surface, and a lesser amount from lakes and soil on land.

Most evaporation occurs at the ocean's surface, and near the equator. Evaporation rates are higher near the equator because the angle of sunlight is more vertical in those regions. Right along the equator, however, evaporation is slightly decreased relative to surrounding areas due to the frequent formation of clouds.

Evaporation Feedback High levels of evaporation, such as those observed over the Gulf Stream, can increase air humidity and promote the formation of clouds, which in turn can slow down the evaporation process.

Through the process of respiration, plants and animals also release water vapor. In respiration, food is broken down to release energy needed by the organism, and six water molecules are produced for each molecule of glucose. In plants, this water, along with water absorbed through the roots, transpires into the atmosphere through leaf pores as water vapor.

(13) **CCC Patterns** A narrow region of high evaporation in the Atlantic Ocean, east of North America, coincides with the Gulf Stream. A similar region exists in the Pacific Ocean, south of Japan. It corresponds to the Kuroshio Current. Explain why you think water is evaporating more rapidly from these currents.

....

....

....

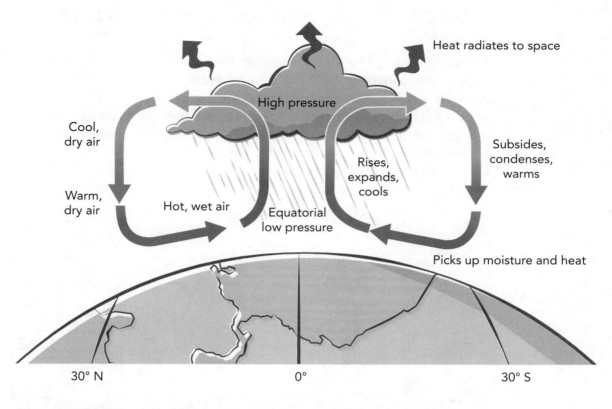

Cool, dry air

Warm, dry air

Hot, wet air

High pressure

Rises, expands, cools

Equatorial low pressure

Heat radiates to space

Subsides, condenses, warms

Picks up moisture and heat

30° N   0°   30° S

Convection in the Atmosphere

The air of the atmosphere is moved by convection. This convection is driven by the heating of air near Earth's surface from sunlight. The warm air expands, making it buoyant and causing it to rise. As the air rises and expands it cools, causing water vapor within it to condense and form tiny water droplets, creating clouds and eventually rain. The dryer air is pushed away from the equator by more rising air, which, now being cold and dense, falls back to Earth's surface. That air then flows across Earth's surface back towards the equator, as what are called the trade winds, warming over time until it is buoyant enough to rise again.

14. **CCC Cause and Effect** All else being equal, air volume increases when pressure decreases. Use this relationship to explain why warm air at the equator rises up through the less dense air above it. 🖉

....

....

....

....

Atmospheric Pressure and Wind

Winds are a result of pressure differences in the atmosphere at Earth's surface, with air moving from regions of high pressure to regions of low pressure. These patterns are constantly shifting, day to day and season to season, causing our weather. Differences in pressure can occur for several reasons, but are usually the result of differences in heating rates. These differences can result from factors such as the changing locations of ocean currents and the movement of clouds.

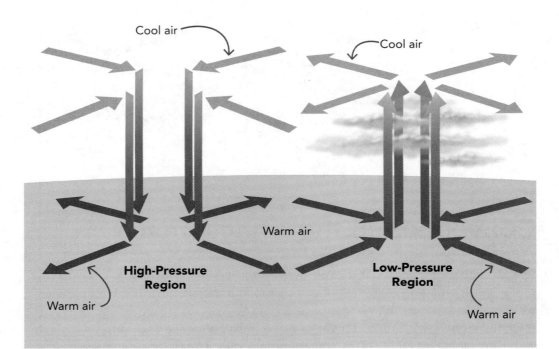

Pressure Systems At an area of low air pressure at the surface, moist warm air flows toward the center of the low pressure before rising, cooling, forming clouds, and then flowing away from the area. At areas of high pressure, dry cold air high in the atmosphere falls and warms as it approaches the surface. The air then flows away from the area.

(15) **CCC Cause and Effect** In the diagram, clouds form over the low-pressure region where air is rising, while at the high-pressure region, sunlight hits the ground as cold air is sinking. Explain why this pattern might change and reverse over time.

....

....

....

....

Global Atmospheric Circulation

Due to Earth's size and rate of rotation, the general global pattern of air circulation is broken up into six cells. The locations and structures of these cells are always shifting, day-to-day and season-to-season. In the Northern Hemisphere, the bottom of the Hadley Cell forms winds that blow toward the west (trade winds), and the bottom of the Ferrel Cell forms winds that blow from the west (westerlies). This is why most of the weather in the United States goes from west to east.

Latitude Pressure Zones Places where air is rising are low-pressure zones. Places where the air is falling are high-pressure zones.

Some of the air that rises at about 60° north and south flows toward the poles, where it falls as very cold and dry air, producing **Polar cells**.

Ferrel cells form around 50–60° north and south. Air masses tend to rise, creating rainfall. Air then flows toward the equator at high altitudes, falling back at around 30° N and S.

Subpolar low

Polar High

Polar cell

Polar easterlies

60°

Ferrel cell

Polar front

Hadley cell

30°

Westerlies

Subtropical high

Horse latitudes

Hadley cell

0°

Trade winds

Equatorial low

Equator

Doldrums

Hadley cell

Trade winds

Warm air at the equator rises and cools, forming **Hadley cells** that cause heavy cloud cover. Most of Earth's rain falls here. The cool dry air falls at roughly 30° N and S.

(16) **SEP Develop and Use Models** Use the model of atmospheric circulation to explain why most of the world's deserts are roughly 30° north, 30° south, or at the poles. 🖉

....

....

Humidity and Condensation

Humidity The amount of water vapor that can exist within air changes depending on temperature. Warmer air can contain a greater amount of water vapor than colder air. **Relative humidity** is a measure of the percentage of water vapor in the air compared to the maximum amount the air can hold at that particular temperature. If the humidity is high, the air feels damp and sticky. The dew point occurs when the relative humidity reaches 100%. At this point, no more water can be held in the air, and droplets of liquid water or crystals of ice will begin to form. Clouds are visible because they consist of tiny condensed ice crystals or water droplets.

Water Vapor and Temperature Dew and frost usually form late at night or early in the morning, when the air gets colder than the point of 100% humidity. As the temperature falls, the air can hold less water vapor, so dew or frost forms on surfaces such as the grass.

Water Content of Air at 50% and 100% Relative Humidity

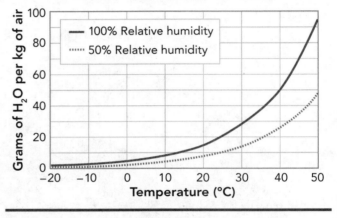

(17) **CCC Patterns** Examine the graph of relative humidity compared to temperature for a city over a 3-day period. The temperature reaches a peak at about 3 pm on Day 3. Estimate how much water vapor is in the air at that time. ✏️

Relative Humidity and Temperatures in Chicago, Illinois for December 1–3, 2017

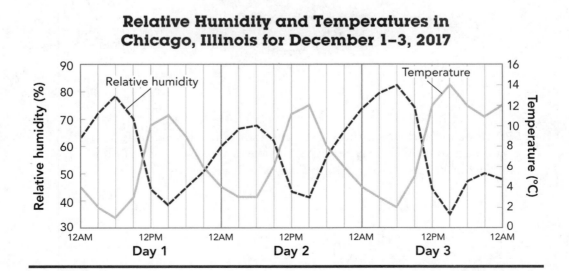

Types of Precipitation

How do different types of precipitation form?

Interacting Air Masses When warm air encounters a colder, denser air mass, the warm air is pushed up and over the colder air, forming clouds that may produce different types of precipitation.

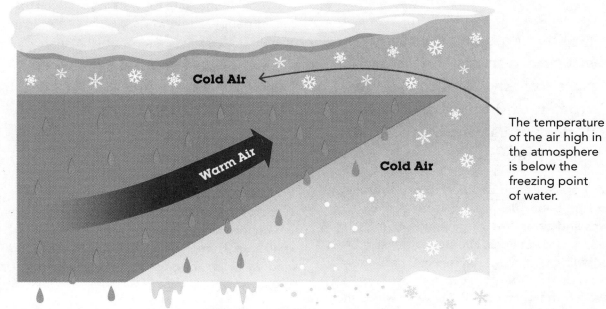

Cold Air

Warm Air

Cold Air

The temperature of the air high in the atmosphere is below the freezing point of water.

The type of precipitation that reaches the ground is dependent on the **temperature of the air** it falls through and the **temperature near the surface**.

Frozen precipitation melts as it falls, reaching the ground as **rain.**

Frozen precipitation melts as it falls but refreezes on cold surfaces becoming **frozen rain.**

Frozen precipitation melts in a shallow layer of warm air then refreezes into **sleet** before reaching the surface.

Snow falls through a continuous column of cold air, never melting before reaching the surface.

Precipitation When the humidity is 100% and air temperature continues to drop, water vapor will continue to condense and eventually fall to the ground as **precipitation.** Air temperature usually drops when one air mass is lifted during a collision with another, denser air mass. The form that the precipitation takes depends on the temperatures of the colliding air masses.

(18) **CCC Energy and Matter** In the diagram, notice that freezing rain and sleet fall as liquid rain through the cold air mass before freezing. Use what you know about the energy of changes of state to explain this phenomenon. ✏️

....

....

....

Severe Weather

Humans rely on precipitation for fresh water and for agriculture, but under certain conditions severe weather can pose a natural hazard and can be damaging and life-threatening.

▶ **When cold fronts collide with warm fronts, the warm air is quickly lifted and cools rapidly, and this can create storms with strong winds and lots of precipitation.**

Heavy precipitation can lead to catastrophic flooding. Snow blizzards can shut down towns and cities. Freezing rain can tear down trees and power lines. Hailstones the size of baseballs can damage houses and cars. In certain cases, tornadoes can spin off along these storm fronts, creating intense winds that can exceed 400 km/hr and tear up everything in their paths. Fortunately, real-time ground and satellite radar monitoring can identify places where severe weather is likely to occur, and provide the data for warning systems that can let people know when it is time to evacuate or seek shelter.

Hurricanes and typhoons are examples of **tropical cyclones**, which are large, rapidly rotating storm systems with high winds, a low-pressure center ("eye"), and spiraling arms of thunderstorms. Hurricanes tend to develop in tropical latitudes over warm water, which causes rising masses of humid air. Earth's Coriolis effect causes cyclones to rotate, taking evaporated water vapor from a very broad area and concentrating intense rainfall into a very small area. Human risks from hurricanes include wind damage, flooding, and coastal storm surges.

Paths of hurricanes near North and Central America The map shows the paths of hurricanes of varying intensities in the Atlantic and Pacific oceans. Note the large number of hurricanes that enter the Gulf of Mexico or come up the east coast of the United States.

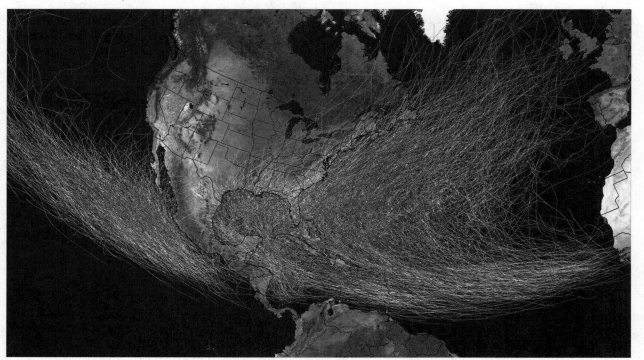

19 **SEP Develop and Use Models** On the weather map, draw where you might expect the warm and cold fronts to be a day later. Mark the part of the map that will see a drop in temperatures over the next day. ✏️

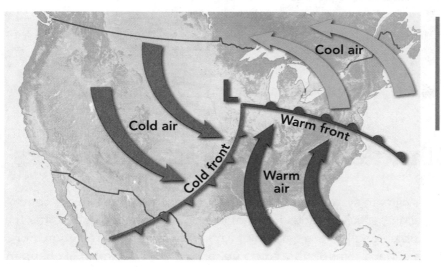

Colliding Air Masses
Moving air masses are often shown on weather maps with arrows. Severe storms are likely to occur where a cold air mass is colliding with a warm air mass.

Revisit

INVESTIGATIVE PHENOMENON

GO ONLINE to Elaborate and Evaluate your knowledge of Earth's energy budget by completing the class discussion and data analysis activities.

In the CER worksheet, you provided evidence and reasons to explain what causes droughts. With a partner, reevaluate the evidence cited in your arguments.

20 **SEP Engage in Argument** How do you think California's geographic location might limit the amount of precipitation it gets? ✏️

....

....

....

....

....

....

....

Atmospheric System Feedbacks

GO ONLINE to Explore and Explain climate forcing and atmospheric system feedbacks.

Climate Forcings and Feedbacks

Earth's climate system and therefore its surface temperature are controlled by sunlight, which includes forms of electromagnetic radiation other than just visible light, such as ultraviolet (UV) and infrared (IR) radiation. For Earth's surface temperature to go up, one of three factors must happen: (1) an increase in incoming sunlight (due to changes in the sun's activity), (2) a decrease in how much sunlight gets reflected from the surface back out into space, or (3) an increase in how much of that energy is kept by greenhouse gases. These factors driving the climate are called **climate forcings,** and there is a large number of Earth system impacts and feedbacks that result from them.

Tropical Deforestation Removing large portions of tropical rainforests generates both cooling and warming climate forcings. The bare ground reflects more sunlight back out into space than the highly absorbing forest, so this has a cooling effect. However, a larger effect is the warming due to the release of the forest's carbon dioxide into the atmosphere and the absence of those trees that otherwise would have continued absorbing carbon, so the net result of deforestation is warming.

Albedo of Various Surfaces

What are **the albedos** of different types of surfaces?

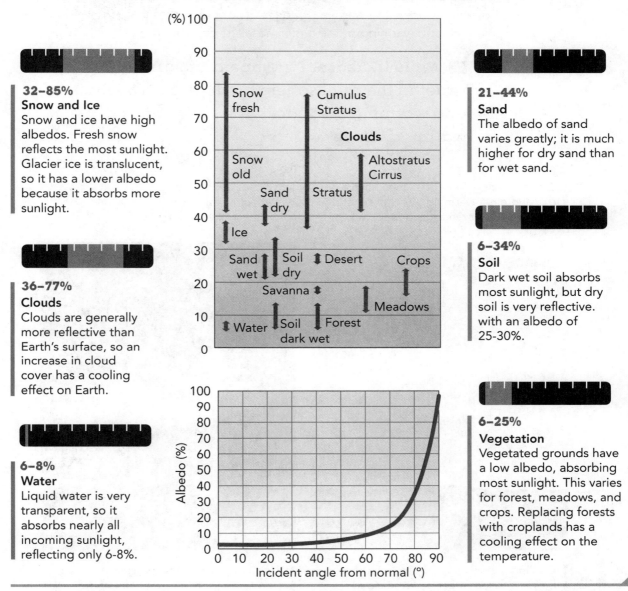

32–85%
Snow and Ice
Snow and ice have high albedos. Fresh snow reflects the most sunlight. Glacier ice is translucent, so it has a lower albedo because it absorbs more sunlight.

36–77%
Clouds
Clouds are generally more reflective than Earth's surface, so an increase in cloud cover has a cooling effect on Earth.

6–8%
Water
Liquid water is very transparent, so it absorbs nearly all incoming sunlight, reflecting only 6-8%.

21–44%
Sand
The albedo of sand varies greatly; it is much higher for dry sand than for wet sand.

6–34%
Soil
Dark wet soil absorbs most sunlight, but dry soil is very reflective. with an albedo of 25-30%.

6–25%
Vegetation
Vegetated grounds have a low albedo, absorbing most sunlight. This varies for forest, meadows, and crops. Replacing forests with croplands has a cooling effect on the temperature.

Albedo is the proportion of incoming sunlight that reflects off of an object's surface. On Earth it is an important factor for retaining solar energy and therefore for climate. Albedo varies for different materials and also by incident angle; it increases as the angle of light relative to the surface increases, and so is naturally higher at Earth's poles.

(21) **SEP Analyze and Interpret Data** Construct an explanation for why croplands would have a higher albedo than forests. ✏️

....

....

Evaporation Feedbacks

An increase in Earth's temperatures causes an increase in evaporation and precipitation as the warming of ocean water increases evaporation from its surface and warming of the air increases its capacity to hold water vapor.

▶ **While increases in temperature and in water in the atmosphere produce both cooling and warming feedbacks, the net result is a warming effect.**

Cloud Forcing Though clouds have a net cooling effect during the day and a net warming effect at night, the overall effect is warming, providing a net reinforcing feedback for atmospheric warming.

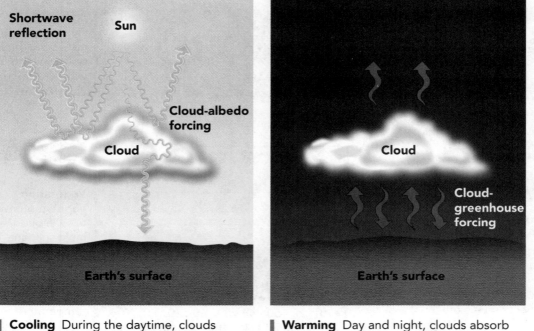

Cooling During the daytime, clouds have a cooling effect because cloud tops reflect some sunlight (mostly visible wavelengths) back into space. This is a counterbalancing feedback.

Warming Day and night, clouds absorb a portion of the long-wavelength infrared radiation emitted from Earth's surface. The clouds re-emit the infrared radiation, warming the atmosphere. This is a reinforcing feedback.

(22) **SEP Design Solutions** Jet airplanes create long, straight clouds called contrails. How could you change the schedules of airplane flights to reduce their warming impact? ✏️

....

....

....

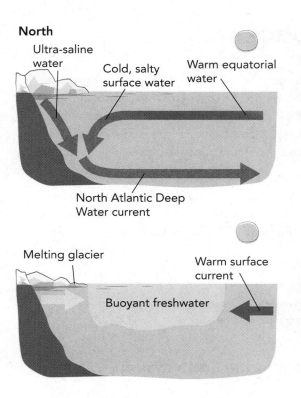

North

Ultra-saline water

Cold, salty surface water

Warm equatorial water

North Atlantic Deep Water current

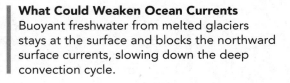

Melting glacier

Warm surface current

Buoyant freshwater

How Currents Work Density differences between the cold and salty polar waters and the warmer equatorial waters drives the global convection cycle of deep ocean currents. In the Atlantic Ocean, ultra-saline water created when sea ice forms joins the cold and salty northward-flowing surface water to form the North Atlantic Deep Water current that drives Atlantic Ocean Circulation.

What Could Weaken Ocean Currents Buoyant freshwater from melted glaciers stays at the surface and blocks the northward surface currents, slowing down the deep convection cycle.

The Ocean and Carbon Dioxide

The ocean is involved in several feedbacks affecting carbon dioxide in the atmosphere. Ocean waters provide a strong counterbalancing feedback to global warming by absorbing CO_2 from the atmosphere, reducing the greenhouse effect. About 30% of the CO_2 that humans have released in the past century has been absorbed by the ocean.

However, reinforcing feedbacks also exist. When ocean water warms, it can hold less dissolved CO_2 than it otherwise would. This means more CO_2 in the atmosphere and more greenhouse warming. In addition, as water at the poles warms, the difference in temperature between equatorial waters and polar waters decreases, slowing the pattern of global ocean circulation, and reducing the ocean's ability to remove CO_2 from the atmosphere.

(23) **SEP Construct and Use Models** You have probably had the experience of leaving a cold bubbly soda out in the open and finding that it had gone flat when it warmed up. (The bubbles are CO_2.) Explain how this phenomenon can be used to model the ocean's ability to store CO_2. 🖉

....

....

....

Biomass Feedbacks

The biosphere provides a strong counterbalancing feedback for global warming because plants absorb carbon dioxide. The more carbon dioxide in the atmosphere, the larger the biomass of the biosphere becomes, removing about a quarter of the CO_2 that humans release into the atmosphere each year. It is unclear how long this feedback will exist.

Only about 45% of the CO_2 that humans release into the atmosphere stays there. About 30% is absorbed by the ocean, and 25% by plants. Human release of CO_2 has more than doubled in the past 50 years, but plants and the ocean have removed more than half of it. Biomass absorption varies with climate fluctuations.

Biosphere Carbon The biosphere is estimated to contain about 550 billion tons of carbon, mostly in forest trees. Each year, plants produce new biomass containing over 100 billion tons of carbon.

Carbon Dioxide and the Earth System

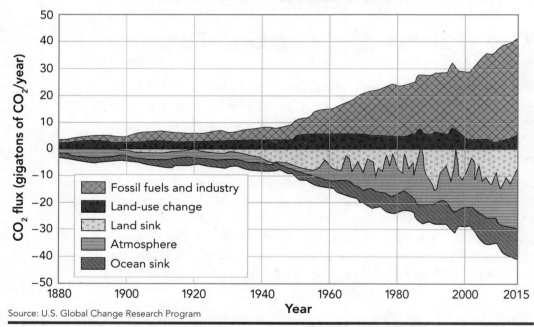

Source: U.S. Global Change Research Program

(24) SEP Design Solutions Describe what humans can do in the future using the biosphere to reduce CO_2 levels in the atmosphere. ✏️

....

....

Methane Hydrate Feedbacks

Two significant reinforcing feedbacks, one in the frigid tundras and another in offshore ocean sediments, occur with the vast amounts of frozen methane gas hydrates called clathrates. Rapid warming in the Arctic is melting the permafrost of the tundras and releasing methane (a powerful greenhouse gas), driving more warming. Methane is also released when offshore waters warm, melting their frozen clathrates. The huge volume of offshore clathrates poses a serious threat for global warming.

Atmospheric Methane Global atmospheric methane levels have been rising due to many human factors, including agriculture, but the melting of clathrates is a significant one. Methane in the atmosphere converts into carbon dioxide in about a decade, but while it remains it is more than 20 times more powerful as a greenhouse gas.

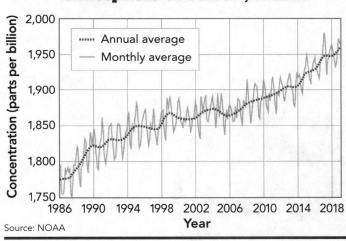

Methane (CH_4) in the Atmosphere at Barrow, Alaska

Concentration (parts per billion) vs. Year

- ...... Annual average
- —— Monthly average

Source: NOAA

Burning Methane Clathrate It might be strange to see a piece of ice burn, but this isn't ordinary ice. This is a piece of methane clathrate—a combination of frozen methane and water.

(25) **SEP Analyze and Interpret Data** Notice how the amount of methane measured in the atmosphere at Barrow, Alaska changes over time. Construct an explanation for why the trend may continue upward in the future. ✎

....

....

....

Surface Radiation Feedbacks

Feedbacks and Equilibrium One of the most important counterbalancing feedbacks is surface radiation feedback—the release of more and more energy as an object gets hotter. This means the more an object heats up, the faster it also cools off. Hotter objects release electromagnetic radiation at shorter wavelengths than cooler objects. The sun emits short-wavelength visible light because its photosphere is about 5800 K. In contrast, a person emits long-wavelength infrared radiation because the skin's surface is only 310 K (37°C). In addition, each square meter of the sun's visible surface emits a lot more energy than a person does. The energy emitted per square meter is proportional to T^4 – the fourth power of the temperature. The sun's surface temperature is 17 times hotter than that of a person, but it releases energy at a rate that is 80,000 times greater, for each square meter. So, as Earth's surface temperature increases, the amount it radiates back out into space also increases, until it approaches an equilibrium and stops getting hotter. However, it also means that if the greenhouse effect keeps increasing, Earth's surface will keep getting hotter as that equilibrium shifts over time.

Planetary Atmospheres The atmospheres of Venus, Earth, and Mars have very different temperatures and pressures, but Mars and Venus have runaway greenhouse feedbacks. Both planets have atmospheres of about 96% CO_2 (compared to only 0.04% for Earth).

Venus
Surface Temperature: 462°C
Atmospheric pressure: 91 Atm

Earth
Surface Temperature: 15°C
Atmospheric pressure: 1 Atm

Mars
Surface Temperature: −63°C
Atmospheric pressure: 0.003 Atm

(26) **SEP Construct Explanations** From what you know about differences between the surfaces of Venus, Earth, and Mars, construct an explanation for why Earth's atmosphere contains such a smaller percentage of CO_2 than both of its neighbors, Venus and Mars. ✏️

....

....

The Impact of Small Temperature Changes Earth's average surface temperature is about 15°C. If this temperature were to increase, the planet would emit more radiation. How significant would this change be? Suppose that the average temperature increases from 15°C to 20°C. The amount of radiation emitted at each temperature may be estimated by reading the peak spectral intensity of the corresponding black-body curve. On the graph, the 20°C curve has a peak spectral intensity of about 27.5. The graph does not include a 15°C curve, but we can estimate a value of 25.5 by interpolating between the 20°C and 30°C curves.

Black-Body Curves for Typical Terrestrial Temperatures

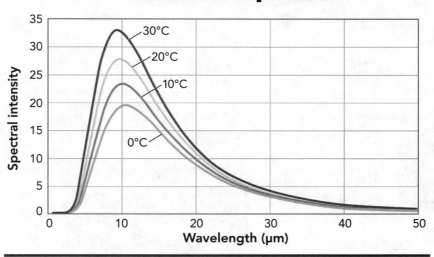

Ideal Curves Most objects do not radiate like perfect black bodies, but the curves reflect the general behavior of matter at different temperatures.

To calculate the percentage increase in temperature, we must use the Kelvin scale: 15°C = 288 K; 20°C = 293 K. The temperature increased by 1.7%, a factor of 1.017. But the spectral intensity increased by 7.8%, a factor of 1.078 (from 25.5 to 27.5). This is because spectral intensity increases with the fourth power of the temperature. We can verify this by raising the temperature change factor (1.017) to the fourth power: $(1.017)^4 = 1.07$, which is approximately the spectral intensity increase factor.

(27) **SEP Develop and Use Models** Use the information provided by the 30°C curve in the graph to estimate the percent increase in Earth's emitted radiation if the surface temperature of the planet increased from 15°C to 30°C. ✎

Arctic Sea Ice Feedbacks

A very significant reinforcing feedback occurs with ice in the Arctic Sea because ice is much more reflective (albedo between 35 and 80%) than ocean water (albedo = 6%). As the sea warms and more ice melts, the exposed ocean water absorbs more sunlight, accelerating the warming.

Arctic Sea Ice Melts The cycle begins with warm water and air melting the thin, floating arctic ice sheet. Global warming has significantly reduced its size over the past century.

Albedo Decreases As the reflective sea ice disappears, it leaves the darker ocean water exposed, which absorbs more of incoming sunlight during summer months, when the sun shines 24 hours a day in the Arctic Circle.

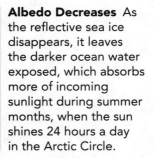

Temperatures Rise The added sunlight causes the Arctic water to warm, and it couples with the atmosphere to cause it to warm as well. The result is more melting of Arctic ice, and the cycle repeats.

(28) **SEP Analyze and Interpret Data** The graph shows the extent of sea ice over the past 1400 years. How much did the area of ice change prior to 1800? How much is the loss of sea ice area since 1800? ✏️

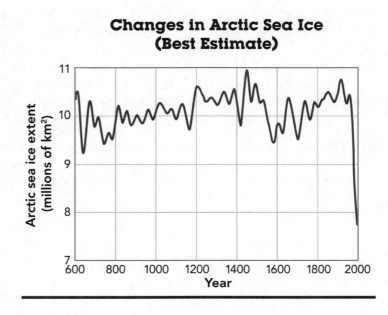

Changes in Arctic Sea Ice (Best Estimate)

Glacier Feedbacks

The melting of glaciers provides additional reinforcing feedbacks that lead to a decrease in ice. When glaciers melt, their fronts recede to higher elevations, exposing rock underneath. This rock absorbs more sunlight than the highly reflective ice and snow, and this warms the ground and leads to more melting. In addition, the loss of water due to the shrinking area of ice reduces the amount of regional water that evaporates and sublimates. This can reduce the snowfall that is needed to replenish the constantly flowing glaciers.

(29) CCC Stability and Change If the area exposed in the image of the glacier in the Purcell Mountains occurred over a period of 25 years, estimate the years until the rest of the glacier melts. 🖊

....

Receding Glacier Trees have yet to grow in the area left exposed from a receding glacier in the Purcell Mountains of British Columbia.

Revisit

INVESTIGATIVE PHENOMENON 🖥

GO ONLINE to Elaborate on and Evaluate your knowledge of atmospheric feedback systems by completing the class discussion and engineering design activities.

In the CER worksheet, you drafted a scientific argument about the possible causes of droughts. With a partner, reevaluate the evidence cited in your arguments.

(30) SEP Engage in Argument Describe a reinforcing or counterbalancing factor you think can cause droughts in California. Explain your reasoning. 🖊

....

....

....

....

....

....

Long-Term Climate Factors

 GO ONLINE to Explore and Explain the factors that cause climate to change over very long periods of time.

Climate Zones: Latitude and Altitude

Earth contains a great diversity of regional climates, which are critical in determining the biomes and communities of life that have evolved across the planet. Maps of Earth's climate zones have a limited usefulness because the zones constantly shift as regional and global climates change. However, these maps reveal that patterns of wet and dry zones are largely a result of latitude and altitude: temperatures decrease toward the poles, or as altitude increases.

Map of Climate Zones The Köppen climate map groups Earth's diverse climates into about a dozen types that allow for an analysis of patterns in climate variations.

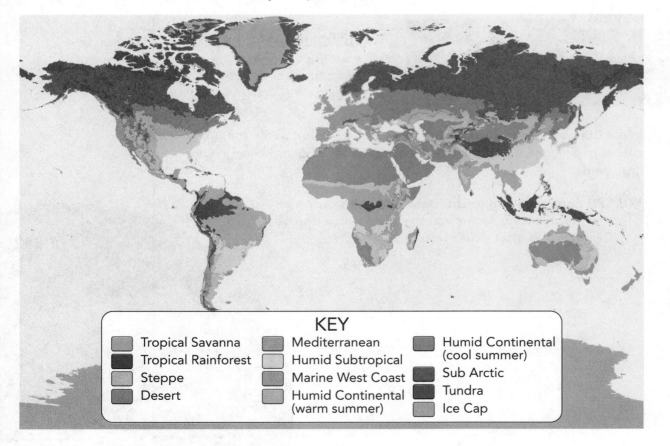

KEY
- Tropical Savanna
- Tropical Rainforest
- Steppe
- Desert
- Mediterranean
- Humid Subtropical
- Marine West Coast
- Humid Continental (warm summer)
- Humid Continental (cool summer)
- Sub Arctic
- Tundra
- Ice Cap

Long-Term Changes in Sunlight

The sun is the most important factor in Earth's weather and climate. Earth's surface would be nothing but ice if it were not for sunlight, but the amount of sunlight the planet receives is not constant. Like other stars, the sun changes over its lifetime. The energy of sunlight comes from the nuclear fusion of hydrogen atoms into helium within the sun's core. As the sun runs out of hydrogen, it will fuse helium to make larger elements, getting steadily hotter and more intense. The sun's output is 30% greater than when it formed, 4.6 billion years ago, and increases by 1% every hundred million years. The sun will likely remain a star for 4 to 5 billion years, but it will be hot enough to boil away Earth's ocean in less than a billion years.

Structure of the Sun The sun is primarily made of hydrogen and helium. Because of the extreme temperatures, atoms in the sun exist as a plasma, with electrons stripped off of the nuclei. That plasma forms several different layers.

Energy leaves the sun's **photosphere** primarily in the form of electromagnetic radiation (sunlight).

The sun's energy comes from the fusion of 620 million tons of hydrogen into helium each second in its **core.**

Energy radiates outward from the core through the **radiative zone** as high-frequency gamma rays, taking over 100,000 years to reach the convective zone.

In the **convective zone,** energy is primarily carried from the radiative zone to the sun's outer layers through plasma convection.

(31) **CCC Stability and Change** Liquid water has existed on Earth's surface for at least 4 billion years, even as the sun's energy output has continued to increase. The total area of continents (now 39% of Earth's surface) may have grown in size over Earth's history. Think about what you know about the albedos of land and water. Does an increase in land area explain why Earth's surface hasn't heated to a point that the ocean has boiled away? Why or why not? 🖊

....

....

Past Climates

Determining a history of Earth's past temperature is challenging; scientists infer it from "proxy" data, which are other data sets that are a function of temperature. The most useful recent data set starts with the evolution of hard-shelled life forms at the start of the Cambrian Period, about 540 million years ago. This record shows periods of ice ages (when significant amounts of water were stored on land as glacial ice sheets) and warm periods (when there was little ice). Glacial periods have lasted for tens of millions of years. Earth has been in one such cold period for the past 50 million years. Not much is known about ancient climates for the first three-fourths of Earth's history because so few rocks remain from this time.

Oxygen Isotope Data Past temperatures can be inferred from the ratios of ^{16}O and ^{18}O isotopes in clam shells. Because ^{16}O is lighter than ^{18}O, the ^{16}O isotopes evaporate more easily. Rain, snow, and glaciers therefore contain very little ^{18}O, which stays in the ocean. Time periods that show an increase in ^{18}O in clam shells indicate that a great deal of ice (containing ^{16}O) was stored on land in glaciers.

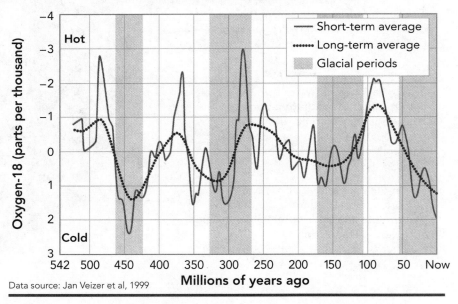

Phanerozoic Climate Change

Data source: Jan Veizer et al, 1999

(32) **SEP Analyze and Interpret Data** Calculate the mean time between the starts of cold glacial periods over the past 500 million years.

Changing Composition of Earth's Atmosphere Earth's surface was blistering hot in its early years. It was almost completely molten, and greenhouse gases such as methane, water vapor, and carbon dioxide dominated the atmosphere. Life and the ocean gradually removed most of Earth's atmospheric CO_2.

Composition of Earth's Atmosphere

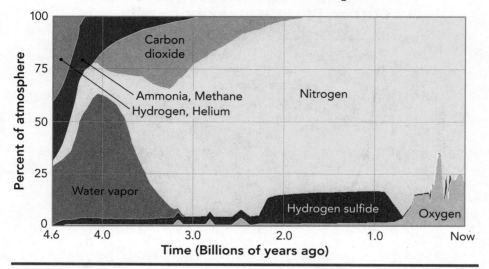

Life and Carbon Dioxide

Life has had a dramatic effect on all of Earth's surface systems, especially the atmosphere. If not for plant life and the ocean, the atmosphere would be mostly carbon dioxide. The ocean began removing carbon dioxide from the atmosphere more than 4 billion years ago. The later expansion of photosynthetic plant life brought atmospheric CO_2 levels nearly to zero (0.04%), keeping Earth's surface from becoming too hot and uninhabitable. The atmospheric carbon removed by life was stored away in the ground as rocks such as limestone and fossil fuels such as coal, oil, and natural gas.

(33) SEP Construct Explanations Explain why it would make sense that the amount of water vapor in Earth's atmosphere would decrease as Earth's surface cooled. Where did that water go? ✏️

....

....

....

....

....

Atmospheric Carbon Dioxide and the Diversity of Life The levels of atmospheric CO_2 have fluctuated over Earth's history, as have the number of genera, which are groups of similar species. Scientists do not have a good way to measure the volumes of past biomass, but the diversity of life can be used as a rough indicator of the degree to which life had expanded.

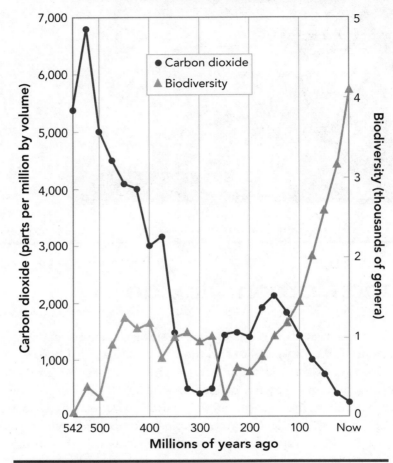

Carbon Dioxide and Biodiversity

CO_2 and Biodiversity Over the past 542 million years, the amount of carbon dioxide in the atmosphere has decreased while the diversity (and number) of living things has increased.

(34) **SEP Analyze and Interpret Data** Observe the correlation between the patterns of the two curves. Land plants evolved about 470 million years ago and expanded across the continents, developing into forests. Explain the carbon dioxide curve during this time. ✏️

....

....

....

Volcanic Activity and CO$_2$

While not occurring now, there have been times in Earth's history, usually associated with the initial arrival of mantle plumes of hot rock at the surface, when vast amounts of lava have erupted for millions of years. This volcanic activity has triggered extended warm periods.

◼ **Extended periods of volcanic activity add large amounts of CO$_2$ to the atmosphere.**

| **Areas of Large Flood Basalts** Basalt rock forms from cooling lava. Due to mid-ocean ridge volcanism, the ocean seafloor is mostly basalt. However, there are times when large volcanoes have erupted for millions of years, sometimes in the middle of plates. These regions are called **flood basalts.**

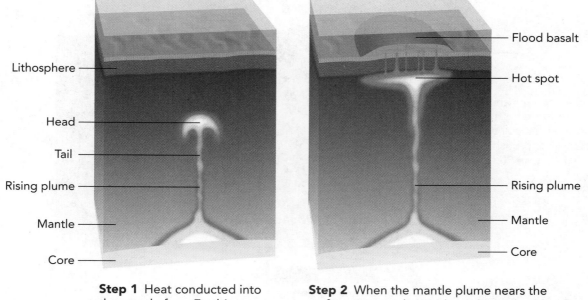

Lithosphere

Head

Tail

Rising plume

Mantle

Core

Flood basalt

Hot spot

Rising plume

Mantle

Core

Step 1 Heat conducted into the mantle from Earth's core can cause a plume of hot mantle rock to rise a few centimeters per year toward the surface.

Step 2 When the mantle plume nears the surface, it spreads out along the underside of the lithosphere. Heat from the plume melts part of the lithosphere above it, causing eruptions of magma that then cool to form flood basalts.

(35) **SEP Construct Explanations** The "Deccan Traps," large flood basalts covering much of western India, formed around 66 million years ago. What effects did their formation likely have on Earth's atmosphere? Explain. ✏️

....

....

Erosion and Carbon Dioxide

The chemical weathering of rocks removes CO_2 from the atmosphere, reducing the greenhouse effect. Carbon dioxide in the atmosphere reacts with water vapor to form carbonic acid (H_2CO_3), which makes rain water slightly acidic and accelerates the weathering of minerals. The carbon, often in the form of bicarbonate ions (HCO_3^-), enters the ocean. It becomes part of the shells of marine organisms, and when they die, is stored away under the seafloor as sedimentary limestone. Periods of increased erosion, such as when large mountain ranges are uplifted, can contribute to global cooling through the removal of CO_2 from Earth's surface systems.

Erosion of the Himalayan Plateau The high erosion rates of the Himalayan Plateau over the past 50 million years have removed significant amounts of CO_2 from the atmosphere.

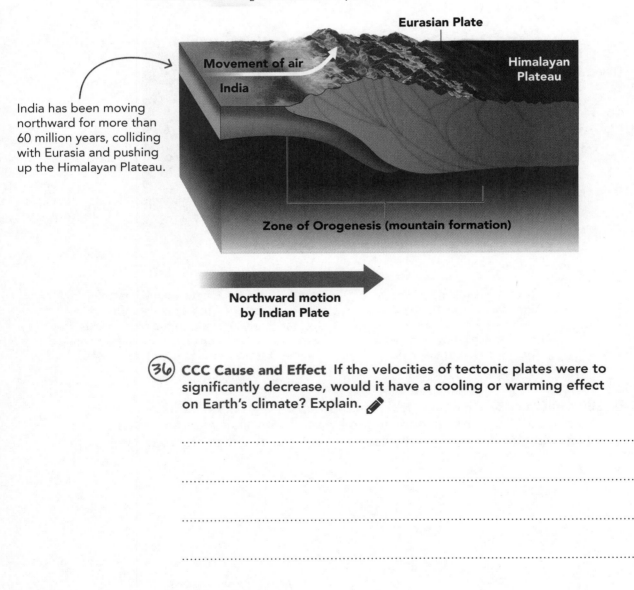

India has been moving northward for more than 60 million years, colliding with Eurasia and pushing up the Himalayan Plateau.

Eurasian Plate

Movement of air

India

Himalayan Plateau

Zone of Orogenesis (mountain formation)

Northward motion by Indian Plate

(36) **CCC Cause and Effect** If the velocities of tectonic plates were to significantly decrease, would it have a cooling or warming effect on Earth's climate? Explain. 🖊

....

....

....

....

Climates During Pangaea (350–250 Million Years Ago) India and Australia show evidence of large glaciers 300 million years ago because at that time they were adjacent to Antarctica, near the South Pole. Patterns of past regional climates on continents only make sense when the locations of the continents in the past are considered.

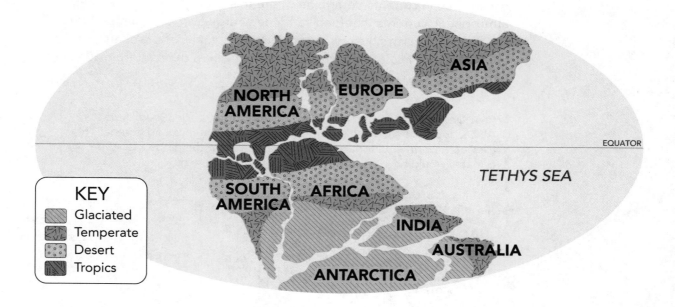

KEY
- Glaciated
- Temperate
- Desert
- Tropics

Continent Distributions and Ocean Currents

Continental Distribution Due to plate tectonics, the sizes and locations of continents have continually changed over the past 4 billion years. Regional climates are affected by the locations of the continents in relation to atmospheric circulation cells and air currents. Fragmented continents experience steadier climates due to the moderating effect of the surrounding ocean water. Large supercontinents tend to have monsoon climates, with alternating wet and dry seasons.

The amount of continent surface that is above sealevel is also an important climate factor. Though continents occupy 39% of Earth's surface, about 8% of this surface is now underwater in the form of continental shelves. Due to differences in albedo of land and water, a reinforcing feedback occurs during ice ages when glaciers accumulate on land: sea level drops, shorelines recede, and less ocean surface results in less sunlight absorbed by the low-albedo ocean.

37 **CCC Cause and Effect** The United States has the largest deposits of coal in the world. Coal forms from fossilized swamp vegetation. Use the map to explain why most of these coal deposits likely formed between 350 and 250 million years ago. ✏️

....

....

....

Ocean Circulation Patterns Ocean currents are a major climate factor because ocean water stores an enormous amount of energy and ocean currents move this energy around the planet in the form of heat. Not only does ocean water cover most of Earth, but it absorbs 94% of the sunlight that hits it. Therefore, most of the sun's energy ends up in the ocean. Ocean currents determine where this energy ends up, warming atmospheric currents that then carry the energy over continents. During the course of Earth's history, changes in the outlines of the continents have altered ocean circulation patterns, affecting where the heat from sunlight ultimately ended up.

Past Ocean Surface Currents Only 50 million years ago, South America, Africa, and Australia were separated from North America and Eurasia. This allowed a warm equatorial current to travel around the globe. Regional climates would have been very different than they are now.

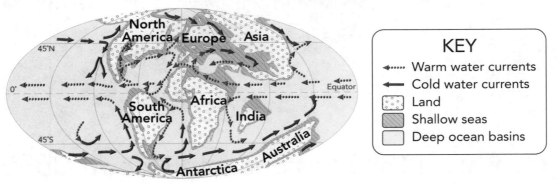

Revisit

INVESTIGATIVE PHENOMENON

GO ONLINE to Elaborate on and Evaluate your knowledge of long-term climate factors by completing the peer review and writing activities.

In the CER worksheet, you drafted a scientific argument about the possible causes of droughts. With a partner, reevaluate the evidence cited in your arguments.

(38) **SEP Engage in Argument** How does the vicinity of the Pacific Ocean affect California's climate? Explain.

....

....

....

....

....

Short-Term Climate Factors

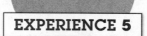 **GO ONLINE** to Explore and Explain the short-term and intermediate-term factors that affect Earth's climate.

Cycles within Cycles

Climate Cycles Earth's climate at any given time is a function of long-, intermediate-, and short-term factors. As a result, there are climate cycles within cycles within cycles. At the moment, Earth has been cooling over the long term for the past 60 million years, cooling over the intermediate term since the peak of the present interglacial period (7500 years ago), and warming over the short term from human contributions. Importantly, scientists are beginning to understand how all of these different factors combine to affect global climates.

Solar Fluctuations A graph of annual average global temperatures shows the contributions from different factors. Part of the wobble results from an 11-year cycle of fluctuating solar output.

The overall upward trend is a result of the increase in greenhouse gases such as carbon dioxide from the human combustion of coal, oil, and natural gas.

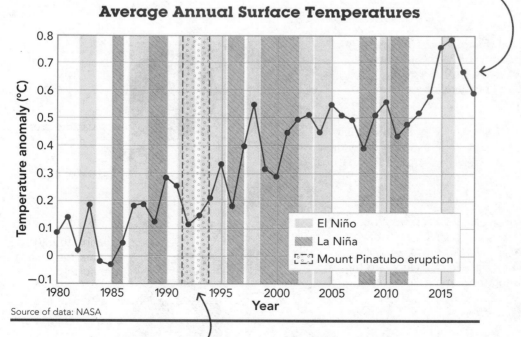

Average Annual Surface Temperatures

Source of data: NASA

The eruption of Pinatubo caused global cooling, even though this occurred during an El Niño period, when global climates would otherwise have been warmer than usual.

El Niño / La Niña The shaded bars show times of El Niño and La Niña currents in the Pacific Ocean. Heat is borrowed from the Pacific Ocean during El Niño episodes, so mean surface temperatures increase.

Milankovitch Cycles

How do Earth's orbital cycles affect its **long-term climate variations?**

Orbital Parameters Earth's long-term climate variations are dominated by forces outside of our planet: the gravitational tugs of other planets, primarily Jupiter and Saturn. The variations in **three orbital parameters, called the Milankovitch cycles**, control the timing of ice ages and other intermediate-term climate changes.

Eccentricity The longest of the Milankovitch cycles is the change to the shape of Earth's orbit around the sun that occurs on a scale of **100,000 to 413,000 years.**

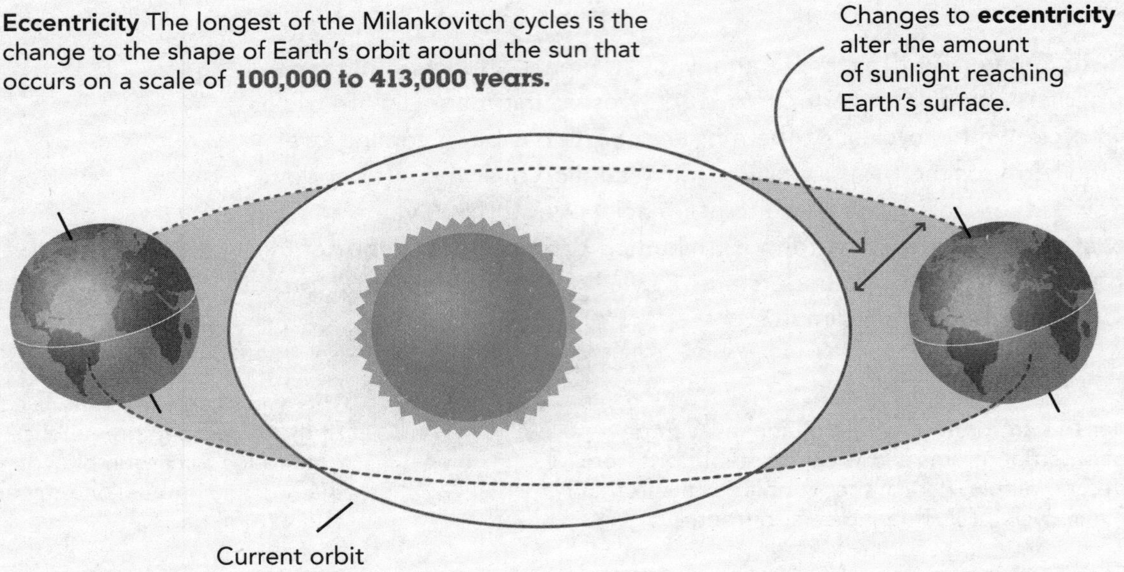

Changes to **eccentricity** alter the amount of sunlight reaching Earth's surface.

Current orbit

Tilt Gradual changes occur to the tilt, or obliquity, of Earth's rotation axis about every **41,000 years.** The moon's gravity helps stabilize Earth's tilt.

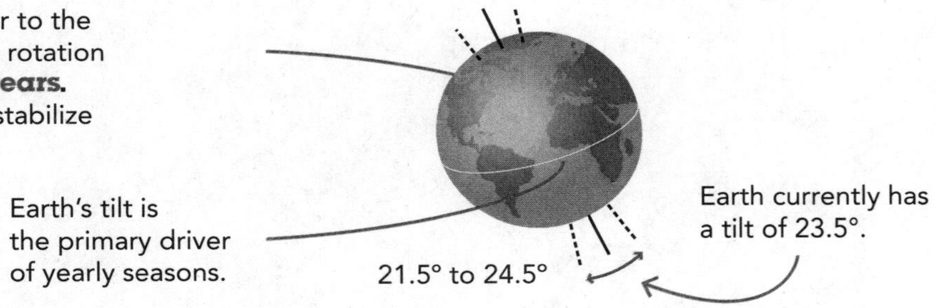

Earth's tilt is the primary driver of yearly seasons.

21.5° to 24.5°

Earth currently has a tilt of 23.5°.

Precession Like a wobbly toy top, Earth also wobbles on its axis every **19,000 to 24,000 years**, changing which hemisphere points toward the sun during the summer and winter.

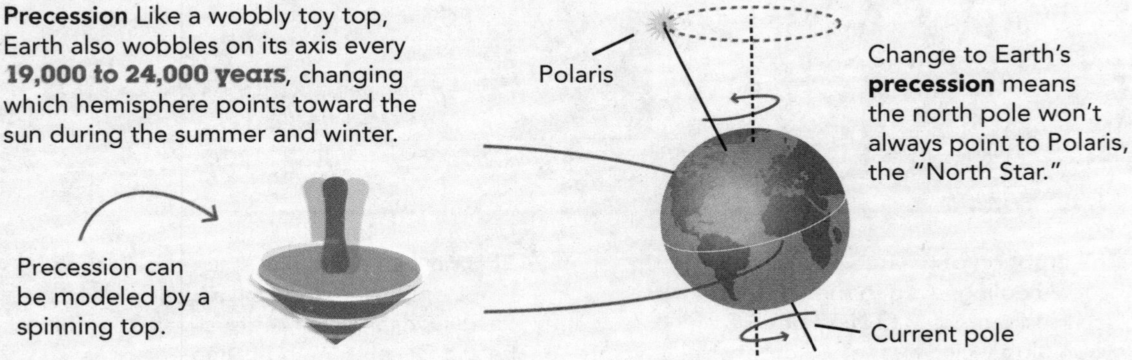

Polaris

Change to Earth's **precession** means the north pole won't always point to Polaris, the "North Star."

Precession can be modeled by a spinning top.

Current pole

Solar Variations The variation in Earth's eccentricity is the only one of the three Milankovitch cycles that actually changes the total amount of sunlight Earth receives in a year. However, the three cycles work together in important ways. A planet moves faster in its orbit when it swings by closer to the sun, and more slowly when it is farthest from the sun. Continents are more reflective than ocean water, and most continents are in the Northern Hemisphere. Therefore, whether the Northern or Southern Hemisphere points toward the sun when Earth swings closest to the sun affects how much total sunlight Earth absorbs in a year. The tilt of Earth's axis as it passes close to the sun also impacts how much sunlight is reflected or absorbed.

Orbital Cycles and Global Climate The graph shows the calculated Milankovitch cycles over the past million years, as well as how they would sum up ("Solar Forcing") at a location 65°N. The bottom curve shows Earth's actual global temperature record, based on the ice core record.

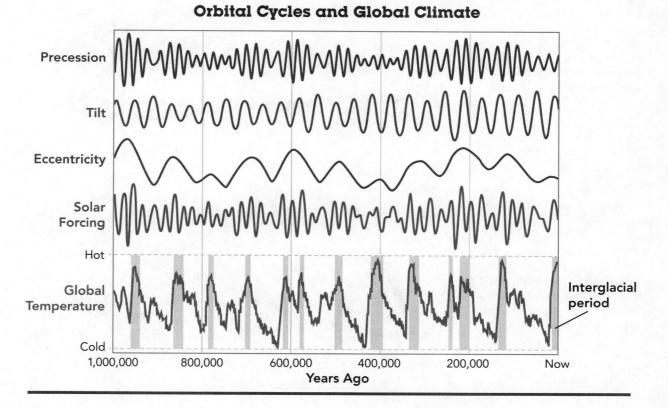

Orbital Cycles and Global Climate

(39) **SEP Develop and Use Models** Study the curve for stages of glaciation and then study the curve showing eccentricity. Describe how well the two curves correspond to one another. Explain what this suggests about the possible cause of the recent cycle of ice ages. ✏️

....

....

....

Ocean/Atmosphere Circulation Changes

Ocean currents are constantly shifting in many different ways. Because of the ocean's important role in moving heat around the planet, these shifting ocean currents are responsible for much of the regional climate variations that occur over the time scale of decades. Sometimes, these variations repeat with enough regularity that they are given names. The most important of these is the

El Niño Southern Oscillation (ENSO). During average times, there is a steady westward current along the equatorial regions of the Pacific Ocean that brings warm water to the western Pacific. However, this current is altered during El Niño and La Niña phases. The results are changes in global atmospheric currents and the distribution of heat around the planet.

El Niño During an El Niño, warm waters in the western Pacific start flowing towards the east. The polar atmospheric jet stream carries warm and dry air to central North America. The Pacific jet stream is strong and brings cooler air and lots of rain to southern North America.

La Niña During a La Niña, the warm westward equatorial ocean current gets stronger, bringing more warm water to the west Pacific. A high-pressure zone in the North Pacific brings cold air with frequent rains to central North America, and warmer drier air to the south.

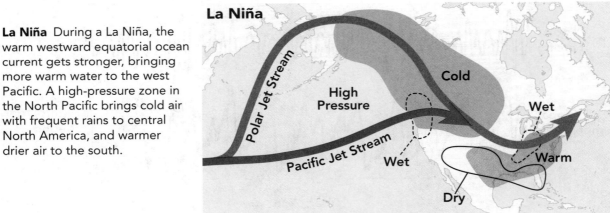

(40) **SEP Analyze and Interpret Data** Suppose that you are a farmer living in Texas. Would you prefer an El Niño or La Niña phase of Pacific Ocean oscillation? Use the maps to construct an explanation to support your response. ✏️

....

....

Variations in Solar Output

Shorter-Term Fluctuations The amount of light Earth receives from the sun fluctuates over the time scale of decades to centuries, affecting global temperatures. The sun's magnetic field flips polarity approximately every 11 years (the full cycle lasts about 22 years), and the total amount of radiation Earth receives varies by about 0.25 W/m² over this cycle.

The number of sunspots also varies over an 11-year cycle, correlated with the irradiance. This is useful because we have records of the number of sunspots going back to 1610, when Galileo first started using telescopes to observe the sun. This extends our record of the solar cycle back 400 years.

> **Sunspots** Sunspots are not physical objects, but slightly cooler regions of the sun's photosphere. The arcing solar prominences leave and return to the sun at the locations of the sunspots. When the sun's surface is hotter and energetic, there are more prominences and sunspots.

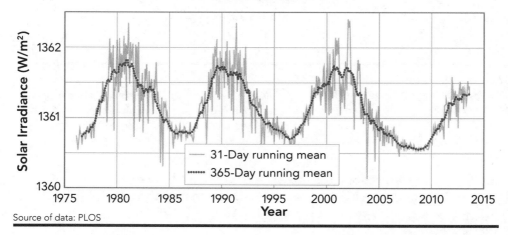

Solar Irradiance

Source of data: PLOS

> **Solar Irradiance** Due to the reversals of the sun's magnetic field, the amount of sunlight reaching Earth's orbit fluctuates by about 1 W/m², approximately between 1360.7 and 1361.7 W/m². However, because this sunlight gets distributed across the sphere of Earth's surface, averaging about 340 W/m² at any point on Earth's surface, the climate forcing from these sunlight fluctuations is about 0.25 W/m².

Longer-Term Fluctuations The amount of sunlight Earth receives also fluctuates over centuries. A useful proxy for this is the record of carbon-14 (^{14}C) production in the atmosphere. Carbon-14 decays over time, but it is replenished when cosmic rays from distant supernovae interact with nitrogen-14 (^{14}N) in the air. When the sun is more active, its stronger solar wind interferes with the cosmic rays, slowing ^{14}C production. The ^{14}C record for the past thousand years shows several pronounced dips that correspond to four distinct episodes of cold temperatures during the Little Ice Age, which extended from about 1300 to 1850. These periods of low solar activity—the Wolf, Spörer, Maunder, and Dalton minima—were times of extreme cold, frequent crop failures, famines, and human conflict. The impacts of the Little Ice Age on human cultures were large, even though the global decrease in temperature was only about 0.5°C.

Solar Activity from ^{14}C Production The record of changes in ^{14}C production serves as a proxy for solar activity. The production of ^{14}C decreases (negative values) when solar activity increases.

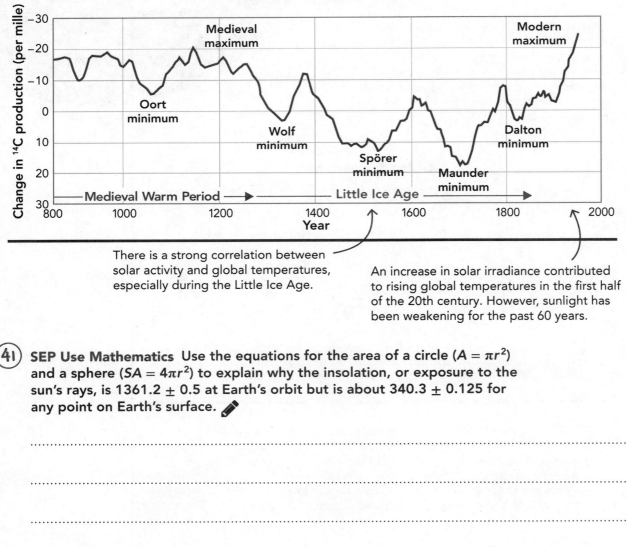

Carbon–14 Over Time

There is a strong correlation between solar activity and global temperatures, especially during the Little Ice Age.

An increase in solar irradiance contributed to rising global temperatures in the first half of the 20th century. However, sunlight has been weakening for the past 60 years.

41 **SEP Use Mathematics** Use the equations for the area of a circle ($A = \pi r^2$) and a sphere ($SA = 4\pi r^2$) to explain why the insolation, or exposure to the sun's rays, is 1361.2 ± 0.5 at Earth's orbit but is about 340.3 ± 0.125 for any point on Earth's surface. ✏️

....

....

....

....

Volcanic Eruptions

Cooling Effects Volcanic eruptions can increase global warming through the release of CO_2, but they have more significant short-term cooling effects. Erupted sulfur dioxide (SO_2) reacts with water vapor in the atmosphere to form tiny droplets (aerosols) of liquid sulfuric acid (H_2SO_4). These aerosols and volcanic ash block out sunlight and cause a cooling period that can last for years or much longer for large eruptions. Several historical periods of cold temperatures, agricultural failure, and famines correlate with large volcanic eruptions.

Average Surface Temperature Changes

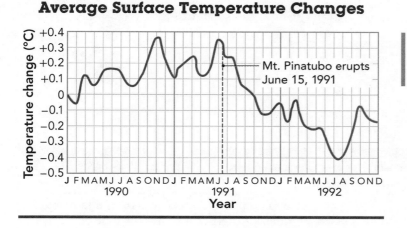

Mt. Pinatubo erupts
June 15, 1991

Pinatubo Temperature Impact Global temperatures dropped by more than a half-degree over the year following the eruption of Mt. Pinatubo.

Mt. Redoubt (Alaska) The eruption of Mt. Redoubt in 2009 ejected vast volumes of volcanic rock, ash, and millions of tons of sulfur dioxide (SO_2) into the atmosphere.

Erupted ash and sulfuric acid (H_2SO_4) aerosols block out a portion of sunlight (yellow arrows), reflecting it back into space, causing a net cooling effect.

Historic Impacts There have been many climate-altering volcanic eruptions over the past 1000 years. The effects of these eruptions have been quantified in records of ice cores and tree-ring growth, as well as documented in historical records. The release of millions of tons of sulfate aerosols affects climates by altering atmospheric patterns, causing extreme weather events such as snow in the summer, flooding, or droughts, as well as crop failures, famines, epidemics, and large-scale human migration.

Large Eruptions Most of the volcanic eruptions that altered global climates have occurred within the Ring of Fire, the belt of subduction zones that borders much of the Pacific Ocean.

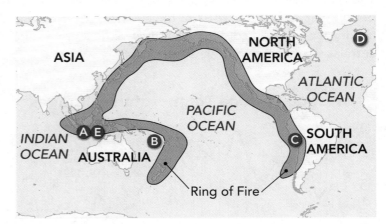

	Large Volcanic Eruptions		
Year	Volcano, Location	H$_2$SO$_4$*	Impact
Ⓐ 1257	Rinjani/ Samalas, Lombok (Indonesia)	~158	global cold temperatures, crop failures, and famines; helped trigger the start of the Little Ice Age
Ⓑ 1452	Kuwae, Vanuatu	~250–400	tree growth stunted globally; severe famines in China; Yellow River frozen for 20 km out to sea; contributed to the 2nd phase of the Little Ice Age
Ⓒ 1600	Huaynaputina, Peru	55	severe cold and famines in Northern Hemisphere, particularly Russia; agricultural collapses in South America and Europe
Ⓓ 1783	Laki, Iceland	120	global freezing; droughts and famines in Africa and Southern Asia; severe weather and crop failures in Europe; contributed to the French Revolution
Ⓔ 1815	Tambora Sumbawa (Indonesia)	90–120	extreme cold and flooding in Europe; extreme cold and famines in Eastern North America, driving the settling of western US territories; extreme flooding in south Asia, triggering a global cholera pandemic

*Volume of sulfate aerosols (million tonnes)

42 **SEP Construct Explanations** Examine the map of the Ring of Fire. Construct an explanation for why most large-scale volcanic eruptions occur in and around the area highlighted on the map. ✏️

....

....

....

Climate and Humans

Prehistoric Impacts Climate has impacted human history in many more ways than just volcanic eruptions. When climates were favorable, humans flourished and populations expanded. When climates shifted and became unfavorable, crops failed, populations diminished, civilizations collapsed, and conflicts between cultures increased.

▶ Trends in climate change have historically determined where agriculture could and could not be practiced, shaping the course of human civilizations.

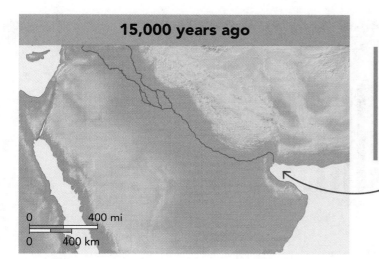

15,000 years ago

0   400 mi
0   400 km

Persian Gulf, 15,000 Years Ago Sea-level rise and changes in coastlines are significant impacts of climate change on humans. Melting glaciers at the end of the last ice age caused sea levels to rise almost 130 meters (400 feet). About 15,000 years ago, there was no Persian Gulf.

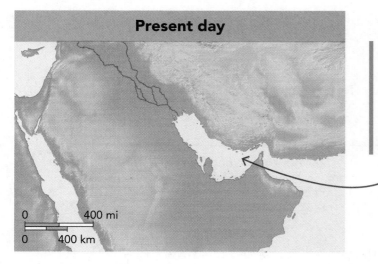

Present day

0   400 mi
0   400 km

Persian Gulf, Today As the sea-level rose, the fertile deltas of the Tigris and Euphrates Rivers were flooded, and shorelines rapidly advanced inland. Early settlements had to be abandoned and are now under the Persian Gulf. Many early cultures share stories of expulsion from their homelands, as a result of rising sea levels.

(43) **SEP Use Mathematics and Computational Thinking** Examine the two maps. The current shape of the Persian Gulf has changed little in the past 6000 years. Calculate how fast the Persian Gulf coastline moved landward between 15,000 and 6,000 years ago. ✏️

Historic Climate Events A good example of the impact of past climate changes on human history can be seen in the rise and fall of the Roman and Byzantine empires. An important natural cycle for people in the Mediterranean region was the annual flooding of the Nile river, which peaked around October of each year. The monsoon flooding carried water and rich sediments onto the lands, which allowed for crops to be grown. During about 50 BCE to 250 CE, frequent flooding of the Nile allowed for plentiful harvests that helped the Roman empire grow to a large size. After that time, regional climates changed. The annual Nile floods got smaller and harvests decreased. At the same time, periods of extreme severe weather and resulting famines increased. The Roman and Byzantine empires weakened under the increasing famines, and were eventually overrun by Eurasian tribes such as the Huns, Goths, Visigoths, and Vandals.

Extreme Climate Events of the Roman Empire

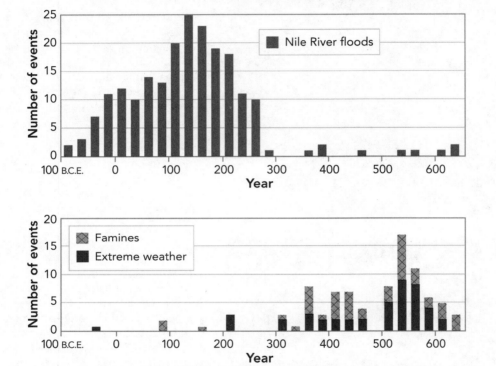

Climatic Changes Historical evidence shows a strong inverse correlation between crop-supporting Nile River floods (top) and periods of both famines and extreme weather, which includes extreme heat, cold, drought, or precipitation (bottom).

(44) SEP Analyze and Interpret Data In the years 536 and 540 there were very large volcanic eruptions (in Iceland and Central America). What evidence do you see of this in the graph? ✏️

....

....

....

Humans and Present-day Climate For 4.6 billion years, many natural factors have changed climate in different ways. Some changes have been gradual; others, immediate and catastrophic. Currently, however, humans are driving climate change faster than any of these natural causes. The most significant impacts are due to rising levels of atmospheric greenhouse gases from the burning of fossil fuels and agricultural land practices.

Climate Forcing Factors Human impacts to the climate system can be quantified in terms of how they affect Earth's surface energy budget, which starts with 340 W/m² of incoming sunlight. The graph shows changes between the years 1750 (pre-industrial) and 2011. Different human activities cause either warming or cooling, but the net effect is now over 2 W/m² of warming, which is driving up Earth's temperature. The contribution from changes in sunlight (solar irradiance) is shown for comparison.

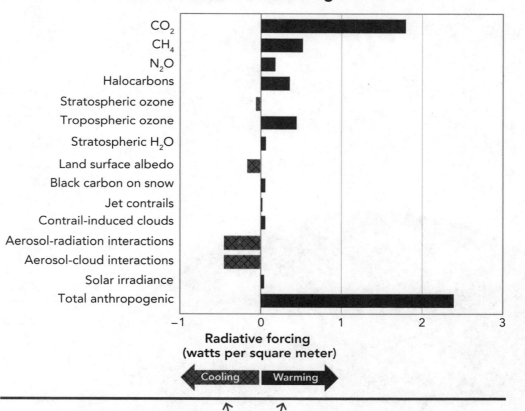

Near-Term Climate Forcing Factors

Cooling factors include deforestation and aerosols in air pollution. Both increase Earth's albedo, which reflects more sunlight back into space.

The greatest warming factors are the release of greenhouse gases (carbon dioxide, methane, nitrous oxides, and halocarbons), but also tropospheric ozone, soot on snow, and airplane contrails.

GO ONLINE to Elaborate on and Evaluate your knowledge of short-term climate factors by completing the peer review and data analysis activities.

In the CER worksheet, you drafted a scientific argument to explain what is causing droughts in California. With a partner, reevaluate the evidence cited in your arguments.

45 **SEP Engage in Argument** Based on what you've learned in this investigation, revisit and answer the question "What is causing drought in California?" Explain. ✏️

....

....

....

....

....

....

GO ONLINE to Evaluate what you learned about the factors and feedbacks that affect Earth's climate by using the available assessment resources.

In the Performance-Based Assessment, you modeled the feedbacks among different Earth systems by growing plants in a closed container. Wrap up your analysis by answering the following question.

46 **SEP Use Models** Suppose there is a small variation in the amount of energy flowing into Earth's surface system. Under what conditions is it possible for that small variation to cause significant changes in the system? ✎

....

....

....

....

....

47 **Revisit the Anchoring Phenomenon** How does what you learned in this investigation help you understand why we are seeing more extreme weather? ✎

....

....

....

....

....

....

....

GO ONLINE to engage with real-world phenomena by watching a video and to complete a CER interactive worksheet.

What is causing an increase in floods?

Global Climate Change

Local weather is strongly influenced by global climate factors. Changes to the global climate can result in changes to local weather, increasing the chances of extreme weather events, such as droughts and floods. Once you have viewed the Investigative Phenomenon video and used the Claim-Evidence-Reasoning worksheet to craft an explanation, answer the following questions about things that might cause an increase in floods.

(1) **CCC Energy and Matter** Where does the water that causes a flood come from? Why is the flooded area not inundated by water all the time? 🖊

....

....

....

....

....

(2) **CCC Patterns** What type of information would you look for in meteorological records to identify patterns in the locations, frequency, or intensity of flooding around the world? How long a period of time would you need records for in order to identify global patterns in flooding? 🖊

....

....

....

....

....

The Chemistry of Earth's Atmosphere

 GO ONLINE to Explore and Explain the chemistry of Earth's atmosphere and how it affects climate.

The Greenhouse Effect

Climate change is one of the most interesting topics of geoscience because it combines the sun's fluctuations, planetary orbits, atmospheric chemistry, radiation physics, ocean circulation changes, and biomass and land feedbacks. It is also a highly relevant topic because of its impacts on human society—past, present, and future. Currently, the biggest changes to climate involve increasing greenhouse gas concentrations, so to understand climate change, we first need to understand the greenhouse effect.

Earth's Energy Budget The greenhouse effect is part of Earth's surface energy budget, which begins with incoming radiation from the sun, mostly as visible light.

Thermal radiation lost to space: 200 W/m²

Thermal radiation radiated to space from surface: 40 W/m²

Solar radiation absorbed by Earth's systems: 241 W/m²

Energy absorbed by gases in the atmosphere: 77 W/m²

Heat and energy in the atmosphere

Energy reradiated into the atmosphere: 464 W/m²

Energy reradiated back into the Earth system: 340 W/m²

The Greenhouse Effect
Greenhouse gas absorption: 358 W/m²

Energy absorbed by Earth's land and ocean surface: 163 W/m²

Energy radiated from Earth's surface: 504 W/m²

Greenhouse Gases

All gases absorb electromagnetic radiation, but each gas absorbs radiation only of specific wavelengths. **Greenhouse gases** are particularly effective at absorbing wavelengths that correspond to infrared radiation, the kind of energy that Earth's surface emits. Most of Earth's atmosphere is nitrogen and oxygen, which absorb very little infrared radiation.

Greenhouse gases exist only in small amounts, but they absorb enough heat to keep Earth's surface about 35°C warmer than it otherwise would be. The **global warming potential (GWP)** is a measure of the heat-trapping capacity of a greenhouse gas over a given period of time, compared to that of a similar amount of CO_2. Except for the chlorofluorocarbons, which have been banned because they destroy the protecting ozone layer, the amounts of all greenhouse gases are increasing due to human activities.

Effects of Greenhouse Gases Different gases warm the atmosphere to different degrees, and they remain in the atmosphere for different amounts of time, so they have very different long-term warming effects.

Human-Released Greenhouse Gases						
Gas	**Carbon dioxide (CO_2)**	**Methane (CH_4)**	**Nitrous Oxide (N_2O)**	**CFC-11**	**CFC-12**	**HCFC-22**
Atmospheric Lifetime (years)	multiple	~12	~114	45	100	12
GWP for 20 years	1	86	268	7,020	11,000	5,160
GWP for 100 years	1	34	298	5,350	10,900	1,810
Concentration in 2019	415 ppm	1,866 ppb	332 ppb	228 ppt	504 ppt	233 ppt
Annual % increase	0.5	0.3	0.3	−0.9	−0.4	4.3
Total Greenhouse forcing (W/m²)	1.82	0.48	0.17	0.26 (all CFCs)	N/A	0.05 (all HFCs)

(3) CCC Address Questions About the Natural World The GWP of N_2O is higher than that of methane and changes less when calculated for 20 and for 100 years. Why does the GWP of nitrous oxide change less, and why does methane have a large total greenhouse forcing contribution? ✎

....

....

....

....

Oscillations of a Water Molecule

How do individual **atoms vibrate** within the H₂O structure?

Water Vibration Modes Molecules vibrate at frequencies that depend on their mass, their size, and the types of vibrations allowed by their structure. The different kinds of vibrations can all occur at the same time.

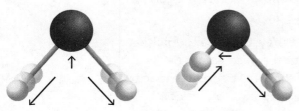 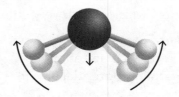

The distances between atoms of the water (H₂O) molecule can **stretch in and out** like a spring. This can occur **symmetrically**, with both hydrogen atoms going in and out together, or **asymmetrically**, with one going in when the other goes out.

The water molecule can oscillate by **bending the arms** of the hydrogen atoms out and in, with the angle between them alternately increasing and then decreasing.

The water molecule can **rotate back and forth** around an axis of rotation, a process called **libration**. This twisting can occur around the x-axis, y-axis, or z-axis, and each mode has a different frequency of oscillation.

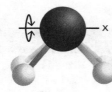 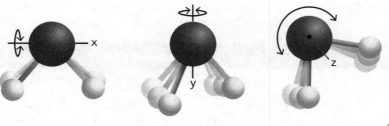

Radiation: Absorption and Reradiation

When gas molecules absorb electromagnetic radiation, the radiant energy transforms into kinetic energy of the molecule. The motions of the molecule become more energetic. Eventually, the molecule reemits that energy as radiation, but until it does, the molecule moves with more kinetic energy. These motions take three general forms: stretching, bending, and twisting. Because different molecules have different sizes and shapes, they stretch, bend, and twist at different frequencies. It is similar to the way that bells of different sizes and shapes make different sound pitches and tones. This is why different gases absorb and reradiate radiation at different wavelengths.

4 **SEP Engage in Argument from Evidence** Water vapor has more distinct ways to absorb radiation than oxygen gas does. Make a claim, based on the diagrams, as to why this might be. ✏️

....

....

....

Water and Ozone

Water and Water Vapor The most powerful greenhouse gas is water vapor (H_2O), which accounts for about 50% of the total absorption of infrared radiation in the atmosphere. Clouds (liquid and solid water) account for another 20%, and carbon dioxide, methane, and everything else absorb the remaining 30%. However, water vapor also absorbs some wavelengths of incoming sunlight, so it has both warming and cooling effects.

■ Water vapor abundance in the atmosphere is impacted indirectly, not directly, by human activities.

Oxygen and Ozone Ozone (O_3) is a powerful absorber of the sun's ultraviolet radiation, which is dangerous to living tissues. This is why the ozone layer in the stratosphere is so important. International action was taken to stop the release of chlorofluorocarbons when it was discovered that those gases were destroying stratospheric ozone.

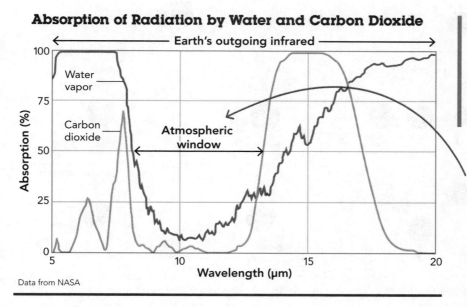

Absorption of Radiation by Water and Carbon Dioxide

Data from NASA

Atmospheric Window Most of Earth's outgoing infrared radiation occurs in the range of about 5 to 20 micrometers (μm), which corresponds to a gap in the absorbance spectrum of both carbon dioxide and water vapor.

Although carbon dioxide has almost no absorbance in the 8–13 μm range, water vapor does. An increase in atmospheric water vapor would close this window (the water vapor curve will move upward, and greenhouse warming would increase).

(5) **CCC Matter and Energy** Construct an explanation for why an increase in atmospheric carbon dioxide would lead to an increase in atmospheric water vapor. ✏

....

....

....

....

Carbon Dioxide and Methane

In general, a molecule will have more absorption modes if it has more atoms and if the molecule is asymmetrical. For example, oxygen gas (O_2) has fewer absorption modes than water (H_2O) or carbon dioxide (CO_2) because there are fewer ways to arrange the smaller number of atoms. However, CO_2 has fewer absorption modes than H_2O because its molecule is linear and therefore is more symmetrical than water vapor's.

The atomic isotopes involved also affect the oscillation. For common carbon dioxide molecules, the carbon atoms can be ^{12}C or ^{13}C and the oxygen atoms can be ^{16}O, ^{17}O, or ^{18}O. Each of the possible combinations will have a different mass distribution and therefore absorb radiation at different wavelengths.

Oscillation and Radiation Absorption Symmetric molecules such as carbon dioxide and methane don't have a molecular dipole in the ground state. Asymmetrical vibrations, librations, and bending produce a structure with a molecular dipole.

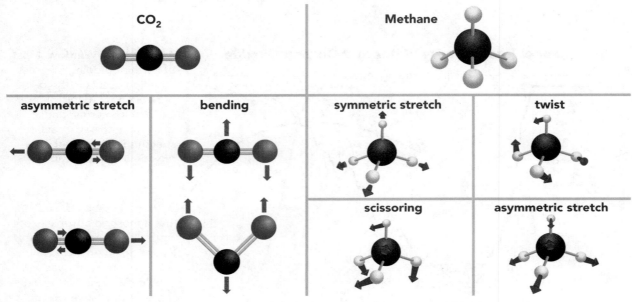

Carbon dioxide has two main modes of oscillation that will absorb infrared radiation: **bending** and **asymmetric stretching**.

Of methane's four oscillating modes, only the scissoring and asymmetric stretch modes have both the carbon and hydrogen atoms moving, which causes a change in the dipole moment of the bonds and absorbs infrared radiation.

6 SEP Develop and Use Models Both CO_2 and H_2O have one atom surrounded by two atoms of a different element. Explain why you wouldn't expect CO_2 and H_2O to have modes of oscillation at the same frequencies. ✏️

....

....

....

Incoming and Outgoing Radiation

Incoming Radiation Most (55%) of the incoming solar radiation passes through Earth's atmosphere and reaches the surface. Of the sun's energy that reaches Earth's solid surface, about 12% gets immediately reflected back out to space, and the rest is absorbed by Earth's surface.

Of the 45% that doesn't reach the surface, about half gets reflected back out to space by Earth's atmosphere and half is absorbed by Earth's atmosphere. The absorbed radiation is largely ultraviolet radiation absorbed by oxygen and ozone molecules and short-wavelength infrared radiation.

(7) **CCC Matter and Energy** The dashed curve shows the average amount of radiation emitted by each square meter of Earth's surface. On its way up, some of that energy is absorbed or scattered by the atmosphere. The solid curve shows the amount that would be observed looking down from the "top of the atmosphere" (TOA). Explain why there are "dips" in that curve. ✏️

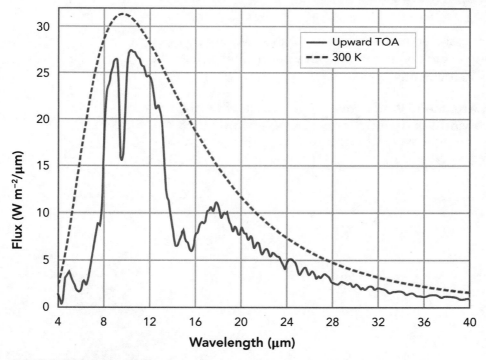

Transmission of Earth's Emitted Radiation

MODTRAN® is a registered trademark owned by the United States Government as represented by the Secretary of the Air Force. Chart provided courtesy of Spectral Sciences, Inc.

....

....

....

Outgoing Radiation Earth's surface warms as it absorbs incoming sunlight, but not indefinitely. It reradiates roughly the same amount of energy it receives, but in the long-wavelength infrared spectrum. The infrared radiation is absorbed by greenhouse gases at the wavelengths corresponding to their different modes of molecular oscillation.

Only about 10% of Earth's outgoing infrared radiation passes directly out into space, mostly through an atmospheric "window," such as the broad notch seen in the total absorption curve at wavelengths of about 8 to 12 μm. About half of the radiation absorbed and reemitted by greenhouse gases goes back to Earth's surface. This energy warms Earth's surface and is reradiated again, with most being absorbed once again by the greenhouse gases. If the amount of greenhouse gases increases, the amount of energy stuck in this loop increases.

Revisit

INVESTIGATIVE PHENOMENON

GO ONLINE to Elaborate and Evaluate your knowledge of greenhouse gases by completing the class discussion and data analysis activities.

In the CER worksheet assigned at the beginning of this investigation, you drafted a scientific argument about floods. With a partner, reevaluate the evidence cited in your arguments.

8 **SEP Engage in Argument** Water covers about 71% of Earth's surface, and it absorbs and releases energy more slowly than rock does. How might water at Earth's surface contribute to the greenhouse effect? 🖉

....

....

....

....

....

....

....

....

Evidence of Climate Change

📶 **GO ONLINE** to Explore and Explain past changes to Earth's climate.

Ice Cores and Ice Ages

Glacier ice forms from the compaction of snow year after year, building up a record of climate that extends back millions of years. The isotopes in the ice provide clues about temperature—the heavy isotopes ^{18}O and ^{2}H (deuterium) are less abundant when temperatures are cold. Ice core analysis reveals a repeating pattern of long, cold "ice ages" separated by brief, warm periods called interglacials. This roughly 100,000-year-long cycle is largely a result of oscillations in the elliptical shape of Earth's orbit around the sun.

In some cases, ice cores have been shaved into slices about 120 micrometers thick so that monthly temperature, pollen, and volcanic ash changes can be observed.

Paleoclimate Reconstructions Scientists use data from ice cores, including analysis of gases from bubbles trapped in the ice and other inclusions, to reconstruct past temperature changes.

The amount of carbon dioxide stored in the ocean changes as a function of temperature. As temperatures have changed, atmospheric CO_2 levels have also changed.

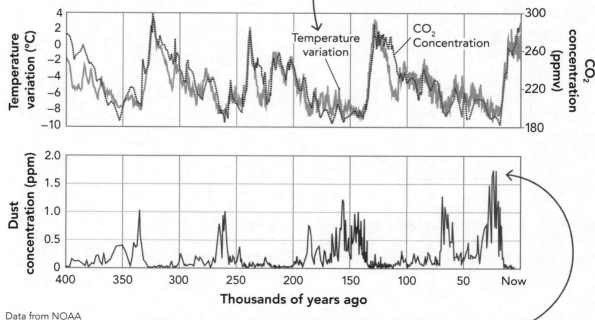

Data from NOAA

Ice also contains dust and ash particles that settled to the ground as the ice formed. These particles can be used to reconstruct the extent of deserts and the timing of volcanic eruptions.

Sea Level Change and Civilization

At the peak of the last Ice Age, about 26,000 years ago, there was so much ice on land in the form of continental glaciers that the level of the ocean was almost 125 m (about 400 ft) lower than it is today. So much continental shelf area, now offshore, was exposed that the world had almost 25% more land. When the Ice Age ended about 15,000 years ago, temperatures rose, glaciers melted, and the sea level started rising.

▶ Permanent human civilizations began just 11,000 years ago, partly because global temperatures warmed and stabilized, allowing for the beginnings of agriculture.

Rapid Sea-Level Rise A sea level rise of 125 m can cause shorelines to advance inland hundreds or thousands of kilometers.

Global sea levels and shorelines have stayed remarkably stable over the past 6,000 years, allowing the establishment of large permanent coastal communities.

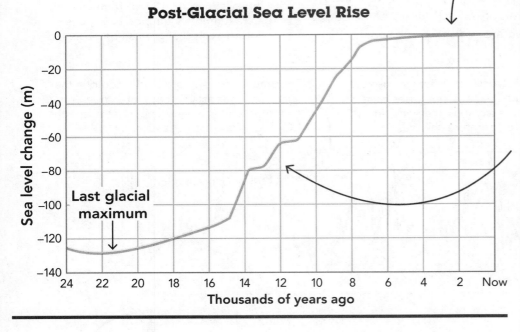

Post-Glacial Sea Level Rise

Last glacial maximum

At the end of the last Ice Age, the global average temperature rose about 8°C and glaciers rapidly melted. Global sea levels rose more than 125 m (about 400 ft).

(**9**) **SEP Analyze and Interpret Data** Sea levels rose most rapidly between 15,000 and 8,000 years ago. Use the graph to calculate the rate of sea level rise during this time, both in meters per century and mm per year. ✏️

Melting Ice and Rising Sea Levels

Sea levels started to rise again about 200 years ago, when the burning of fossil fuels released carbon dioxide into the atmosphere during the Industrial Revolution. The rate of current sea level rise, more than 3 mm/yr, is equally due to the melting of alpine and tidewater glaciers, the melting of Antarctic and Greenland ice, and thermal expansion of ocean water as it warms. As water warms, its rate of expansion also increases. Because of the long circulation time of deep ocean currents, the warming today will cause elevated sea levels for thousands of years.

Melting Ice Together, Greenland and Antarctica are now losing more than a half-trillion tons of ice each year. If all glaciers melted, sea levels would rise approximately 68 m (around 220 ft).

Ice Sheet Mass Loss in Greenland and Antarctica

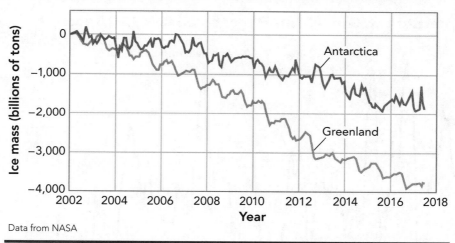

Data from NASA

(10) **SEP Analyze and Interpret Data** On the graph of sea level change, draw two separate straight lines through the curve, one for 1993–2011, and the other from 2011–2018. Use a star to identify the time frame during which the rate of sea-level change was higher. ✎

Global Mean Sea Level, 1993–2018

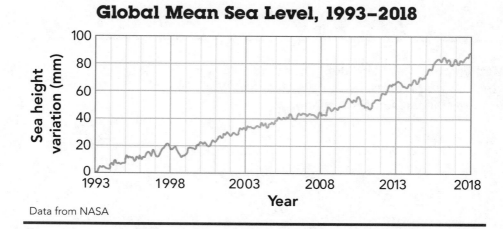

Data from NASA

Ice Cores and Human History

Ice cores have revealed climate variations not only over the past 800,000 years, but also within the last 10,000 years. Within this period, average regional temperatures have fluctuated by a few degrees. Some of the temperature swings for the past 4,000 years correlate with human mass migrations, human population changes, and the rise and fall of civilizations.

For example, ice cores contain a layer of ash from a large volcanic eruption in Iceland during the year 536. The ice also recorded a severe drop in temperatures that followed over the next decades. Widespread famines resulted around the world and allowed the first recorded global plague pandemic to spread, killing up to 100 million people.

11) CCC Stability and Change Fit a straight line through this curve of the temperatures in Greenland over the past 8,000 years. ✏️

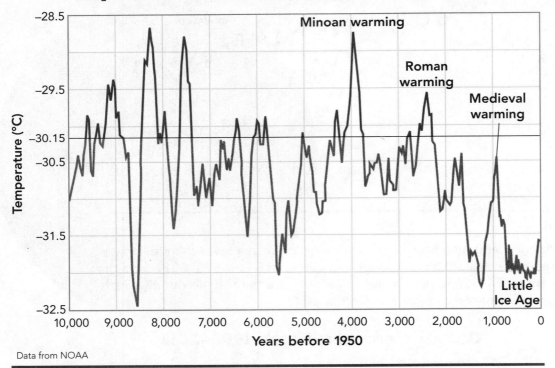

Temperature in Greenland Over the Last 10,000 Years

Data from NOAA

12) SEP Use Mathematics Calculate the general trend of the curve. (Note: This graph ends just before the year 1950. Global temperatures have increased since then.) ✏️

Varves, Corals, and Tree Rings

Varves Some lakes contain a record of annual sediment layers called **varves**, which are characterized by larger particles deposited by spring storms separated by finer particles that accumulate the rest of the year. Varves are very useful for studying regional climates over the past few thousand years. They also contain pollen, which shows the kinds and amounts of plants that grew nearby.

Fossil Corals Corals grow by making calcium carbonate layers from ions in seawater. These layers change in density as water temperature and availability of

nutrients change. The composition, thickness, and color of these annual layers provide a record of ocean temperature, ocean pH, and regional rainfall amounts.

Tree Rings The widths of annual tree rings vary depending on seasonal light and water availability. By comparing living trees with dead trees and with boards used for ancient ships and houses, scientists have established a continuous tree-ring record extending back more than 10,000 years in places.

13 **SEP Analyze and Interpret Data** PDSI, or Palmer Drought Severity Index, is a measure of ground dryness and is positive for wet times and negative for dry times. A severe drought that occurred in the New York City region in the 1960s is pointed out on the graph. Circle other times of significant drought suggested by the data. ✎

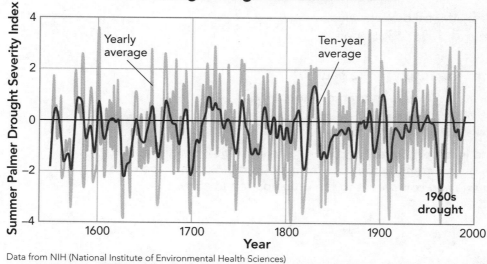

Tree-Ring Drought Reconstruction

Data from NIH (National Institute of Environmental Health Sciences)

Analyzing Graphs to Find Ancient Ocean Temperatures

Recent correlations between sea surface temperature (SST) and coral oxygen isotope anomalies can be used as a proxy for ancient temperatures. For the past 85 million years, Earth has been in a gradual cooling phase. The average $\delta^{18}O$ anomaly has increased by about 4.0 units. Use the correlation between the graphs to calculate the amount of SST cooling over this period. (Assume that the correlation is linear.)

ANALYZE List the knowns and unknown.

Knowns	Unknown
$\delta^{18}O$ and SST values for 1945–1995	change in average SST (ΔSST) over 85 million years = ?
change in average $\delta^{18}O$ anomaly over 85 million years = 4.0 units	

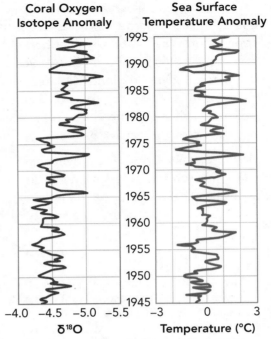

Coral Oxygen Isotope Anomaly   Sea Surface Temperature Anomaly

Data from: Urban, F.E. J. Cole, and J.T. Overpeck, 2000, Influence of mean climate change on climate variability from a 155-year tropical Pacific coral record. Nature 407, 989-993.

CALCULATE Solve for the unknown.

Use the data from the graphs to find the difference between the minimum and maximum values for $\delta^{18}O$ and SST between 1985 and 1990.

Total variation in $\delta^{18}O$ = −4.5 −(−5.3) = 0.8 $\delta^{18}O$ units

Total variation in SST = −1.5°C − 2.0°C = −3.5°C

Correlate the variations by dividing the total variation in SST by the total variation in $\delta^{18}O$.

$$\frac{-3.5°C}{0.8 \; \delta^{18}O \; units} = -4.4°C/\delta^{18}O \; unit$$

Multiply $\Delta\delta^{18}O$ by the calibration value to determine the average SST change.

$$\Delta SST = 4.0 \; \delta^{18}O \; units \times \frac{-4.4°C}{\delta^{18}O \; unit} = \boxed{-18°C}$$

EVALUATE Does the result make sense?

The result suggests SST were, on average, about 18°C warmer 85 million years ago.

(14) **SEP Analyze and Interpret Data** For coral $\delta^{18}O$ and for SST find the curves that best fit the overall trend in the data from 1945 to 1995. Take the ratio of the two amounts and compare it to the ratio you found above.

GO ONLINE for more practice problems.

Medieval Climate Anomaly and Little Ice Age

Climate changes have been connected to large changes in past human populations. One example is the global plague pandemic known as the Black Death that occurred during the 1300s, during which 70% of the human population of Western Europe died.

Black Death In the mid-1300s, the bubonic plague may have caused as many as 100 million human deaths, killing a large percentage of Western Europeans.

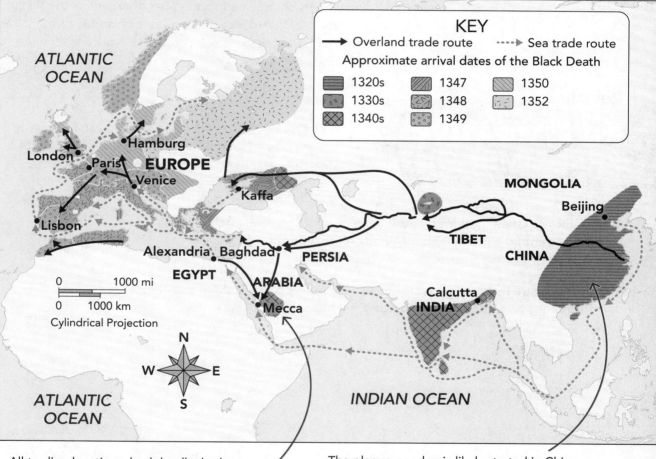

All trading locations, both landlocked centers and ocean ports, became nucleation points for the plague.

The plague pandemic likely started in China, exacerbated by extreme flooding events, which are estimated to have killed 7 million people in 1332 alone.

15. **SEP Analyzing and Interpreting Data** The plague began to spread within China around 1330; it reached England and Ireland in 1349. Using distances on the map, calculate the average rate of spread of the pandemic (in km/yr). ✏️

The Little Ice Age and Its Consequences The Black Death illustrates the link between historical events and climate changes. Following several centuries of relatively stable and warm climates, Mt. Rinjani in Indonesia erupted, ejecting over 250 million metric tons of sulfate aerosols into the atmosphere. This reduced sunlight for decades and caused cold rains, crop failures, and famines. This was the start of the **Little Ice Age,** which lasted about 500 years and had several periods of colder temperatures that correlate with periods of decreased solar activity and sunlight.

The Little Ice Age also affected the European exploration of North America. During the warm Medieval times, the North Atlantic was relatively free of ice, and Vikings settled in Iceland, Greenland, and Canada. But as the Little Ice Age progressed, increasing levels of North Atlantic sea ice made fishing and ocean trade difficult and contributed to the abandonment of the Viking colonies in Greenland and North America. During later episodes of the Little Ice Age, large numbers of European fur traders came to North America to capture beavers for fur hats and coats.

Revisit

INVESTIGATIVE PHENOMENON

GO ONLINE to Elaborate on and Evaluate your knowledge of climate change by completing the class discussion and data analysis activities.

In the CER worksheet assigned at the beginning of this investigation you drafted a scientific argument about floods. With a partner, reevaluate the evidence cited in your arguments.

(16) **SEP Engage in Argument** Describe how melting ice could affect the frequency and intensity of flooding events. ✏

....

....

....

....

....

....

....

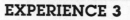
Anthropogenic Carbon Emissions

📶 **GO ONLINE** to Explore and Explain anthropogenic carbon emissions and their effects on Earth's atmospheric chemistry and climate.

Carbon Dioxide and Temperature

Whether over hundreds of millions of years, hundreds of thousands of years, or just the past hundred years, global temperature and atmospheric carbon dioxide concentrations are highly correlated with each other. If some other factor changes the temperature, such as when Earth's orbital parameters drive the Ice Age cycle, carbon dioxide levels change in response.

When atmospheric carbon dioxide levels change, temperature responds in parallel. This is what has been happening since the start of the Industrial Revolution, first with the burning of coal and then with the burning of oil and natural gas. Global temperatures had generally been falling for the past 7,500 years, but are now rising quickly.

| **Global Average Temperature** Globally averaged temperatures have increased steadily over the past 120 years. Temperatures fluctuate from year to year due to several factors, but the overall upward trend correlates with the concentration of carbon dioxide. | Atmospheric CO_2 levels fluctuated between 170 and 280 ppm for the past million years, but are now more than 415 ppm and rising. Temperatures are following suit. |

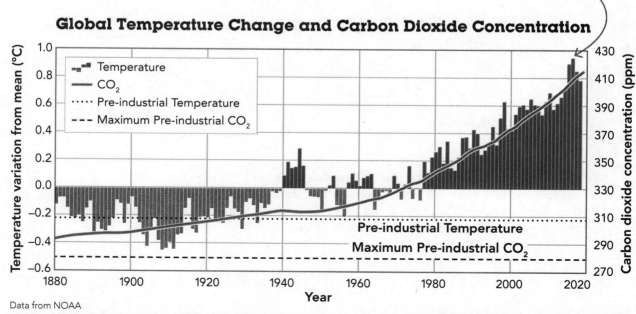

Global Temperature Change and Carbon Dioxide Concentration

Data from NOAA

Greenhouse Gas Release

Atmospheric concentrations of most major greenhouse gases—including carbon dioxide, nitrous oxide, and methane—are increasing due to human activities. However, the concentrations of most chlorofluorocarbons, or CFCs, are slowly declining. CFCs are refrigerants released by human industry that destroy ozone. A nearly global ban on them was enacted in 1989. However, these molecules have very long atmospheric lifetimes and will continue to damage the ozone layer for centuries.

Greenhouse Gas Concentrations Carbon dioxide concentrations show seasonal fluctuations due to summer/winter vegetation cycles, and nitrous oxide and methane exhibit annual cycles due to agricultural practices.

Atmospheric Carbon Dioxide (CO_2)

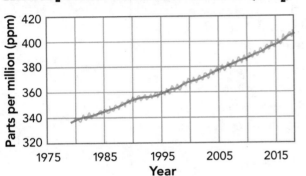

Atmospheric Methane (CH_4)

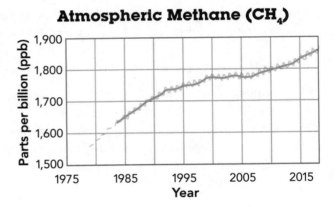

Atmospheric Nitrous Oxide (N_2O)

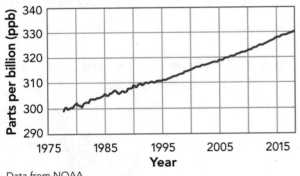

Other Important Gases

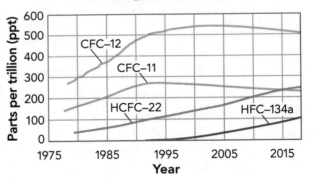

Data from NOAA

17 **SEP Develop and Use Models** The horizontal axes are the same for these curves; the vertical axes are not. Calculate the percentage increase from 1980 to 2018 for the CO_2, N_2O, CH_4, and HCFC-22 curves. Which of these had the largest percentage increase during this time? ✏️

Global Temperature Anomalies Over 100 Years These maps compare the surface temperatures in 1917 and 2017 to the average temperature over the time period of 1951–1980.

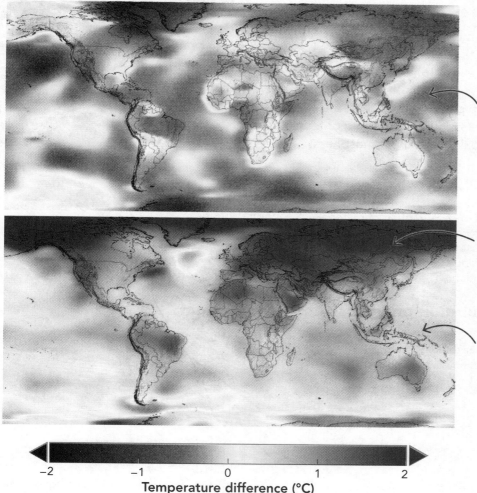

In the early 1900s most places on Earth were colder than the 1951–1980 average.

Land areas generally warm faster than the ocean, but Arctic regions have warmed at twice the rate of the rest of Earth's surface.

Most places on Earth are now warmer than the 1951–1980 average.

-2   -1   0   1   2

Temperature difference (°C)

Regional Temperature Changes

Earth's average global surface temperature is increasing, but temperatures everywhere aren't getting hotter. Some places are colder now, on average, than they were 100 years ago. Annual variations in weather are much greater than gradual climate shifts. In the central U.S., temperatures may change more than 30°C in a single day, which is much larger than the 1°C increase in average global temperature. However, it is significant that there are now more than twice as many record high temperatures, at any given place and time, than there are record low temperatures.

(18) **SEP Constructing Explanations** Some of the few geographic regions in the 2017 map that are colder than the 1951–1980 average are off the coasts of Greenland and Antarctica. Construct an explanation for this observation.

Human Population and Consumption

The impact of global warming is amplified by Earth's large human population, which exceeds 7.5 billion people and grows by another billion every 15 years. In addition, the standard of living is improving for more people. Every day, on average, another 300,000 people get access to electricity and clean water, which requires increased burning of fossil fuels. This releases more carbon dioxide into the atmosphere.

Trends in Population Growth and GDP Gross domestic product, or GDP, and population growth provide insight into rates of consumption of material and energy resources. Any plans for dealing with future climate change must take into account the growth rates of human population and per-capita production and consumption.

Populations have increased so fast that more than 7% of all humans who have ever lived are alive today.

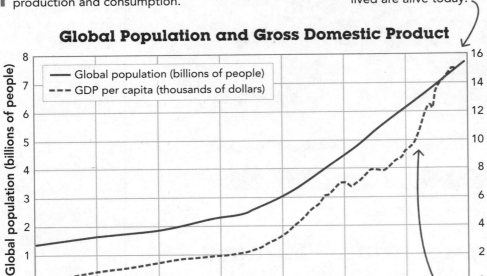

Global Population and Gross Domestic Product

- Global population (billions of people)
- GDP per capita (thousands of dollars)

Global GDP is a measure of the value of all goods and services produced by humans in the world. GDP has steadily increased as population increased.

Data from: Broadberry, S., Campbell, B. M., Klein, A., Overton, M., & Van Leeuwen, B. (2015). British economic growth, 1270–1870. Cambridge University Press and The United Nations.

(19) CCC Energy and Matter The number of people living on Earth cannot increase indefinitely. Explain what you think the limiting factor will be, and how many people Earth will hold at its maximum. ✏️

....

....

....

Carbon Isotopes and Fossil Fuels

In light of the correlations between human activities and the increases of greenhouse gases in the atmosphere, it may seem logical to conclude that human activities play a major role in recent global warming. However, it is important to demonstrate whether human-released CO_2 is primarily responsible for the atmospheric CO_2 rise, or if the CO_2 could be coming from some other reservoir, such as the ocean, soil, or volcanoes.

Of stable carbon isotopes, 98.9% is ^{12}C and 1.1% is ^{13}C. However, the $^{13}C/^{12}C$ ratio is even lower for plants. It is much easier for plants, on land and in the ocean, to use ^{12}C than ^{13}C to convert sunlight and carbon dioxide into food during photosynthesis. Therefore, biomass is very low in ^{13}C, and, as a result, so are fossil fuels, which form from ancient biomass. Thus, the relative concentrations of these two isotopes of carbon in atmospheric CO_2 can help scientists determine the source of the recent CO_2 emissions.

Carbon Isotopes and Carbon Source For the atmosphere, the $\delta^{13}C$ is naturally about −6.5. The $\delta^{13}C$ differs for different carbon sources. This value is around −4 for volcanic emissions, −7 for weathered rock, and −25 for biomass and fossil fuels.

The strong correlation between the increase in CO_2 and decrease in $\delta^{13}C$ is evidence that human-burned fossil fuels are driving the $\delta^{13}C$ value down.

The $\delta^{13}C$ value shows how much of the C in CO_2 is in the form of ^{13}C.

Atmospheric $\delta^{13}C$ is now −8.5 and not −25 because most atmospheric CO_2 is still from other sources, but the amount from fossil fuels is rapidly increasing.

Relative Concentration of ^{13}C in the Atmosphere

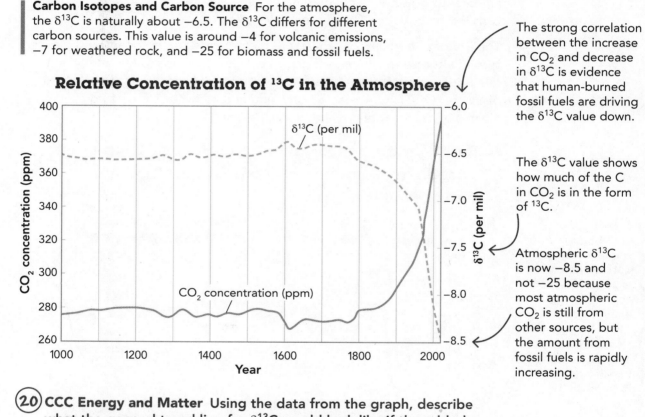

20 **CCC Energy and Matter** Using the data from the graph, describe what the general trend line for $\delta^{13}C$ would look like if the added atmospheric CO_2 since 1800 came from volcanic eruptions. Compare that trend to the expected $\delta^{13}C$ trend if the added CO_2 since 1800 came from weathering rock. 🖉

....

....

....

Sources of Anthropogenic Carbon

The term **anthropogenic** is used to describe anything caused or produced by humans. As of 2019, humans released about 10 billion tons of carbon into the atmosphere per year (10 Gigatons/yr). Most of this carbon comes from the burning of fossil fuels to get energy for electricity, transportation, industry, agriculture, and heat. Fossil fuels are concentrated and compacted remains of millions of years' worth of photosynthesis, so they are very energy-dense. In a sense, they contain the stored energy from millions of years of sunbeams.

Coal, Oil, and Natural Gas Humans have been burning coal and oil for more than 2,000 years, but mostly just what could be found at the surface, at relatively low levels. Coal mining increased rapidly in the eighteenth and nineteenth centuries. Coal burning was the major source of anthropogenic carbon well into the 20th century.

The use of petroleum, particularly as fuel for cars, trucks, boats, and planes, surged after WWII, and oil surpassed coal as the major source of human-released carbon until coal-fired power plants had a resurgence at the start of this century. Natural gas, mostly methane, is increasingly being used for electricity, transportation, and home heating.

> ◀️ The main sources of human-released non-fossil carbon are agriculture, biomass burning, and changes in land use.

Fossil Sources of Human-Released Carbon Fossil sources of carbon account for most anthropogenic carbon release (for example, concrete is made from the fossilized carbon in limestone).

Global Fossil Carbon Emissions by Source

Data from: Marland, G, Andres, B and Boden, T. 2007; and CDIC.

Human Greenhouse Gas Emissions
How do **humans** produce **greenhouse gases**?

Greenhouse gases are generated by many different sources. The bar graph shows how different human activities contribute to the overall production of greenhouse gases. The pie charts show how these contributions vary depending on the particular greenhouse gas under consideration.

25.6%
Electrical energy production

15.9%
Industrial processes

13.2%
Transportation fuel

12.1%
Land use, biomass burning

11.6%
Agricultural production

10.5%
Fossil fuel retrieval

7.5%
Residential, commercial

3.6%
Waste disposal and treatment

Carbon dioxide

Most human activities release **carbon dioxide,** especially **electrical power generation,** industrial processes, and transportation.

Methane

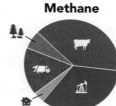

Most **methane** is produced by **agricultural production** (40.8%) and by **fossil fuel retrieval,** processing, and distribution.

Nitrous oxide

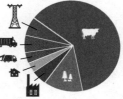

The largest source of **nitrous oxide** is **agricultural production,** which makes 62.5% of the nitrous oxide released by humans.

Greenhouse Gas Emissions by Sector Look around you right now. Everything you see that was human-made involved fossil fuels, including shipping and transportation that brought products to you and any electric lights you are using to see them. But it also takes energy to make energy— about 11% of all human-released greenhouse gases comes from mining, processing, and distributing fossil fuels. Different human practices involve the release of different gases. This makes the reduction of greenhouse gas emissions very challenging.

(21) SEP Use Mathematics and Computational Thinking The amount of carbon humans release is 10 Gt/yr. If this were all in the form of carbon dioxide, how many tons of CO_2 would humans release each year? ✏️

INVESTIGATIVE PHENOMENON

GO ONLINE to Elaborate on and Evaluate your knowledge of carbon emissions by completing the class discussion and data analysis activities.

In the CER worksheet assigned at the beginning of this investigation, you drafted a scientific argument about floods. With a partner, reevaluate the evidence cited in your arguments.

(22) **SEP Engage in Argument** How could anthropogenic greenhouse gas emissions affect the frequency and intensity of flood events? ✏️

....

....

....

....

....

....

Climate Models

 GO ONLINE to Explore and Explain different models of weather and climate.

Physical Models of Weather and Climate

Weather and climate are different, but they both result from interactions among components of the Earth system: the atmosphere, hydrosphere, geosphere, and biosphere. These interactions can be modeled using computer programs. In computer models, the different component systems are joined together by a framework called a *coupler*. By running these programs multiple times using different input parameters, predictions can be made about future weather and climate conditions.

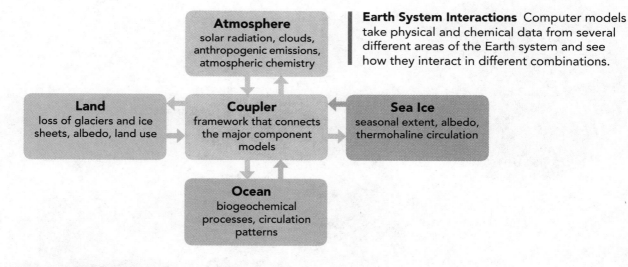

Earth System Interactions Computer models take physical and chemical data from several different areas of the Earth system and see how they interact in different combinations.

Modeling Weather and Climate Data collected by satellites are used to predict atmospheric conditions in both the short-term and long-term future.

Weather models determine what is likely to happen in the next hours or days.

Climate models determine what is likely to happen in the next decades or centuries.

Comparing Weather and Climate Models		
	Weather Model	**Climate Model**
Timescale	Hours to days	Decades to centuries
Time step	Seconds to 10s of seconds	~30 min
Grid size	~1 km	~100 km
Sensitivity	Very sensitive to complete initial conditions	Highly sensitive to boundary values
Interaction	Continuously nudged with new observations	Free-running

Earth System Models

A climate **Earth System Model (ESM)** is a computer model that uses a set of equations to calculate interactions between various parameters in specific geographic locations. The five basic parameters are pressure, temperature, mass, water vapor amount, and momentum. Data are largely collected by satellites.

The model divides Earth into individual 3D grid cells, and the equations are solved for every side of every cell at every time step. Using an ESM to make climate predictions involves starting with current parameters and adding input forcings—such as sunlight, volcanism, and human activities—to predict future conditions (outputs). Accurate input data about all of Earth's systems is needed in order to get reliable outputs.

Model Parameterization Earth's atmosphere, ocean, and land are broken up into small 3D grid cells. The horizontal grid is based on latitude and longitude. The vertical grid is based on altitude, depth, or pressure.

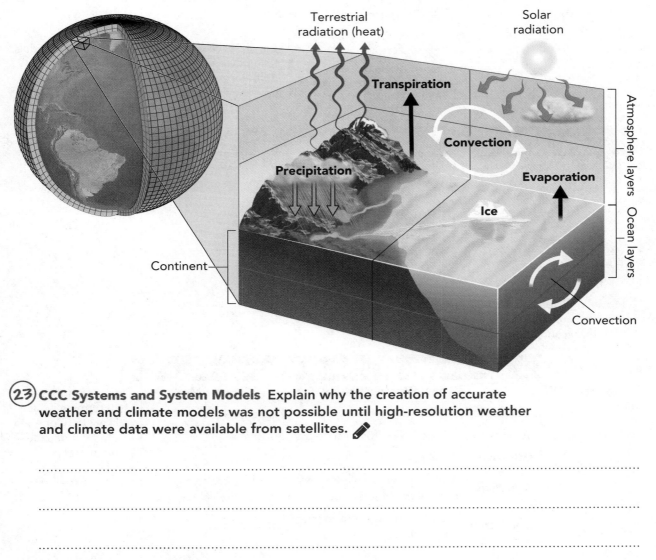

23 **CCC Systems and System Models** Explain why the creation of accurate weather and climate models was not possible until high-resolution weather and climate data were available from satellites. 🖉

....

....

....

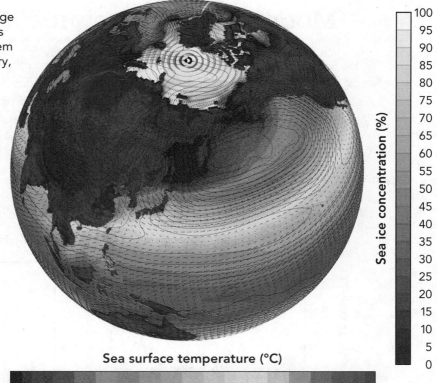

CESM Image This image depicts several aspects of Earth's climate system in the twentieth century, including sea surface temperatures and sea ice concentrations.

Sea ice concentration (%)

100
95
90
85
80
75
70
65
60
55
50
45
40
35
30
25
20
15
10
5
0

Sea surface temperature (°C)

–2 0 2 4 6 8 10 12 14 16 18 20 22 24 26 28 30 32

IPCC Models

The most powerful ESM is the **Community Earth System Model (CESM).** Climate scientists from around the world contribute data to this model, and predictions from the CESM are used in official reports issued by the **Intergovernmental Panel on Climate Change (IPCC).** Climate scientists developed the CESM to make predictions about future climate conditions based on current and projected inputs and conditions.

The 2014 IPCC report used a CESM that divided Earth's surface into 32 atmospheric layers, 60 ocean layers, 25 land layers, and latitude and longitude divisions that were smaller than 1° × 1°. Computations were done for all grid cells at 30-minute time steps, thousands of years into the future.

24 CCC Systems and System Models Climate scientists also use the CESM to create paleoclimate models, or models of past climate conditions. These models use larger map grid cells than future climate models. Why do you think that is? ✏️

....

....

....

....

Models of the Twentieth Century

Scientists are also able to use the CESM to determine which past inputs have contributed to conditions seen in Earth's recent past. They do this by inputting hypothetical initial conditions at some point in the past and then running the program up to the present. If the data projections are inaccurate, then the scientists know that the inputs were wrong.

Modeling Global Temperature History
The CESM was used to identify which inputs (human or natural forcings) were responsible for the pattern seen in Earth's mean global temperature from 1860 to 2010. Note that complex systems, such as climate models, cannot be predicted with total certainty. The shaded areas around the curves represent this uncertainty.

When the model was run using only natural forcings—such as sunlight and volcanism—as inputs, the results showed similar variability but did not match the recent upward trend.

When the model was run using only human forcings—such as greenhouse gas emissions and land use—as inputs, the upward trend was modeled but not the variability.

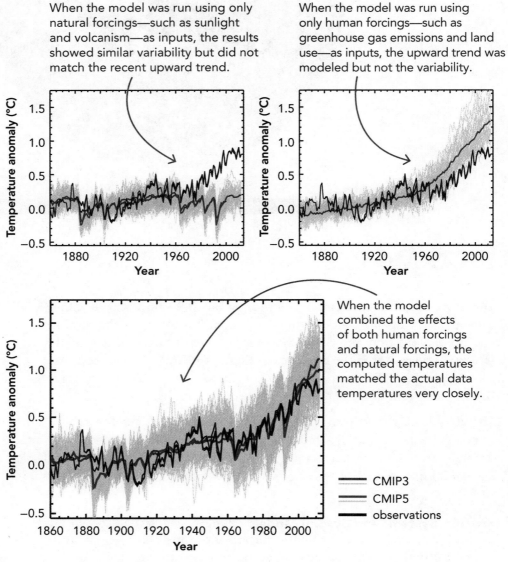

When the model combined the effects of both human forcings and natural forcings, the computed temperatures matched the actual data temperatures very closely.

CMIP3
CMIP5
observations

(25) **SEP Analyze and Interpret Data** Analyze the climate model runs with only human and then only natural climate forcings. Then describe how each contributes to actual recorded temperature data when they are combined. ✏️

....

....

....

Scenarios for the Twenty-First Century

To develop future climate projections, the IPCC has to make some assumptions about global greenhouse gas output in the coming decades. Countries can take an infinite number of pathways, ranging from stopping all fossil fuel use immediately to burning it all as quickly as possible. Not every scenario can be tested, so the IPCC's fifth assessment report (or AR5, published in 2014) picked four different possible Representative Concentration Pathway (RCP) scenarios for the release of greenhouse gases between now and the year 2100. Full climate model runs were then made for each of these four RCPs.

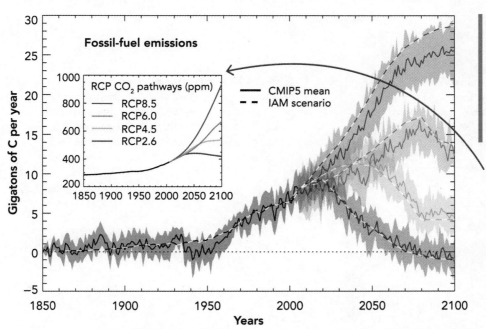

Carbon Emission Pathways The main graph shows the amount of carbon emissions required between now and 2100 in order to produce the CO_2 pathways shown in the inset.

The four RCP scenarios show human-induced radiative forcing, in W/m^2, in the year 2100. The colored lines show Earth's mean atmospheric CO_2 levels between now and 2100, for each scenario.

IPCC Scenarios of Representative Concentration Pathways (RCPs)	
Model	**Description**
RCP8.5	Radiative forcing pathway to 8.5 W/m^2 in 2100 and still rising. "Business as usual" scenario, with greenhouse gas use still increasing in 2100. Least optimistic.
RCP6.0	Radiative forcing pathway to 6 W/m^2 in 2100 and still rising. Carbon emissions peak around 2080, then decline.
RCP4.5	Radiative forcing pathway to stable 4.5 W/m^2 level in 2100. Carbon emissions peak around 2040, then decline.
RCP2.6	Radiative forcing pathway to 2.6 W/m^2 in 2100, already declining. Carbon emissions peak around 2020 and drop to zero around 2080. Most optimistic.

26 **CCC Stability and Change** Describe which of the four RCP scenarios you see as being the most likely, and why. ✏️

....

....

Projected Temperatures

In all of the scenarios of the IPCC AR5 report, temperatures will be warmer in the year 2100 than they are now. This is not surprising for the RCP8.5 scenario, with continued aggressive fossil fuel burning. However, this also occurs for the other three scenarios, where greenhouse gas emissions start to decline before the end of the century. There are several reasons for this. Some greenhouse gases remain in the atmosphere for a long time and continue to trap Earth's infrared radiation long after they are released. The ocean also has a long circulation time, so the large amounts of heat that are currently being pumped into the deep ocean will come back up centuries later to rewarm the atmosphere.

Projected Radiative Forcings These curves show predicted radiative forcings from the release of greenhouse gases, reduction of light reflected from Earth's surface due to sea ice melting, human-released aerosols, and soot.

Projected Temperatures These curves show predicted global temperature changes in response to the four RCP scenarios shown at left. Note that for RCPs 4.5, 6.0, and 8.5, temperatures continue to rise for centuries.

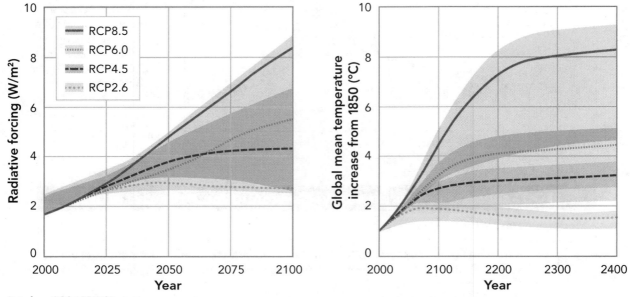

Data from IPCC AR5 WG1

(27) **SEP Analyze and Interpret Data** Continents warm faster than the ocean, so assume that land temperatures increase 20% faster than the global average. For scenario RCP8.5, how much warmer are average land temperatures expected to be in the year 2300 (with respect to 1850), converted to °F? What temperature would that make your town right now?

Regional Temperature and Precipitation Projections

Computations made by the CESM allow scientists to predict the likely climate conditions for all regions of the globe. It is instructive to use the most optimistic (RCP2.6) and the least optimistic (RCP8.5) scenarios to provide a bracket for predicting future conditions. What will likely occur is probably somewhere in between these two scenarios. While the RCP2.6 and RCP8.5 models differ in the magnitudes of their predicted changes, their patterns are generally similar.

Future Regional Temperatures We can expect continents to warm about 50% faster than ocean basins. The Arctic region will experience the accelerating melting of permafrost, sea ice, and the Greenland glacier.

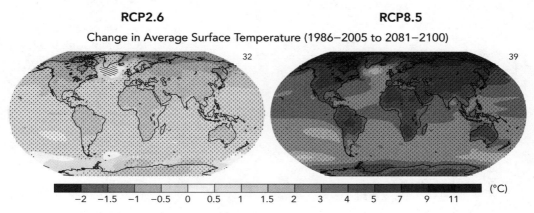

RCP2.6   RCP8.5

Change in Average Surface Temperature (1986–2005 to 2081–2100)

-2 -1.5 -1 -0.5 0 0.5 1 1.5 2 3 4 5 7 9 11 (°C)

Future Regional Precipitation In general, the dry desert regions about 30° north and south of the equator will get drier. The moist tropical regions will get wetter, and the poles will also see an increase in precipitation.

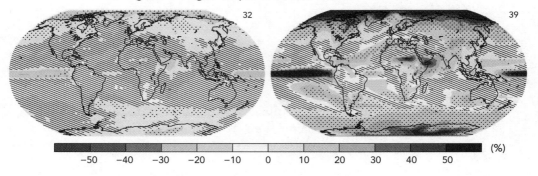

Change in Average Precipitation (1986–2005 to 2081–2100)

-50 -40 -30 -20 -10 0 10 20 30 40 50 (%)

28 **SEP Analyze and Interpret Data** One of your classmates wants to move to Italy when she retires because she likes a cool and moist climate. Using the maps, explain whether you think her decision is good or not, and why. ✏️

....

....

Projected Sea Level Rise

As global temperatures increase, ice will melt and sea water will warm and expand. The last time there were more than 415 ppm CO_2 in the atmosphere (the level in the year 2019) was 3.6 million years ago, when sea levels were 15–25 meters higher. At that level, nearly every coastal town or city around the world would be flooded. In all climate models, sea levels, which have been stable for 6,000 years, will keep rising, but it is uncertain how quickly.

Rate of Sea Level Rise Most ecosystems and human systems cannot adapt to sea level rise greater than 1 m. Even a rise of less than 0.5 m can endanger coastal areas around the globe. How much sea levels will rise in the future depends on how much atmospheric CO_2 levels are increased by human activities.

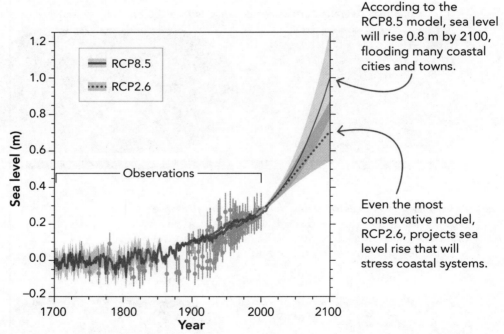

According to the RCP8.5 model, sea level will rise 0.8 m by 2100, flooding many coastal cities and towns.

Even the most conservative model, RCP2.6, projects sea level rise that will stress coastal systems.

Data from *Climate Change 2013*, IPCC.

(29) **CCC Stability and Change** Explain the role that water's latent heat of melting plays in controlling the rate of sea level rise. ✏️

....

....

....

....

Projected Changes in Extreme Weather

One result of global warming is an increase in regional temperature differences. Models show that these differences can lead to increased episodes of extreme weather—such as more intense tornadoes and hurricanes—more frequent short-term precipitation events, and more intense droughts and floods. One climate model prediction that is perhaps surprising is that nearly all of the world will experience more extended five-day precipitation events. Even in places that are predicted to get less total rainfall, the rainfall will occur in a small number of more intense precipitation events. This will result in more flooding worldwide.

(30) **SEP Analyze and Interpret Data** Climate models predict an increase in the intensity of both heavy precipitation events and droughts. On the map of consecutive dry days, circle the regions that are projected to have more frequent consecutive dry days but also increased maximum five-day precipitation events. ✏️

Maximum Five Day Precipitation   RCP8.5: 2081–2100

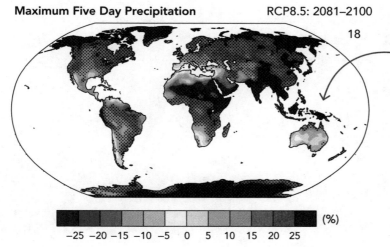

Intense precipitation events are projected to increase for nearly every land region, even those regions that are expected to receive less annual water.

Consecutive Dry Days   RCP8.5: 2081–2100

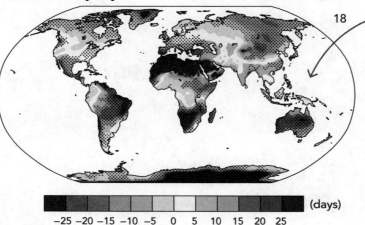

Regions that are already dry and suffer frequent droughts will experience even more frequent dry periods.

GO ONLINE to Elaborate on and Evaluate your knowledge of climate models by completing the peer review and data analysis activities.

In the CER worksheet assigned at the beginning of this investigation, you drafted a scientific argument about floods. With a partner, reevaluate the evidence cited in your arguments.

31 **SEP Engage in Argument** What do CESM projections say about the likelihood of flooding in the future? ✏️

....

....

....

....

....

....

Consequences of Climate Change

GO ONLINE to Explore and Explain the effects to Earth's systems of continued climate change.

Droughts

Climate change has an impact on numerous Earth systems. Many of these impacts directly affect people. For example, humans depend on food produced by agriculture for survival. Currently, 40% of global land area is used to grow crops and raise livestock. But in 15 years, there will be an additional billion people on Earth to feed. Climate models suggest that parts of the world are expected to receive less rainfall and experience more frequent extended droughts in the near future, negatively impacting the ability of their societies to grow food crops.

IPCC climate models predict increased droughts in the Southwest U.S. and in Central America. Similar droughts occurred in those regions during the warm Medieval Climate Anomaly. One tree-ring data set in the Southwest U.S. shows that almost no rain fell for a period of 40 years, around 1160–1200. It is likely that these droughts contributed to the collapse of some of the native American Ancestral Puebloan cultures, as well as the Mayan cultures in Central America.

Drying Up Cachuma Lake in California's Santa Ynez Valley is in danger of disappearing. Recent droughts in many southwestern U.S. states seem to be repeating the climate pattern seen during the Medieval Climate Anomaly.

133

Extreme Precipitation

Over the past 50 years, there has been a significant increase in the number of extreme one-day precipitation events worldwide. Climate models suggest that the trend of extreme precipitation will continue as global temperatures increase. Even regions that are predicted to receive less overall rainfall will likely find that rain will fall in a smaller number of more intense downfalls.

A similar pattern of correlation can be observed in other weather-related phenomena, such as hurricanes, tornadoes, and droughts. One example of record-breaking flooding occurred in 2018, when up to 3 feet of water rained in parts of North Carolina due to Hurricane Florence.

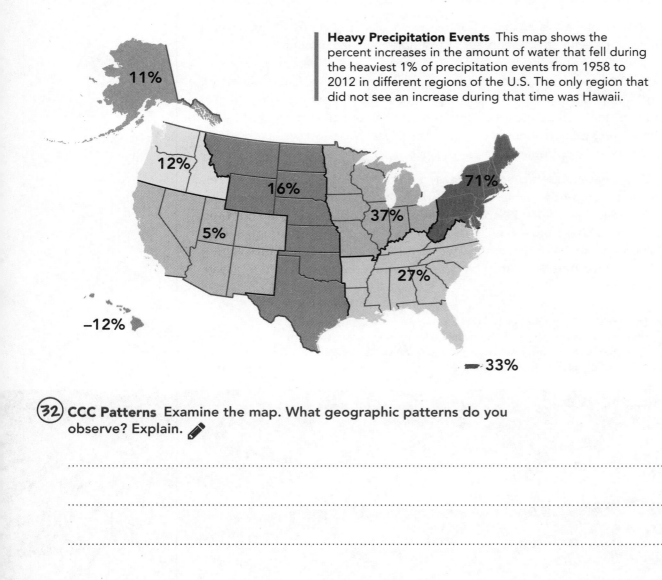

Heavy Precipitation Events This map shows the percent increases in the amount of water that fell during the heaviest 1% of precipitation events from 1958 to 2012 in different regions of the U.S. The only region that did not see an increase during that time was Hawaii.

32 **CCC Patterns** Examine the map. What geographic patterns do you observe? Explain. ✏️

....

....

....

....

As more rain falls in shorter amounts of time, the frequency and intensity of flooding increase. Floods pose many hazards to communities, including physical injury or loss of life, destruction of homes and infrastructure, and pollution of drinking water.

Computational weather models can now reliably forecast dangerous flooding up to three days in advance, allowing for planned evacuations and greatly reducing loss of life. However, floods still have many negative longer-term impacts, including financial loss, destruction of food crops, and the forced relocation of residents.

Patterns in the magnitude and frequency of extreme weather events, such as droughts or heavy precipitation events, may be observable on one time scale and not exist at other scales. That is why scientists observe daily changes, annual changes, and decadal averages.

33 SEP Analyze and Interpret Data The bars in the graph show annual data for extreme one-day precipitation events in the contiguous United States as a percentage of land area. The line shows the trend in annual data using a nine-year weighted average. This line averages data over a nine-year period, but gives more weight to the middle year. There are other ways to represent trends within a data set on a graph. Try the following:

a. For each 10-year period (1960s, 1970s, etc.), circle the top of the highest year's bar. Then draw a set of lines, left to right, connecting your circles.

b. Draw a single straight line that best fits all of the years (the tops of the bars).

c. Draw two straight lines, one between 1910–1960, the other between 1960–2015, that best fit the data in two parts.

Extreme One-day Precipitation Events 1910–2015, Contiguous United States

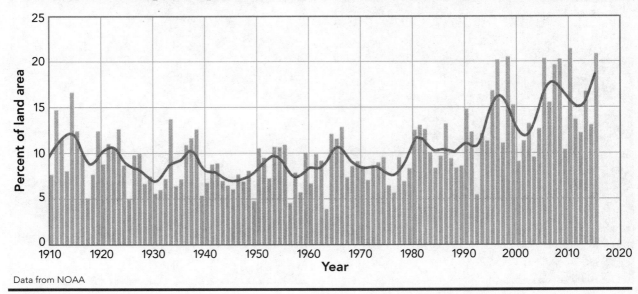

Data from NOAA

Disappearing Glaciers

One of the most important impacts of climate change is the loss of glaciers. In many parts of the world, glaciers store water throughout the year and slowly feed rivers, keeping them flowing. Many rivers originate in alpine glaciers, so the loss of this ice threatens human water supplies. The slow release of glacial water is also important for recharging depleted groundwater reservoirs.

Global Glacial Mass Loss Data show an overall decrease in glacial mass over the past 40 years. Glaciers are becoming both shorter and thinner.

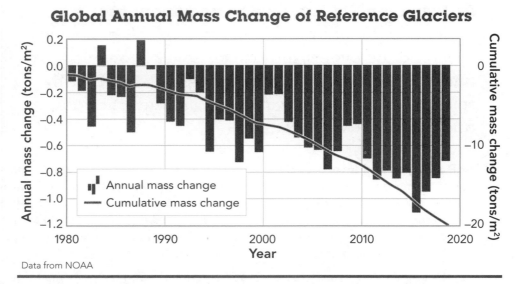

Global Annual Mass Change of Reference Glaciers

Data from NOAA

(34) **Stability and Change** These two photos of Grinnell Glacier in Glacier National Park, Montana, were taken 43 years apart. Trace the outline of the glacier in each photo using one color. Then, using a second color in the right-hand photo, trace where you think the glacier is today.

1938

1981

Glaciers and Sea Level Melting glaciers contribute to a rise in sea levels. Nearly 3 billion people live within 100 miles of a coastline, where rising sea levels increase the risk of flooding. The risks are worse in flat areas such as river deltas, which often have high populations. In some areas, the risk is exacerbated by sea surges during large storms, such as hurricanes. However, the hazards are not limited to storms. Already, many coastal areas experience so-called *sunny-day flooding*, where the streets of coastal towns now regularly flood during peak monthly high tides.

Coastal Flooding Relatively small increases in sea level can affect large areas of land, depending on the topography. Many coastal areas, such as this portion of the California coast, are relatively flat, allowing the sea to encroach well inland from the current shoreline.

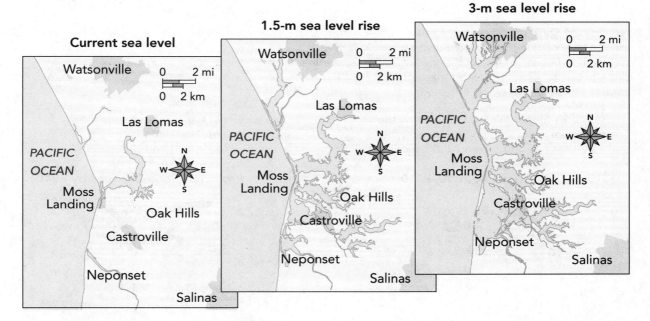

(35) **CCC System and System Models** Use the scale on the map to determine how far inland Castroville is currently. Explain how a 1.5 m sea-level rise could flood parts of Castroville.

....

....

....

....

Impact on the Biosphere

Human activities are changing Earth's biomes at rates not seen in millions of years, to the extent that humans now have their own geologic time period, the **Anthropocene**. Climate change is a significant part of this impact. Plant and animal species evolve to thrive in areas with particular patterns of temperature and precipitation, and if these patterns change faster than species can adapt, they may be decimated, or even go extinct. Climate change can also encourage the spread of invasive species—such as the kudzu vine or pine beetle—into new areas, competing with local species that are struggling under the new conditions. Changing climate patterns affect human food crops as well. Many crop plants that once grew well in certain areas are struggling with rising temperatures and no longer thrive in the same zones.

Northward Shift Plant hardiness zones define geographic areas where certain plants thrive under a particular set of climate conditions. These conditions are largely a function of average annual extreme low temperatures. Zone 4 has the coldest temperatures while Zone 10 has the warmest.

The widths of the colored bands show the locations of the plant zone boundaries over the 10-year period between 2000 and 2010.

The widths of the colored bands show how the plant zone boundaries are projected to expand and shift by 2040.

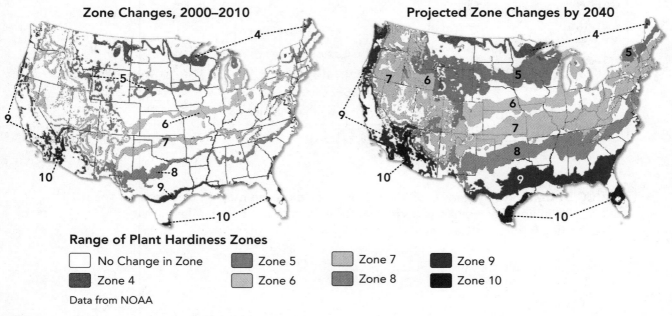

Zone Changes, 2000–2010

Projected Zone Changes by 2040

Range of Plant Hardiness Zones

☐ No Change in Zone ▨ Zone 5 ▨ Zone 7 ■ Zone 9
▨ Zone 4 ▨ Zone 6 ▨ Zone 8 ■ Zone 10

Data from NOAA

36 **SEP Use Mathematics and Computational Thinking** Obtain a map of Missouri and use the information in the future map to compute the rate at which the southern border of Plant Zone 7 will be moving northward. ✎

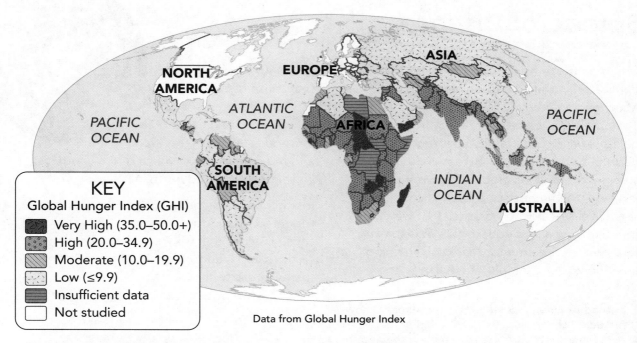

KEY

Global Hunger Index (GHI)

- Very High (35.0–50.0+)
- High (20.0–34.9)
- Moderate (10.0–19.9)
- Low (≤9.9)
- Insufficient data
- Not studied

Data from Global Hunger Index

Famine Susceptibility Global Hunger Index (GHI) values are calculated using data about child undernourishment and mortality. High GHI values indicate countries where climate change and other local factors have caused food shortages.

Famines and Wildfires

Climate and Hunger The correlation between climate change and famine is strong. Famines triggered by volcanic eruptions or decreases in sunlight have had an impact on the rise and fall of past civilizations, and famines will become more frequent as the impacts of global warming are felt. Unfortunately, some of the areas most at risk of famine due to climate change are also areas where hunger is already widespread and where population growth rates are high—such as Africa, India, and Southeast Asia.

Wildfire Incidence Wildfires in California are connected to the El Niño / La Niña Southern Oscillation cycle, and this connection extends to other forms of climate change as well. Areas of increased dryness will become susceptible to more wildfires, especially if climates shift to alternating periods of extreme precipitation followed by drought.

37 CCC Cause and Effect Construct an explanation to explain why alternating periods of extreme precipitation and drought might lead to an increase in the number of wildfires. ✎

....

....

....

Spread of Diseases

Rising global temperatures have also been implicated in the spread of infectious diseases. Many bacteria thrive at warmer temperatures. The number of cases of infection from *Salmonella, E. coli, Campylobacter,* and other harmful bacteria greatly increases during summer months. As global temperatures increase, the number of cases will continue to rise. Disease-carrying parasites that were once found only near the equator are now thriving farther from the equator thanks to warming conditions. For example, the Asian tiger mosquito carries viruses that cause diseases such as yellow fever and West Nile fever. This mosquito arrived in the U.S. in the 1960s and has spread across much of the southeast, west into Texas, and north into New York.

In addition, many global pandemics have been triggered by sudden changes in climate, which cause famines that weaken human immune systems and lead to the migration of humans to new areas to find food.

Spread of Deer Tick Habitats These maps show projected changes in the distribution probabilities of tick populations that carry Lyme disease in the eastern U.S.

Lyme-infected ticks have spread through most of the Southern U.S. and New England.

Tick populations are expected to expand northward and inland in the coming decades.

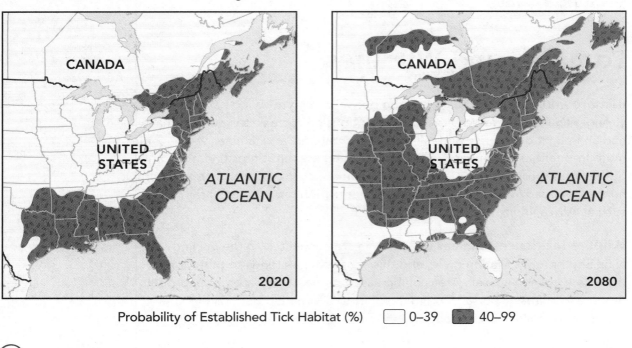

Probability of Established Tick Habitat (%) ☐ 0–39 ▨ 40–99

38 **SEP Analyze and Interpret Data** Based on these maps, which U.S. states are expected to see the biggest increase in the distribution of ticks bearing Lyme disease between now and 2080? Which states could see the biggest decrease? ✎

....

....

Climate Change, Migration, and Conflict

How might **climate change** affect **human social interactions?**

Shifting Climate Average **global temperatures rise** as a result of human carbon emissions.

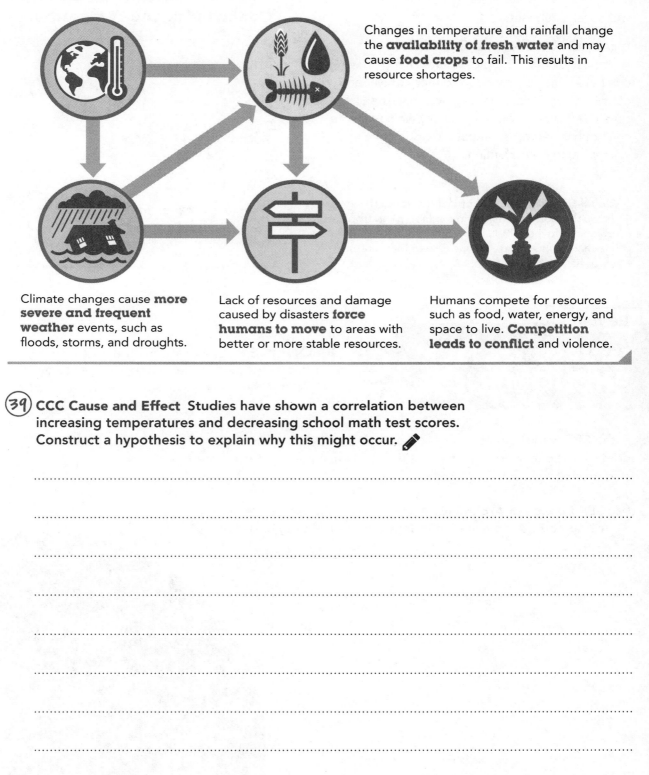

Changes in temperature and rainfall change the **availability of fresh water** and may cause **food crops** to fail. This results in resource shortages.

Climate changes cause **more severe and frequent weather** events, such as floods, storms, and droughts.

Lack of resources and damage caused by disasters **force humans to move** to areas with better or more stable resources.

Humans compete for resources such as food, water, energy, and space to live. **Competition leads to conflict** and violence.

(39) **CCC Cause and Effect** Studies have shown a correlation between increasing temperatures and decreasing school math test scores. Construct a hypothesis to explain why this might occur. ✏️

....

....

....

....

....

....

....

Impact on Human Societies

Displacement of Populations A changing climate can have many negative impacts on human populations, including flooding, drought, disease, and famine. These events often result in the mass migration of large numbers of people to new areas, creating potential for conflict with local inhabitants.

Increased Conflict and Civil Unrest

Historically, times of rapid climate change have correlated with increased incidences of war and conflict. Even today, many regions experiencing severe political conflicts are places where climate change has negatively impacted agriculture and caused hunger and famine.

Global Conflict Risk in Tropical Regions This graph shows the percent change in conflict risk in tropical regions (between 30°N and 30°S) as a function of the change in average Pacific Ocean temperatures, which have a strong effect on tropical climates.

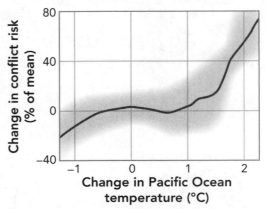

Conflict Risk and Temperature

Data from Hsiang et al., Quantifying the Influence of Climate on Human Conflict. Science, Vol. 341, Issue 6151, September 13, 2013.

Revisit

INVESTIGATIVE PHENOMENON

GO ONLINE to Elaborate on and Evaluate your knowledge of climate change impacts by completing the class discussion and data analysis activities.

In the CER worksheet assigned at the beginning of this investigation, you drafted a scientific argument about floods. With a partner, reevaluate the evidence cited in your arguments.

(40) SEP Engage in Argument What further evidence for increasing floods could you offer, having completed this learning experience? ✏️

....

....

....

....

....

....

Responses to Climate Change

 GO ONLINE to Explore and Explain responses and proposed solutions to climate change.

Solving Global Warming

Halting further ecological damage by climate change will require a combination of technological innovation, political will, and a shift in cultural practices. People need to either reduce the emissions of greenhouse gases or remove them from the atmosphere. Preventing gases from being emitted in the first place is much easier than trying to remove them, and that's where low-carbon communities come in.

Reducing Emissions Governments can provide tax incentives to help individuals make low-carbon investments, such as electric cars and solar panels. Increased use of energy-efficient public transportation and sustainable agricultural practices also help to reduce a community's carbon output.

Low-Carbon Communities Cities that employ "green" technologies and urban planning strategies can significantly reduce their carbon footprints. Such cities are the key to sustainable development.

Drivers of Climate Change There are five principal drivers of climate change at work in society today. Implementing changes that will combat these drivers will require international cooperation at an unprecedented level. Economic legislation may be required to encourage efficient practices and deter the release of greenhouse gases. In all areas, education will be needed in order to develop intelligent uses of resources.

Five Ways to Reduce the Drivers of Climate Change

Carbon Economics		**Reveal "true costs" of fossil fuels** Fossil fuels have maintained their dominance in the marketplace in part because their "true costs"—costs associated with damage from carbon emissions—have been passed on to taxpayers. Imposing a carbon tax would allow renewable energy sources to compete fairly in the energy marketplace.
Carbon Subsidies		**Remove fossil fuel subsidies** An estimated $5 trillion in global subsidies are provided to the fossil fuel industries each year—more than a half-trillion in financial aid and the rest in the form of exemptions for "true costs." If not for these subsidies, fossil fuels might have been abandoned long ago for financial reasons.
Renewable Energy		**Implement clean energy sources** The use of electricity from sources such as wind, solar, and hydroelectric power releases little or no greenhouse gases. In many regions, wind and solar are already cheaper than fossil fuels.
Modern Agriculture	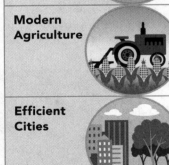	**Adopt "green" farming practices** Sustainable agricultural practices can help combat climate change and also be more profitable. These practices involve the intelligent use of water, fertilizers, and pesticides. They also include appropriate crop selection, crop timing, and crop rotation.
Efficient Cities		**Design low-carbon communities** Designing systems of transportation, architecture, urban design, and industry with energy efficiency in mind will greatly reduce energy demands and greenhouse gas emissions. Changing business practices, such as using teleconferencing instead of airplane travel, will also reduce climate impacts.

(41) **SEP Engage in Argument from Evidence** Which of these five drivers will be the hardest to reduce? Explain your reasoning. ✏️

....

....

....

....

....

Energy Sources

Humans use energy at an enormous rate—about 20 TW (terawatts), or 20 trillion joules per second. This is equivalent to the work that would be done if every person on the planet bench-pressed a set of 580-lb weights one meter every second. Fossil fuels have been doing most of this work for us, but fortunately there is a cleaner, cheaper, and inexhaustible source of energy: the sun.

Global Energy Sources Most of the energy used by humans comes from fossil fuels, including oil, coal, and natural gas. A smaller percentage comes from renewable sources.

For many years, the largest low-carbon sources of energy have been hydroelectric and nuclear fission.

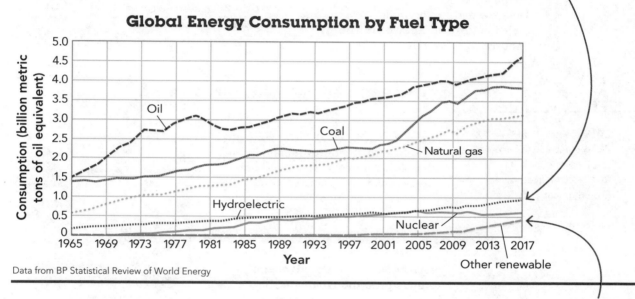

Global Energy Consumption by Fuel Type

Data from BP Statistical Review of World Energy

Although solar and wind still provide a small percentage of the global energy supply, they are now the fastest-growing energy sources.

Solar Energy About 125,000 TW of sunlight reaches Earth continuously—that's more than 6,000 times what humans use. We need only a tiny fraction of this to meet all our energy needs. Commercial solar panels are approaching 20% efficiency, and large solar farms yield almost 10 W/m².

Other Renewable Sources of Energy Research in materials has allowed wind turbines to continue to get lighter, larger, and cheaper. There are many designs of wind turbines. The largest has three blades spanning >150 m and yields 8 MW, enough to power over 6,500 houses. There are other low-carbon sources of energy, but they are not growing as rapidly as wind and solar.

One of these other low-carbon sources of energy is geothermal energy. In some places, it is possible to use Earth's internal heat as a clean, renewable source of energy. Geothermal energy is produced from the decay of radioactive materials below Earth's surface and the loss of heat originally produced during Earth's formation. Where easily accessible, near hot spot volcanoes, for example, this energy can be used to produce electricity for homes and industries.

Global Growth of Renewable Energies

How fast are **low-carbon energy** sources **growing globally?**

2018 electricity in GW: **178**
2018 electricity as a % of total electricity: **5.8%**
2013–2018 average annual growth in capacity: **13.5%**

Wind Farms of **wind turbines** can yield about 2.5 W/m² while the land is used for other purposes. This combination is ideal for the windy **agricultural plains** of the central U.S.

2018 electricity in GW: **492**
2018 electricity as a % of total electricity: **16.2%**
2013–2018 average annual growth in capacity: **2.7%**

Water Hydroelectric power requires large areas and is only cost-effective in a few parts of the world. Nevertheless, it is the **largest renewable energy source** in current use.

2018 electricity in GW: **71**
2018 electricity as a % of total electricity: **2.3%**
2013–2018 average annual growth in capacity: **28%**

Solar About 125,000 TW of **sunlight reaches Earth continuously**—more than 6,000 times what humans use. Large solar farms yield almost 10 W/m².

Nuclear Nuclear fission **does not release greenhouse gases,** but it raises a variety of environmental concerns and is very expensive.

2018 electricity in GW: **296**
2018 electricity as a % of total electricity: **9.8%**
2013–2018 average annual growth in capacity: **1.3%**

(42) **CCC Influence of Engineering and Technology on Society** Humans use electricity at a rate of approximately 3 TW (3000 GW). If this and the growth rate of solar power stayed the same, in how many years would solar energy be able to supply all of the world's electricity needs?

Transportation

Motorized vehicles are major contributors to carbon emissions. In fact, about one-fifth of global human-released CO_2 comes from transportation. Fortunately, advances in battery technology are driving the transition from combustion-engine to electric vehicles. The greatest challenges remain for ocean shipping and air travel. Ocean freighters could use nuclear power. Planes will likely continue to run on the combustion of liquid fuels, but can greatly reduce CO_2 output by using lightweight materials and flying with full passenger loads.

Electric Vehicles Cars and trains that run on electricity generated by renewable energy sources provide transport without the release of greenhouse gases.

Energy Use per Mode of Transportation			
Mode of Travel	**Efficiency (J/m per person)***	**Mode of Travel**	**Efficiency (J/m per person)***
Bicycle	~100	Combustion-engine Car	600–1000
Walking	~200 (depending on diet)	Ferry Boat	~750
Electric Train	50–300	Airplane	~1500
Electric Car	120–180	Ocean Liner	3400–6600
Bus	200–700	Helicopter / Private Jet	~5400
Hybrid Car	350–500	Jet Ski	~18,000

* Assumes that large passenger vehicles are full (and cars have four people)

43 **SEP Engage in Argument from Evidence** Suppose a group of people are planning to drive between cities in combustion engine cars. Use data from the table to outline the conditions under which they would or would not use less energy than flying. ✏️

....

....

....

....

....

....

Home Heat Loss
In this enhanced infrared image of a house on a cold day, heat loss is indicated by color.

Areas of high heat loss are shown in red. Areas of the highest rates of heat loss are shown in white.

The lowest rates of heat loss are occurring in places shown in blue.

Infrastructure

Older homes, schools, and other buildings are not very energy-efficient. Much of the energy used to heat and cool them is lost to the environment. In fact, more than 10% of total human greenhouse gas emissions come from heating and cooling older buildings. Newer structures built with modern "green" architecture require much less energy to heat in the winters and air condition in the summers. Rooftop solar panels and heat pumps also greatly reduce energy needs.

▶ A sustainable city functions as a system made up of smaller subsystems, including public transportation, embedded green spaces, and recycling programs.

44 **CCC Influence of Engineering, Technology, and Science on Society and the Natural World** In the infrared photo of the house, which areas are experiencing the highest rates of heat loss? Propose an engineering solution to reduce loss in these areas. 🖉

....

....

....

....

Carbon Capture and Sequestration

If humans continue to burn fossil fuels, we will need to find ways to prevent the resulting carbon dioxide from entering the atmosphere. The removal and containment of excess carbon dioxide is known as carbon capture and sequestration (CCS). Carbon dioxide can be captured by stripping it out before the fuel is combusted, or by using chemicals to separate it from exhaust gases. The carbon dioxide can then be used for industrial processes or sequestered away in reservoirs.

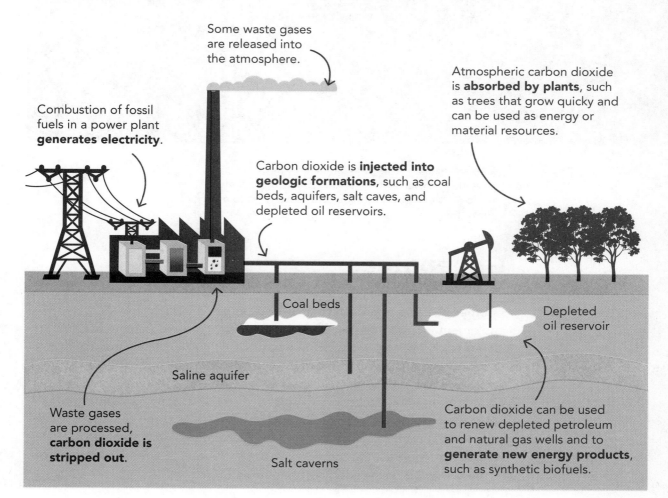

Some waste gases are released into the atmosphere.

Combustion of fossil fuels in a power plant **generates electricity**.

Carbon dioxide is **injected into geologic formations**, such as coal beds, aquifers, salt caves, and depleted oil reservoirs.

Atmospheric carbon dioxide is **absorbed by plants**, such as trees that grow quicky and can be used as energy or material resources.

Coal beds

Depleted oil reservoir

Saline aquifer

Waste gases are processed, **carbon dioxide is stripped out**.

Salt caverns

Carbon dioxide can be used to renew depleted petroleum and natural gas wells and to **generate new energy products**, such as synthetic biofuels.

(45) CCC Science Addresses Question About the Natural and Material World
Carbon dioxide can also be sequestered by combining it with quicklime (CaO) to produce limestone (CaO + CO_2 → $CaCO_3$). Unfortunately, this process requires a lot of energy. Provide a proposal for where this energy might come from that does not further contribute to global warming. ✏

....

....

....

Capturing CO$_2$ Fans pull exhaust from this waste incineration plant into the collectors, where a filter removes the carbon dioxide and converts it to a pure form that can be used industrially or sequestered.

Geoengineering

Another possible approach to reversing climate change is the implementation of massive, planet-wide geoengineering projects. One idea is to dump large amounts of iron or other nutrients into the ocean to encourage massive blooms of phytoplankton that would absorb CO$_2$. Another is to build large-scale devices to remove CO$_2$ directly from the air. Yet another involves pumping massive amounts of aerosols into the atmosphere to partially block out sunlight. However, some climate models suggest that artificial aerosols might inadvertently reduce precipitation, worsening droughts. We must proceed with caution in any large-scale effort, as there may be unintended consequences.

46 CCC Influence of Engineering, Technology, and Science on Society and the Natural World Describe a situation where an engineering solution to one problem could inadvertently create a new problem of a different sort. ✏

....

....

....

....

Sustainability

The path to global sustainability will need to be not only scientifically possible, but also economically viable and socially equitable. Governments play an important role in this effort by offering financial incentives and passing laws that cost relatively little to implement but reap enormous savings in money and health over time. However, governments must ensure that these regulations can be implemented equitably and do not put unfair burdens on any one community.

Sustainable Development For a plan of sustainable development to be successful, it must be environmentally sound, socially just, and economically realistic.

Stewardship of local and global resources, environmental justice

Evironmentally sound solutions take into account a balance of Earth systems and blend management and use of natural resources with pollution prevention.

Environmental Responsibility

Subsidies/incentives for use of natural resources, energy efficiencies

Sustainable Development

Social Justice

Economic Growth

Sustainable development plans must promote economic growth through profit and cost savings. They must also take into account the role of money in decision-making.

Socially just solutions are equitable. They improve standard of living, encourage education, and provide equal opportunities.

Workers' rights, business ethics, fair trade

Economics Switching from fossil fuels to wind and solar power will not only reduce greenhouse gases, but save money by reducing health care costs and environmental damage associated with pollution.

Industry The efficiency of industrial practices can be improved to reduce their impact on climate and save money. Factories can use cogeneration, where leftover heat from a factory or power plant is used for other commercial purposes. Advances in materials science can allow machines to run at higher temperatures that make them thermodynamically more efficient.

Forests Tropical rain forests are the lungs of our planet, absorbing much of the CO_2 we produce and releasing the oxygen we breathe. It is tempting for tropical countries to cut down their forests to grow crops or raise cattle, but ironically these are some of the least fertile soils in the world, so tropical-climate agricultural efforts typically fail. International cooperation is needed to provide tropical countries with financial incentives to protect their forests.

Low-carbon Agriculture These soybeans were planted between rows of wheat stubble just after the wheat was harvested, eliminating the need to till the soil. Double cropping increases soil moisture, reduces erosion, and increases profits.

Agriculture Currently, more than 12% of human-released greenhouse gases come from agricultural practices. But research efforts are continually leading to more efficient uses of land, water, and fertilizers. Some agricultural crops have been used to make biofuels for cars, but these fuels are also producers of greenhouse gases. Given increasing global populations, these croplands may be needed instead for growing food.

Social Justice The negative impacts of climate change affect the poor more than the wealthy, both in the U.S. and around the world. Low-income people are more vulnerable to malnutrition following a drought or devastating storm. They are also more likely to live near industrial plants, putting them at greater risk for diseases associated with pollution. International organizations such as the United Nations Framework Convention on Climate Change are needed to ensure that climate decisions that affect people are made as fairly and justly as possible.

47 **SEP Design Solutions** Propose an improvement to a practice at your school that will reduce climate impacts. Be sure to consider economic and social effects of the change alongside environmental consequences. ✏️

....

....

....

....

Calculations Involving Land Area and Wind Power

Wind farms are developing rapidly across the Plains states thanks to their compatibility with farms and pasturelands. Wind farms have an efficiency of about 2.5 W/m². The total area of the U.S. is 9,147,593 km². If the entire energy needs of the U.S. (3.4 TW) were supplied by these wind farms, what percentage of U.S. land would the farms have to occupy?

ANALYZE List the knowns and unknown.

Knowns	Unknown
Wind farm efficiency = 2.5 W/m²	Total area of U.S. land devoted to wind farms = ? %
Total area of the U.S. = 9,147,593 km²	
Total U.S. rate of energy consumption = 3.4 TW	

CALCULATE Solve for the unknown.

Find the area of wind farms needed to supply U.S. energy needs, in m².

$$\frac{3.4 \text{ TW}}{2.5 \text{ W/m}^2} = 1{,}360{,}000{,}000{,}000 \text{ m}^2$$

Convert area to km².

$$1{,}360{,}000{,}000{,}000 \text{ m}^2 = 1{,}360{,}000 \text{ km}^2$$

Calculate what % of U.S. land that value is.

$$\frac{1{,}360{,}000 \text{ km}^2}{9{,}147{,}593 \text{ km}^2} = 15\%$$

EVALUATE Does the result make sense?

The calculated percentage of 15% makes sense because the U.S. consumes a very large amount of energy, and wind farms occupy relatively large areas. Therefore, a significant percentage of the country's surface area would have to be covered with wind farms in order to meet all our energy needs.

48 **SEP Calculate** Solar panel farms have an efficiency of about 10 W/m². What percentage of U.S. lands would solar panels need to occupy in order to meet U.S. energy demands?

GO ONLINE for more practice problems.

INVESTIGATIVE PHENOMENON

GO ONLINE to Elaborate on and Evaluate your knowledge of tools to fight climate change by completing the class discussion and writing activities.

In the CER worksheet assigned at the beginning of this investigation, you drafted a scientific argument about floods. With a partner, reevaluate the evidence cited in your arguments.

49 **SEP Engage in Argument** What engineering solutions to flooding could you offer having completed this learning experience? ✏️

....

....

....

....

....

....

GO ONLINE to Evaluate what you learned about the causes and effects of global climate change by using the available assessment resources.

In the Performance-Based Assessment, you modeled two mechanisms that can remove CO_2 from the atmosphere. Wrap up your analysis by answering the following questions.

50 **SEP Define Problems** To be effective, any method to remove CO_2 from the atmosphere would have to be applied on a very large scale. Choose one of the methods you modeled and use what you learned in this investigation to describe the criteria and constraints of scaling it up. ✏️

Criteria	Constraints

Revisit

ANCHORING PHENOMENON

51 **Connect to Society** Think about the blizzard image presented at the beginning of Storyline 3. Use what you have learned to answer the question "Why are we seeing more extreme weather?"

....

....

....

GO ONLINE for a problem-based learning activity that you can tackle after completing Storyline 3.

The Dynamics of Chemical Reactions and Ocean Acidification

How do our **everyday** activities impact **Earth?**

Investigation 12
Reaction Rates and Equilibrium

Investigation 13
Acid-Base Equilibria

Investigation 14
Ocean Acidification

ANCHORING PHENOMENON

Inquiry Launch The image shows people driving during rush hour, an everyday activity that contributes to climate change. Which other everyday activities can you think of that may also influence Earth's climate?

While not intentional, many of the everyday activities we perform, when added all together, have large-scale effects on Earth and its systems. Write a short list of activities besides driving that you or your family do regularly, and describe how each of the activities likely helps mitigate or contributes to climate change by affecting Earth's atmosphere or ocean. ✏

....

....

....

....

....

....

....

GO ONLINE to engage with real-world phenomena. Watch the anchoring phenomenon video and preview the optional **problem-based learning experience**.

INVESTIGATIVE PHENOMENON

▶ **GO ONLINE** to Engage with real-world phenomena by watching a video and to complete a CER interactive worksheet.

How do limestone caves form?

Reaction Rates and Equilibrium

Limestone caves are underground cavities formed in limestone rock. They often have icicle-like structures hanging from their ceilings and jutting upward from their floors. Once you have viewed the Investigative Phenomenon video and worked on a first draft of a Claim-Evidence-Reasoning exercise to help explain the phenomenon you observed, answer these reflection questions about limestone caves.

1 **CCC Cause and Effect** Some of the structures in the photo appear almost to be flowing. What does that observation indicate about the physical or chemical processes that might be acting in the cave?

....

....

2 **CCC Stability and Change** How would you describe the rate of change in this system? Which observations from the photo or video are evidence that support your conclusion? Fill in the graphic organizer with your answer.

Evidence

Evidence

Evidence

Conclusion

Rates of Reaction

 GO ONLINE to Explore and Explain the relationships among particle collisions, temperature, concentration, and reaction rates.

Expressing Rates of Change

A **rate** is the ratio between two related quantities expressed in different units. Many rates describe how much something changes within a specified amount of time. Such rates can have time intervals ranging from less than a second to centuries or even longer. Average speed is an example of a rate. It is a change in distance over a given interval of time, or Δt.

$$\text{Average speed} = \frac{\text{change in distance}}{\text{change in time}} = \frac{\Delta d}{\Delta t}$$

For example, you can measure the average speed of a car in meters per second or in miles per hour. The measured speed is the same, just expressed in different units. The rates of chemical changes are usually described in terms of changes in concentration over time, although changes in mass, volume, and pressure over time are also used.

Changes Over Time You could measure the area of a banana's skin that turns from yellow to brown as it ripens over several days. That information would allow you to calculate a rate. By weighing it, you might also find that the mass of the banana changes, giving you another rate. As the banana begins to spoil, the change in color tells you that chemical changes are taking place.

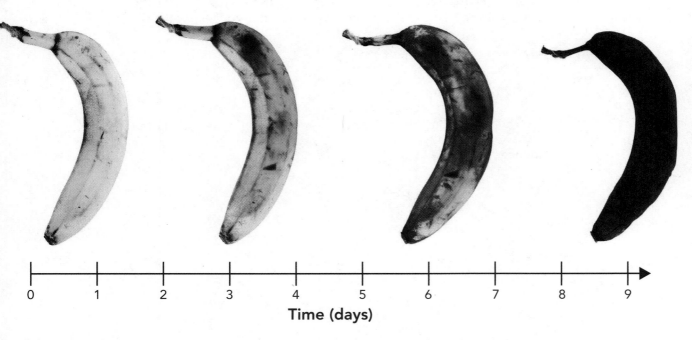

Time (days)

Calculating Reaction Rates

The **reaction rate** is the rate at which the reactants of a chemical reaction form the products. Reactions are commonly described in terms of concentration, written as [X] for a reactant or product X. Over a time interval from t_1 to t_2, the average rate of change of concentration of X can be determined from this relationship:

$$\text{Rate} = \frac{\Delta[X]}{\Delta t} = \frac{[X]_2 - [X]_1}{t_2 - t_1}$$

The calculated average rate can be negative, for a reactant, or positive, for a product. In order to avoid confusion, chemists define a single rate for a reaction that is always positive and can be determined from any reactant or product. It is based on the stoichiometry of the reaction.

For a typical reaction with reactants A and B and product C, the equation $aA + bB \rightarrow cC$ tells you that a moles of reactant A and b moles of reactant B are consumed to produce c moles of product C. Using the stoichiometric equation, you can determine the reaction rate in terms of any reactant or product:

$$\text{Rate} = \frac{-1}{a} \times \frac{\Delta[A]}{\Delta t} = \frac{-1}{b} \times \frac{\Delta[B]}{\Delta t} = \frac{1}{c} \times \frac{\Delta[C]}{\Delta t}$$

Note that in the equation, each reactant has a factor of -1 to ensure the calculated reaction rate is positive.

Concentration Changes Over Time The purple gas iodine (I_2) reacts with hydrogen gas (H_2) to form the colorless gas hydrogen iodide (HI): $I_2(g) + H_2(g) \rightarrow 2HI(g)$. The graph shows the reaction rate by showing how [HI] and [I_2] change over time.

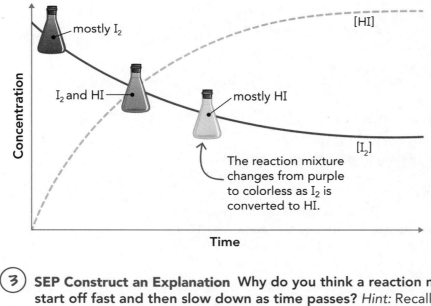

mostly I_2

I_2 and HI

mostly HI

The reaction mixture changes from purple to colorless as I_2 is converted to HI.

[HI]

[I_2]

Concentration

Time

The blue dashed line shows how [HI] changes over time. The line shows that the initial reaction rate is fast ([HI] increases quickly) and then becomes slower over time ([HI] increases slowly).

The purple solid line conveys the same information about reaction rate: the initial rate is fast ([I_2] decreases quickly) and later is slow ([I_2] decreases slowly).

(3) SEP Construct an Explanation Why do you think a reaction might start off fast and then slow down as time passes? *Hint:* Recall what you learned about collision theory in previous Investigations. ✏️

....

....

....

Calculating Reaction Rates

Hydrogen and iodine gas react to form hydrogen iodide, as shown in the equation $H_2(g) + I_2(g) \rightarrow 2HI(g)$. Suppose you are given a time interval from $t_1 = 10$ seconds to $t_2 = 20$ seconds and a change in H_2 concentration from 0.210 mol/L to 0.185 mol/L. Use the reaction rate equation to calculate the average reaction rate during that time period.

ANALYZE List the knowns and the unknown.

Knowns	Unknown
$[H_2]_1 = 0.210$ mol/L	Reaction rate = ? mol/L·s
$[H_2]_2 = 0.185$ mol/L	
$t_1 = 10$ s	
$t_2 = 20$ s	

CALCULATE Solve for the unknown.

Write the equation for average reaction rate.

$$\text{Reaction rate} = \frac{-1}{1} \times \frac{\Delta[H_2]}{\Delta t} = \frac{[H_2]_2 - [H_2]_1}{t_2 - t_1}$$

Substitute the knowns into the equation and solve.

$$\text{Reaction rate} = -1 \times \frac{0.185 \text{ mol/L} - 0.210 \text{ mol/L}}{20 \text{ s} - 10 \text{ s}}$$
$$= \frac{0.025 \text{ mol/L}}{10 \text{ s}}$$
$$= 0.0025 \text{ mol/L·s}$$

EVALUATE Does the result make sense?

The calculated rate, 0.0025 mol/L·s, is slow. That makes sense because the concentration of hydrogen gas changed very little (only 0.025 mol/L) in 10 seconds.

4 For the same reaction between hydrogen and iodine, suppose you have a product concentration of 0.180 mol/L at time $t_1 = 15$ s and a concentration of 0.205 mol/L at time $t_2 = 20$ s. Calculate the average reaction rate for the time interval with respect to the product, HI. ✏️

GO ONLINE for more practice problems.

Collision Theory—a Review

Collisions between molecules drive chemical reactions. Recall that collision theory is a model that is used to relate the properties of the colliding particles to the rates of chemical reactions. According to **collision theory,** in order for a collision to be effective, reactant particles must possess a sufficient amount of kinetic energy to break the necessary bonds in the reactants. They must also collide with the right orientation to form the bonds that make the products. The probability of bonds breaking in a collision depends on the kinetic energy of the collision being sufficient to break the necessary bond or bonds in the reactants.

Understanding Reactant Collisions
How must reactant particles collide to **react and form products?**

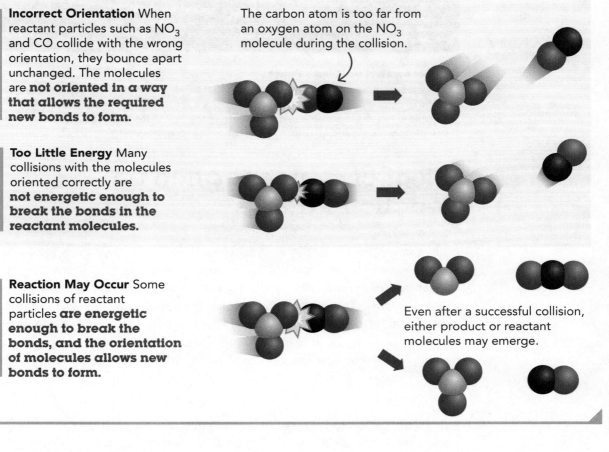

Incorrect Orientation When reactant particles such as NO_3 and CO collide with the wrong orientation, they bounce apart unchanged. The molecules are **not oriented in a way that allows the required new bonds to form.**

The carbon atom is too far from an oxygen atom on the NO_3 molecule during the collision.

Too Little Energy Many collisions with the molecules oriented correctly are **not energetic enough to break the bonds in the reactant molecules.**

Reaction May Occur Some collisions of reactant particles **are energetic enough to break the bonds, and the orientation of molecules allows new bonds to form.**

Even after a successful collision, either product or reactant molecules may emerge.

(5) **CCC Patterns** For reacting gases, what effect do you think reducing the reaction vessel's volume has on the probability of reactant particles colliding and forming products? ✏️

....

....

Concentrated vs. Dilute Reactant Sulfuric acid reacts with the metal zinc to produce hydrogen gas. On the left is a test tube with zinc and concentrated sulfuric acid. The reaction quickly produces a large volume of hydrogen gas bubbles. On the right is a test tube with zinc and dilute sulfuric acid. The reaction goes slowly, producing a small amount of hydrogen gas bubbles.

Effect of Concentration on Reaction Rates

From studying collision theory, you know that the rates of many reactions are dependent on reactant concentrations. In such cases, a higher concentration of reactants means a greater number of reactant molecules in a given volume. The result is more collisions per unit of time and, therefore, more collisions that are likely to lead to a reaction. Increasing concentration produces an increase in reaction rate for those cases. For reacting gases, notice you can increase the concentration by decreasing the volume of the reaction vessel.

SEP Develop Models Develop a molecular-level model that demonstrates what generally happens to particle collisions and reaction rates when higher concentrations of reactants are used. Refer to the reaction of zinc and sulfuric acid in the photo as an example.

Effect of Temperature on Reaction Rates

As the temperature of a reaction system increases, the average kinetic energy of the reactant molecules increases. The increased kinetic energy usually means that molecular collisions have a higher probability of breaking bonds and forming new bonds because the molecules are moving faster and collide with greater force. The increased kinetic energy also means the molecules collide more often. Raising the temperature thus usually has a strong effect in increasing a reaction rate. Similarly, a decrease in temperature causes less frequent collisions, each one with lower energy, usually resulting in a decreased reaction rate.

Warm vs. Cool Reaction Conditions The reaction between magnesium and water produces magnesium hydroxide, which is colorless. In order to make the increasing concentration of magnesium hydroxide visible, an indicator that turns purple is added to the test tubes. The two test tubes have the same amounts of all components; the only difference is the temperature of the contents.

Warm water reacts rapidly with magnesium to produce magnesium hydroxide.

Cool water reacts with magnesium much more slowly.

(7) **CCC Cause and Effect** Food stored in a refrigerator can stay fresh for long periods. However, the same food stored at room temperature quickly spoils. How can you explain the difference in terms of collision theory? ✏️

....

....

....

....

Effect of Particle Size on Reaction Rates

You probably know that crushed ice melts faster than ice cubes, or that a spoonful of granulated sugar dissolves more quickly than a sugar cube. Breaking up the ice or the sugar exposes more surface area, and the increase in surface area means that there is more area available for collisions. The increased surface area leads to an increase in the frequency of collisions and therefore speeds up the physical processes of melting and dissolving. The same is true for chemical reactions.

◗ Increasing a reactant's surface area causes an increase in the reaction rate.

Many chemical manufacturing processes reduce the particle size of the reactants to increase reaction rates. In mining applications, for example, ore is crushed to expose more surface area and optimize the metal extraction process.

Small vs. Large Surface Area When heated in a flame in the presence of oxygen, the iron in steel can combust to form iron oxide. The rate of the reaction differs greatly as a result of the surface area of the metal that is available for collisions with oxygen molecules.

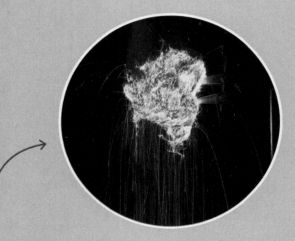

A steel nail, which has a small surface area, glows when it is heated. A tiny amount of iron on the surface of the nail reacts with oxygen to form iron oxide, but there are no sparks.

Steel wool is composed of small strands of steel, which have a large surface area. It reacts with oxygen more readily than the nail, producing a self-sustaining reaction that glows and sparks as the iron combusts.

(8) **CCC Cause and Effect** You may not think of wood as a dangerous material, but sawdust in the air of a woodworking shop can produce an explosion. Explain why sawdust is such a danger. ✏

....

....

....

INVESTIGATIVE PHENOMENON

GO ONLINE to Elaborate on and Evaluate what you learned about reaction rates by completing the peer review and writing activities.

In the CER worksheet you completed at the beginning of the investigation, you suggested a possible explanation for the formation of limestone caves. With a partner, reevaluate the evidence and the explanation you presented.

9 **CCC Cause and Effect** Suppose changes in climate raised the temperature of the limestone rock in a cave by a small amount. What do you think would be the effect on the reactions that form the cave and the structures within it? Cave formation involves many processes, so you only need to discuss the processes you are sure take place. ✏️

....

....

....

....

....

....

The Progress of Chemical Reactions

 GO ONLINE to Explore and Explain what is needed for colliding molecules to undergo a chemical reaction.

Activation Energy

Collision theory helps to explain why changes in conditions, such as temperature, concentration, and particle size can affect reaction rates. Recall that in addition to the correct orientation of the reactants, reactants must have sufficient kinetic energy to break existing bonds. The minimum energy requirement for colliding particles to react is known as the **activation energy.** You can think of the activation energy for a reaction as a barrier that reactants must overcome before products can form.

▶ Increasing the temperature of the reactants is a common way to provide the activation energy needed to start a chemical reaction.

Energy From Friction As the match head moves across the surface, its particles briefly adhere to the surface. Breaking that adhesion makes the particles in the match head vibrate. The energy of vibration supplies the activation energy to ignite the match.

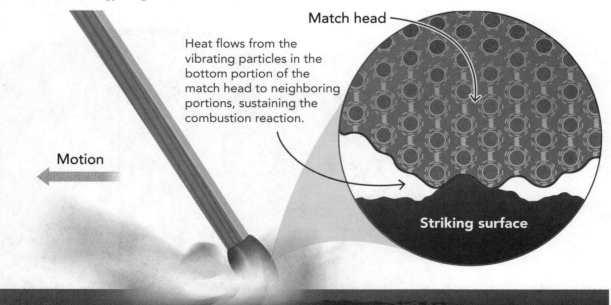

Match head

Heat flows from the vibrating particles in the bottom portion of the match head to neighboring portions, sustaining the combustion reaction.

Motion

Striking surface

Energy Diagrams

The **activated complex** is a transition state that exists for a short period of time in a chemical reaction as the bonds in the reactants are breaking and the bonds in the products are forming. The energy required for reactant particles to form the activated complex is the activation energy.

Understanding Energy Changes in Reactions
What aspects of reactions are modeled in energy diagrams?

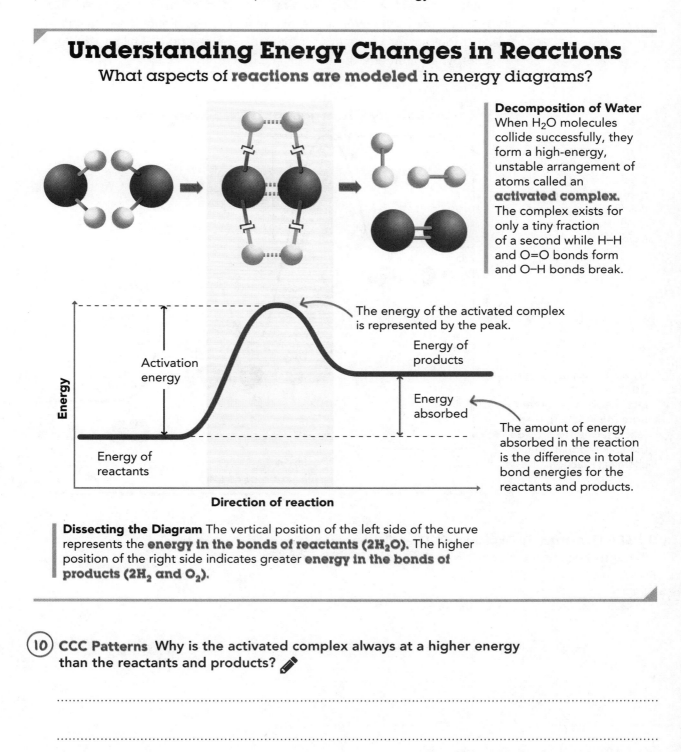

Decomposition of Water
When H_2O molecules collide successfully, they form a high-energy, unstable arrangement of atoms called an **activated complex.** The complex exists for only a tiny fraction of a second while H–H and O=O bonds form and O–H bonds break.

The energy of the activated complex is represented by the peak.

Energy of products

Energy absorbed

The amount of energy absorbed in the reaction is the difference in total bond energies for the reactants and products.

Dissecting the Diagram The vertical position of the left side of the curve represents the **energy in the bonds of reactants ($2H_2O$).** The higher position of the right side indicates greater **energy in the bonds of products ($2H_2$ and O_2).**

(10) **CCC Patterns** Why is the activated complex always at a higher energy than the reactants and products? 🖉

....

....

One-Step and Multistep Reactions

One-step reactions are reactions in which reactants are converted into products in a single step. Most reactions, however, are multistep reactions. A **reaction intermediate** is a product of one step in a multistep reaction and a reactant in a following step. Intermediates are consumed in the formation of the final products.

For multistep reactions, the slowest reaction is called the rate-determining step, and it affects the overall rate of a reaction. The higher the activation-energy requirement for a step, the slower is the reaction. Similarly, the lower the energy requirement, the faster is the reaction.

Energy Changes for a Two-Step Reaction

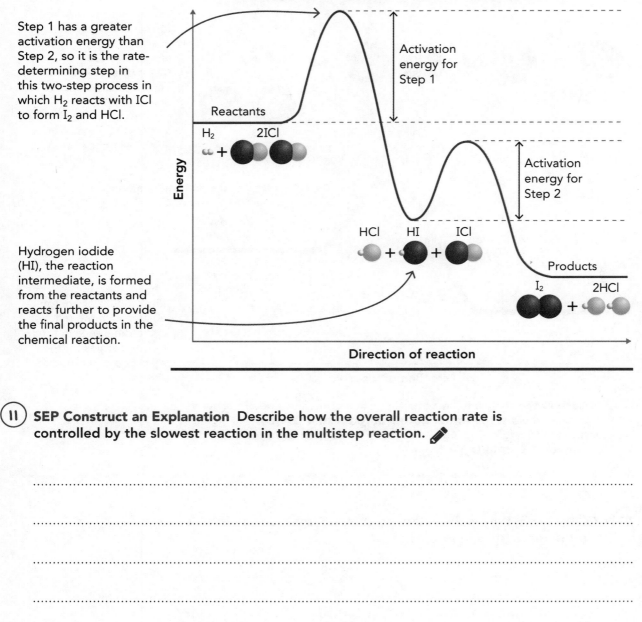

Step 1 has a greater activation energy than Step 2, so it is the rate-determining step in this two-step process in which H_2 reacts with ICl to form I_2 and HCl.

Hydrogen iodide (HI), the reaction intermediate, is formed from the reactants and reacts further to provide the final products in the chemical reaction.

(11) **SEP Construct an Explanation** Describe how the overall reaction rate is controlled by the slowest reaction in the multistep reaction. ✏

....

....

....

....

Lowering Activation Energy

Catalysts Increasing temperature, increasing concentration, or reducing particle size are all ways of increasing reaction rates. Those factors increase reaction rates without affecting the activation energies for the reactions. A **catalyst** is a substance that increases reaction rates by providing a lower energy path for the reaction without being used up during the reaction. The way a catalyst increases a reaction rate is by reducing the activation energy for the reaction. With a lower energy requirement, a greater proportion of the molecules have enough energy to react, and the reaction rate increases.

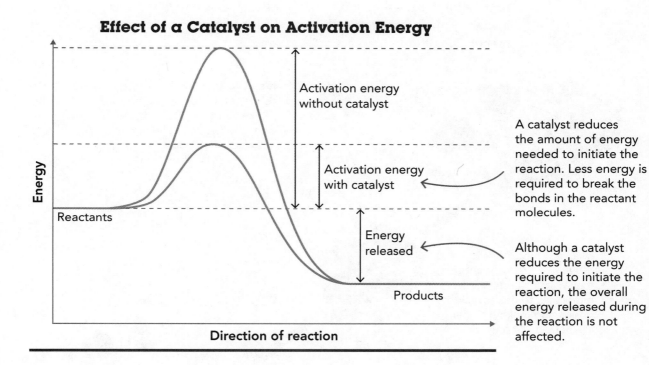

Effect of a Catalyst on Activation Energy

Activation energy without catalyst

Activation energy with catalyst

A catalyst reduces the amount of energy needed to initiate the reaction. Less energy is required to break the bonds in the reactant molecules.

Energy released

Although a catalyst reduces the energy required to initiate the reaction, the overall energy released during the reaction is not affected.

Reactants

Products

Energy

Direction of reaction

12) **SEP Develop a Model** Sketch a graph to show the changes in concentration for the reactants, the product, and the catalyst during this chemical reaction catalyzed by platinum: $2H_2 + O_2 \longrightarrow 2H_2O$. Use the vertical axis of your graph to represent concentration, and the horizontal axis to represent time. 🖉

Enzymes There are many important reactions in living systems that would proceed very slowly under normal conditions. The temperature may not be high enough to supply the activation energy to start the reaction. Reactant concentrations may be too low for reactions to occur quickly. Therefore, a biological catalyst called an enzyme is often needed. Enzymes are proteins or other molecules that fold into specific shapes to form indentations called active sites. There, reactant molecules bond with the enzyme. Enzymes help the reactants interact but are not used up in a reaction.

By bonding with the reactants, an enzyme forms an intermediate complex that lowers the activation energy needed to complete the reaction. An enzyme positions the reactants next to each other with the correct orientation for the reaction to proceed. Enzymes are effective in reactions involving small and large molecules. They also speed up decomposition reactions, not just combination reactions.

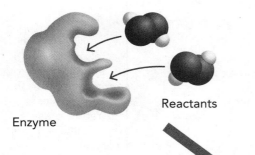

Enzyme

Reactants

How Enzymes Work An enzyme temporarily bonds to the reactants, forming a transition state with a lower energy. The lower energy of the transition state results in a lower activation energy for the overall reaction.

Reactant molecules bond to the active site. The enzyme may twist or bend the molecules to help break the bonds and make it easier for the activated complex to form.

Once the products are formed, they are released, leaving the active site available for other reactant molecules.

Products

(13) **SEP Construct an Argument** Increasing the concentration of reactants in an enzyme-catalyzed reaction increases the rate of the reaction, but only up to a point. Write and support a claim for why enzyme-catalyzed reactions are limited in this manner. ✏

....

....

....

INVESTIGATIVE PHENOMENON

GO ONLINE to Elaborate on and Evaluate what you learned about how reactions occur by completing the class discussion and data analysis activities.

In the CER worksheet you completed at the beginning of the investigation, you suggested a possible explanation for the formation of limestone caves. With a partner, reevaluate the evidence and the explanation you presented.

14 **SEP Plan an Investigation** In this Experience, you have studied both endothermic reactions (in which products have more energy than reactants) and exothermic reactions (in which products have less energy). Are the chemical processes that form a cave and the structures within it exothermic or endothermic? What experiments could you conduct to find out?

....

....

....

....

....

....

Reversible Reactions and Equilibrium

 GO ONLINE to Explore and Explain how reversible chemical reactions respond to changing conditions.

Reversible Reactions

When reactants are brought together, a reaction begins, and product concentrations build up. For some reactions, called **reversible reactions,** product molecules under ordinary conditions can react to form the original reactant molecules. Such a reaction can be represented with a double arrow in a chemical equation. The double arrow shows that the reaction proceeds in both directions.

$$2SO_2(g) + O_2(g) \rightleftharpoons 2SO_3(g)$$

In some reversible reactions, the products are favored. Chemists say that the forward reaction, in which the equation is read left to right, predominates, and they represent such a reaction with this arrow symbol: $\rightleftharpoons$. In other reversible reactions, the reactants are favored. Chemists say that the reverse reaction, in which the equation is read right to left, predominates, and they represent such a reaction with this arrow symbol: $\rightleftharpoons$.

Forward and Reverse Reactions The diagram models what happens at the molecular level for the reversible reaction involving SO_2, O_2, and SO_3. Molecules of SO_2 and O_2 react to form SO_3. As the concentration of the product, SO_3, increases, the reverse reaction is able to proceed at the same time as the forward reaction.

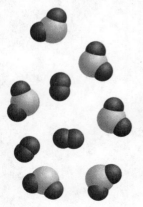

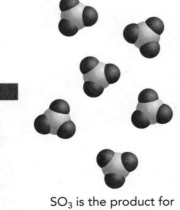

SO_2 and O_2 are reactants for the forward reaction and products for the reverse reaction.

The forward and reverse reactions are both happening, so all reaction species are present at any given time.

SO_3 is the product for the forward reaction and the reactant for the reverse reaction.

Equal Rates When the rate of water entering the bowl and the rate of water exiting the bowl are equal, the water level remains constant. The system is in equilibrium. You can compare the bowl to a reaction system at chemical equilibrium.

Chemical Equilibrium

Reversible reactions eventually reach **chemical equilibrium,** a state of balance in which the rates of the forward and reverse reactions are equal. In other words, the forward and reverse reactions are both happening at the same time and at the same rate.

▶ At equilibrium, the reactant and product concentrations are stable at the macroscopic level, even with constant changes happening at the molecular level.

The relative concentrations of the reactants and products at equilibrium mark the **equilibrium position** of the reaction. Reactions represented using the arrow ⇌ favor the formation of products. In such cases, the equilibrium position is one in which the products are more common. Reactions represented using the arrow ⇌ favor the formation of reactants, and the reactants are more common at equilibrium.

(15) **CCC Stability and Change** Describe an everyday example of a system that achieves a state of balance. Describe how your example is similar to a reaction system at chemical equilibrium. ✏️

....

....

....

Le Châtelier's Principle

Chemical systems typically progress from states that are not in equilibrium to ones that are. But what happens to a system that has reached equilibrium if the conditions change? **Le Châtelier's principle** states that if a chemical system at equilibrium experiences a disturbance, it changes in a way that counteracts the change as it returns to equilibrium. You can apply Le Châtelier's principle to identify potential changes you can make to a reaction system to increase the amounts of desired reaction species at equilibrium.

Disturbing Equilibrium

How does a system at equilibrium respond to a change?

Equilibrium When docked, a ship bobs up and down in the water but maintains a stable position. **A chemical system at equilibrium is similar—the forward and reverse reactions still happen, but there is no net change.**

Without cargo, the ship floats high in the water.

Disturbing the Equilibrium Although the ship-and-water system is a physical system, it responds to a change in a way similar to a chemical system at equilibrium.

Adding cargo will disturb the ship's position in the water.

New Equilibrium The loaded ship reaches a new stable position in the water. **When you change a chemical system at equilibrium, it also shifts to restore the equilibrium.**

With cargo, the ship displaces more water and sinks deeper.

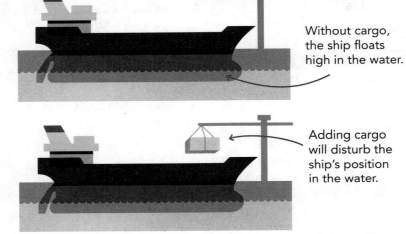

16) **CCC Cause and Effect** Use Le Châtelier's principle to predict what will happen if a chemical reaction system is disturbed by removing the product from the system through a precipitation reaction.

....

....

....

How Concentration Affects Equilibrium

At the molecular level, a disturbance involving a change to one component of a system at equilibrium affects other components. Changing the concentration of one component will change the rate of the forward or reverse reaction—whichever one the changed component is a reactant in—until the forward and reverse reaction rates are equal again. Consider the following reaction:

$$A + B \rightleftharpoons C$$

If a reactant concentration increases, then according to Le Châtelier's principle, the system counteracts the change. The reaction shifts to the right, converting reactants into products and lowering the reactant concentration. If a reactant concentration decreases, the reaction shifts to the left to increase reactant concentrations. Likewise, if product concentrations change, the reaction shifts to the left or the right to offset the change.

Balancing CO_2 and H_2CO_3 Carbon dioxide and carbonic acid in your blood follow this reversible reaction:

$$CO_2(aq) + H_2O(l) \rightleftharpoons H_2CO_3(aq)$$

Le Châtelier's principle explains how the system adjusts to minimize the effects of a disturbance.

Excess H_2CO_3 in the blood is not healthy and is controlled by reducing the CO_2 concentration through rapid breathing. Removing CO_2 causes the reaction to shift to the left and decrease the H_2CO_3 concentration.

The CO_2 in your blood increases as you exercise, and the reaction shifts to the right to decrease the CO_2 concentration and increase the H_2CO_3 concentration.

(17) **SEP Design a Solution** Consider the following reversible reaction: $2CO(g) + O_2(g) \rightleftharpoons 2CO_2(g)$. Describe a way to increase the CO concentration at equilibrium. Explain your reasoning. ✏️

....

....

....

How Pressure Affects Equilibrium

If the volume of a gas mixture is changed, the pressure of the gases also changes. (You can think of a change in volume as a change in concentration, since the number of particles in a given volume changes.) According to Le Châtelier's principle, a disturbance in the pressure of a reaction mixture of gases at equilibrium shifts the system in a direction that offsets the change in pressure. Consider the reaction for the formation of hydrogen sulfide gas.

$$2H_2(g) + S_2(g) \rightleftharpoons 2H_2S(g)$$

When the system shifts to the right, three moles of gas are converted to two moles of gas. A decrease in the number of moles of gas results in a decrease in pressure. Therefore, a change in volume that results in an increase in pressure shifts the reaction to the right to decrease the number of gas molecules. Likewise, if the volume changes so that the pressure decreases, the reaction shifts to the left in order to produce a greater number of gas molecules.

Effect of Increasing Pressure If you push down on the piston, reducing the volume and increasing the pressure, the system shifts in the direction that has fewer molecules of gas.

$3H_2(g)$ $N_2(g)$ $2NH_3(g)$

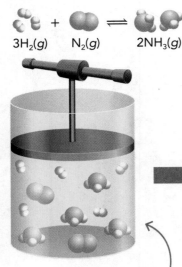

The piston is lowered, squeezing the molecules into a smaller space and increasing the pressure.

The initial mixture has a total of 11 gas molecules.

The final mixture has a total of 9 gas molecules. The shift reduces the pressure to offset the disturbance.

18 **SEP Use Models** Draw what happens to the equilibrium mixture of gases when the pressure increases for the following reaction: $2NO_2(g) \rightleftharpoons 2NO(g) + O_2(g)$. Assume the initial equilibrium mixture has two NO_2, four NO, and two O_2 molecules. ✏

How Temperature Affects Equilibrium

When a system at equilibrium is disturbed by an increase in temperature, the reaction shifts in the direction that tends to decrease the temperature, meaning that it shifts in the direction that absorbs heat. Consider the following reaction:

$$N_2(g) + 3H_2(g) \rightleftharpoons 2NH_3(g) + heat$$

When ammonia is produced from nitrogen and hydrogen gas, heat is a product of the exothermic reaction. Raising the temperature of the reaction under equilibrium conditions causes the reaction to shift to the left, so less heat is released and more reactants are formed. The system absorbs heat to minimize an increase in temperature. Conversely, lowering the temperature shifts the reaction to the right, releasing heat and forming more products. The system produces heat to offset a decrease in temperature.

Effects of Heating and Cooling Nitrogen dioxide (NO_2) is a brown-colored gas produced when colorless dinitrogen tetroxide (N_2O_4) decomposes in the endothermic reaction $N_2O_4 + heat \rightleftharpoons 2NO_2$. The photo shows how the system shifts in response to heating and cooling the reaction mixture.

Warming the equilibrium mixture causes the reaction to shift to the right, absorbing heat. Absorbing heat helps to offset the increase in temperature and results in the formation of more of the brown gas NO_2.

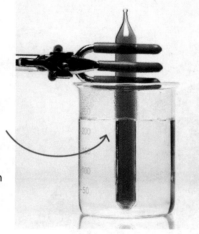

Cooling the equilibrium mixture causes the reaction to shift to the left, releasing heat and increasing the concentration of the colorless gas N_2O_4.

(19) **CCC Stability and Change** When the temperature is lowered for an exothermic reaction at equilibrium, which way does the reaction shift? Explain your reasoning using Le Châtelier's principle. ✏️

....

....

....

INVESTIGATIVE PHENOMENON

GO ONLINE to Elaborate on and Evaluate what you learned about reversible reactions by completing the class discussion and engineering design activities.

In the CER worksheet you completed at the beginning of the investigation, you suggested a possible explanation for the formation of limestone caves. With a partner, reevaluate the evidence and the explanation you presented.

20 **CCC Patterns** Burning coal with a high sulfur content can increase the acidity of precipitation. Using Le Châtelier's principle, explain how the increasing acidity of precipitation affects the processes that form limestone caves. ✏️

....

....

....

....

....

Free Energy and Entropy

⬚ **GO ONLINE** to Explore and Explain how entropy and free energy determine whether a physical or chemical process occurs.

Free Energy and Favorability

You studied enthalpy earlier in this chemistry course, and you know that a negative change in enthalpy ($\Delta H < 0$) for a reaction or a physical change means that the process is exothermic. Combustion is an example of an exothermic reaction that converts essentially all of its reactants to products, and it releases a considerable amount of energy as well.

Free energy is the overall energy change for a process. The overall energy is called "free energy" because it is free to do things, such as work. A process that produces free energy is a spontaneous process, or a **thermodynamically favorable process.** Other processes, such as ammonium chloride dissolving in water in a cold pack, require the addition of energy to go forward. A process that does not release free energy is a nonspontaneous process, or a **thermodynamically unfavorable process.** In addition to enthalpy, the temperature at which the process happens and the organization of the particles (atoms, ions, or molecules) in the system contribute to the free energy.

Limestone Erosion Carbonic acid in rainwater reacts with calcium carbonate in a limestone structure, causing it to erode over time. The reaction is thermodynamically favorable.

$$CaCO_3(s) \quad + \quad H_2CO_3(aq) \quad \rightleftharpoons \quad Ca(HCO_3)_2(aq)$$
Limestone   Carbonic acid   Calcium bicarbonate

Reaction Rate vs. Favorability

From your study of collision theory, you know that whether a reaction is thermodynamically favorable does not determine the rate at which it proceeds. Some thermodynamically favorable reactions are so slow that they appear to be unfavorable. Similarly, some thermodynamically unfavorable reactions occur quickly—once they have enough energy available.

Changing the conditions for a reaction—by raising the temperature, for instance—can speed up thermodynamically favorable reactions. Changing the temperature can also change some thermodynamically unfavorable reactions into favorable reactions.

Decomposing Calcium Carbonate In a lime kiln, calcium carbonate decomposes when heated. The reaction is thermodynamically favorable, but it does not proceed quickly until the reaction system is heated.

$$CaCO_3(s) \xrightarrow{heat} CaO(s) + CO_2(g)$$
Limestone   Lime   Carbon dioxide

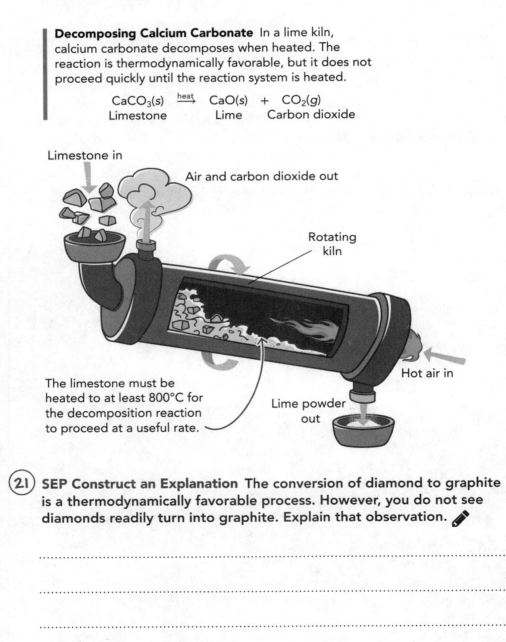

Limestone in

Air and carbon dioxide out

Rotating kiln

Hot air in

The limestone must be heated to at least 800°C for the decomposition reaction to proceed at a useful rate.

Lime powder out

(21) **SEP Construct an Explanation** The conversion of diamond to graphite is a thermodynamically favorable process. However, you do not see diamonds readily turn into graphite. Explain that observation. ✏

....

....

....

Entropy

When looking at a set of thermodynamically favorable processes, you may notice that most of them are exothermic. However, there are many endothermic processes that are thermodynamically favorable. There are also exothermic processes that are thermodynamically unfavorable. To understand the reason for that pattern, it is necessary to look at another aspect of the system: entropy. **Entropy,** S, is a measure of the disorder of a system—the opposite of the order of the system.

> ◼ **Entropy is a concept that describes the behavior of matter and energy within a physical system.**

In general, it is more likely for a system to be disordered than to be highly ordered. The figures show four kinds of change that increase the disorder, or decrease the predictability, of a system: changing state, dividing a substance into smaller parts, increasing the total number of molecules as reactants form products, and raising the temperature.

Changing State Entropy increases as disorder increases. Any state of matter in which the atoms or molecules can move around more, decreasing the organization of the system, has greater entropy. Gases have greater entropy than liquids, and liquids have greater entropy than solids. Therefore, entropy increases in reactions that involve solid reactants forming liquid or gaseous products. Entropy also increases when liquid reactants form gaseous products.

Dividing Into Parts Entropy increases when a substance is divided into parts. For instance, when an ionic or molecular compound dissolves in water, entropy increases. The solid compound, with its molecules or ions neatly organized in a crystal structure, splits up into dissolved molecules or ions. The result is an increase in entropy.

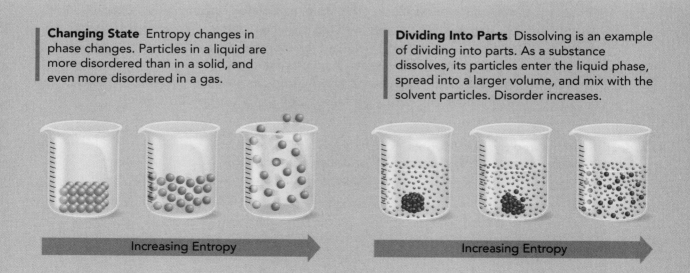

Changing State Entropy changes in phase changes. Particles in a liquid are more disordered than in a solid, and even more disordered in a gas.

Dividing Into Parts Dissolving is an example of dividing into parts. As a substance dissolves, its particles enter the liquid phase, spread into a larger volume, and mix with the solvent particles. Disorder increases.

Increasing Entropy

Increasing Entropy

Increasing the Number of Molecules When the total number of product molecules is greater than the total number of reactant molecules, entropy usually increases. Having more molecules on the product side of a reaction means there is an increase in entropy as the reaction proceeds.

Increasing Temperature Entropy tends to increase when the temperature increases. Particles (atoms, ions, or molecules) in the substance move faster, which increases the disorder of the system.

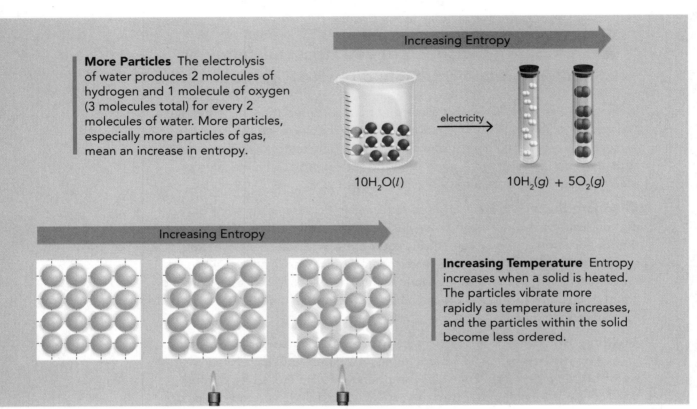

More Particles The electrolysis of water produces 2 molecules of hydrogen and 1 molecule of oxygen (3 molecules total) for every 2 molecules of water. More particles, especially more particles of gas, mean an increase in entropy.

Increasing Entropy

electricity

$10H_2O(l)$

$10H_2(g) + 5O_2(g)$

Increasing Entropy

Increasing Temperature Entropy increases when a solid is heated. The particles vibrate more rapidly as temperature increases, and the particles within the solid become less ordered.

The **second law of thermodynamics** states that the entropy of an isolated system never decreases. Therefore, an isolated system always spontaneously evolves toward the state with the maximum entropy. The second law applies to all isolated systems, including the atoms and molecules in a reaction system that is insulated from its surroundings. Reactions that involve an entropy increase ($\Delta S > 0$) as reactants form products are usually favored, and reactions that involve an entropy decrease ($\Delta S < 0$) are usually not favored.

(22) **CCC Systems and System Models** For each process, predict whether the entropy increases ($\Delta S > 0$) or decreases ($\Delta S < 0$). Discuss the reasoning for each of your answers with a classmate. ✏️

$FeCl_3(s) \xrightarrow{H_2O} FeCl_3(aq)$ ....

$2CO(g) + O_2(g) \longrightarrow 2CO_2(g)$ ....

$2KClO_3(s) \longrightarrow 2KCl(s) + 3O_2(g)$ ....

Changes in Free Energy

Recall that some endothermic reactions and physical changes are thermodynamically favorable, so a process's change in enthalpy being negative or positive does not alone determine whether the process is thermodynamically favorable. As well as the change in enthalpy, you must know the change in entropy for the process. To tell the complete energy story for a process, chemists calculate the change in free energy, ΔG.

$$\Delta G = \Delta H - T\Delta S$$

(Note that the temperature, T, must be expressed in kelvins when using this equation.) Free energy can be either released or absorbed during a physical or chemical process. A process that releases free energy, indicated by a negative ΔG, is thermodynamically favorable. If you examine the equation, you can see that ΔG is always negative for a process that is exothermic and involves an increase in disorder. Such a process is thermodynamically favorable. Again, examining the equation, you can see that ΔG is always positive for a process that is endothermic and involves a decrease in disorder in the system. Such a process is thermodynamically unfavorable.

When a process is exothermic with a decrease in disorder, or endothermic with an increase in disorder, the temperature of the system determines whether the process is thermodynamically favorable.

Combustion The greatest part of the energy from a bonfire is released by the combustion of cellulose, which is composed of large molecules. The combustion products are gases with much smaller molecules.

$C_6H_{10}O_5(s) + 6O_2(g) \rightarrow 6CO_2(g) + 5H_2O(g)$

(23) **SEP Use Mathematical Thinking** Use the equation for ΔG to explain why the burning of a piece of wood or paper, an example of a combustion reaction, is a thermodynamically favorable reaction. 🖉

....

....

....

Determining Thermodynamic Favorability

Calculate ΔG for water freezing at 263.15 K (−10°C). The ΔH value for the process is −6010 J, and the ΔS value is −22.0 J/K. Is the process thermodynamically favored at −10°C?

$$H_2O(l) \rightarrow H_2O(s)$$

ANALYZE List the knowns and the unknown.

Knowns	Unknown
$\Delta H = -6010$ J	$\Delta G = ?$
$\Delta S = -22.0$ J/K	
$T = 263.15$ K	

CALCULATE Solve for the unknown.

Start with the equation for calculating ΔG.	$\Delta G = \Delta H - T\Delta S$
Substitute the knowns into the equation.	$\Delta G = -6010$ J $- 263.15$ K $\times (-22.0$ J/K$)$
Calculate ΔG for the process.	$\Delta G = -6010$ J $- (-5789$ J$)$ $\Delta G = -6010$ J $+ 5789$ J $\Delta G = -221$ J
Interpret the value to determine whether the process is favorable at the stated temperature.	ΔG is negative, so freezing is thermodynamically favorable at −10°C.

EVALUATE Does the result make sense?

The units cancel, and the calculated value has the correct units for energy (joules). Based on observations of water freezing below 0°C (273.15 K), this result makes sense.

(24) Calculate ΔG for water freezing at 295.15 K (22.0°C). Is the freezing of water a thermodynamically favorable process at that temperature? ✏

GO ONLINE for more practice problems.

Freezing The formation of ice crystals with a regular structure shows a decrease in entropy. That decrease in entropy must be offset by a decrease in enthalpy.

Enthalpy, Entropy, and Free Energy

Factors Affecting Favorability Recall that a physical or chemical process is thermodynamically favorable at any temperature if it is exothermic and involves an entropy increase. A process is thermodynamically unfavorable at any temperature if it is endothermic and involves an entropy decrease. For other processes, the thermodynamic favorability depends on the temperature.

Some processes have a decrease in entropy—the particles in the system become more organized—but the processes are still thermodynamically favorable at low temperatures. Consider water freezing as an example. During that phase change, the water molecules become more organized, which is a decrease in entropy. The process is always favorable below 0°C and never favorable at higher temperatures. In a similar way, water boiling is always favorable above 100°C and never favorable at lower temperatures. In both cases, the overall value for ΔG depends on the temperature and on a balance between the relative magnitudes of ΔH and ΔS.

(25) **SEP Construct an Explanation** Explain why the processes of condensation (entropy decreasing) and melting (entropy increasing) are thermodynamically favorable only at relatively low or relatively high temperatures. (*Hint*: Are condensation and melting exothermic or endothermic?) ✎

....

....

....

....

....

Offsetting Unfavorable Factors When a process involves one unfavorable factor (either it is endothermic or it involves a decrease in entropy), the unfavorable factor may be offset by a favorable change in temperature. Such an offset is possible only if the temperature change is paired with a favorable factor (an exothermic process or an increase in entropy).

In either case, the relative magnitudes of ΔH and $-T\Delta S$ determine the favorability of the process.

For every process that has one favorable and one unfavorable factor, there is a unique **crossover temperature** (T_C) at which ΔG is zero. Since $\Delta G = \Delta H - T_C\Delta S = 0$, $\Delta H = T_C\Delta S$, and you can calculate T_C using ΔH and ΔS.

Free Energy and Temperature

How does **temperature** affect the **thermodynamic favorability** of a process?

Modeling Thermodynamic Favorability The magnitude and sign of the free energy change indicate the relative thermodynamic favorability of a process. The magnitudes and signs of the enthalpy and entropy changes, and sometimes the temperature, affect the free energy change. The graph models those relationships.

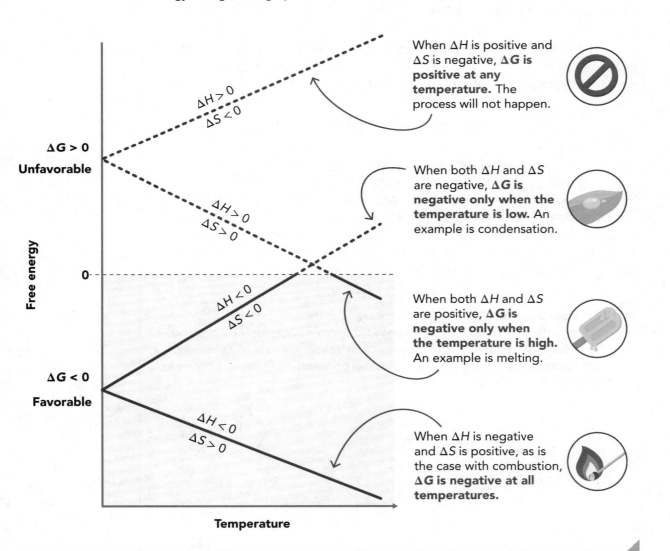

When ΔH is positive and ΔS is negative, ΔG **is positive at any temperature.** The process will not happen.

When both ΔH and ΔS are negative, ΔG **is negative only when the temperature is low.** An example is condensation.

When both ΔH and ΔS are positive, ΔG **is negative only when the temperature is high.** An example is melting.

When ΔH is negative and ΔS is positive, as is the case with combustion, ΔG **is negative at all temperatures.**

Using the Crossover Temperature

Consider the decomposition reaction in which carbon tetrachloride produces graphite and chlorine gas: $CCl_4(g) \rightarrow C(s) + 2Cl_2(g)$. Find the temperature range in which the reaction is thermodynamically favorable. First, calculate the crossover temperature, T_C. Then, determine whether thermodynamically favorable temperatures, T_F, are above or below that temperature. Note that $\Delta H = +95,600$ J and $\Delta S = +148$ J/K.

ANALYZE List the knowns and the unknowns.

Knowns	Unknowns
$\Delta H = 95,600$ J	$T_C = ?$ K
$\Delta S = 148$ J/K	$T_F >$ or $< T_C$?
$\Delta G = 0$	

CALCULATE Solve for the unknowns.

Start with the equation for calculating ΔG, and set ΔG equal to zero.

$$\Delta G = 0 = \Delta H - T_C\Delta S$$

Solve the equation for T_C.

$$T_C = \frac{\Delta H}{\Delta S}$$

Substitute in the known values and solve for T_C.

$$T_C = \frac{95,600 \text{ J}}{148 \text{ J/K}}$$
$$T_C = 646 \text{ K}$$

Determine whether the reaction is favorable above or below T_C. Note that ΔS is positive, so $-T_C\Delta S$ is always negative. ΔG becomes increasingly negative as T increases above T_C.

$$T_F > T_C$$

EVALUATE Do the results make sense?

It makes sense that a decomposition reaction would require high temperatures. If you plug a temperature above 646 K into the formula and solve for ΔG, the result is negative.

26) **Boiling water is an endothermic process. Use a calculation to show that 373.15 K (100.0°C), the boiling temperature for water, is the crossover temperature for the process. Use the values $\Delta H = +44.0$ kJ and $\Delta S = +117.9$ J/K.**

GO ONLINE for more practice problems.

27 **SEP Interpret Data** The table contains the four possible cases for enthalpy and entropy changes in a reaction or physical change. Complete the third column by describing the temperature range in which each sort of reaction or physical change is thermodynamically favorable. ✎

Enthalpy Change	Entropy Change	Favorable?
Negative	Positive	
Positive	Positive	At higher temperatures
Negative	Negative	
Positive	Negative	

Revisit

INVESTIGATIVE PHENOMENON

GO ONLINE to Elaborate on and Evaluate your knowledge of entropy and free energy by completing the peer review and writing activities.

In the CER worksheet you completed at the beginning of the investigation, you suggested a possible explanation for the formation of limestone caves. With a partner, reevaluate the evidence and the explanation you presented.

28 **CCC Energy and Matter** Suppose that one of the processes that forms stalactites in a cave is endothermic and has a negative change in entropy. How much would the temperature need to increase or decrease to halt the process? ✎

....

....

....

....

GO ONLINE to Evaluate what you learned about reaction rates and equilibrium by using the available assessment resources.

In the Performance-Based Assessment, you explained the results of your investigations for the effects of changing reaction system conditions on equilibrium and reaction rate. Wrap up your explanation by answering the following questions.

29) **SEP Construct an Explanation** In measuring the variation with concentration for the rate of decomposition of hydrogen peroxide, what did you observe? Explain your observation in terms of collision theory.

....

....

....

....

....

30) **SEP Construct an Explanation** In measuring the variation with temperature for the dissolution of sodium acetate, what did you observe? Explain your observation in terms of collision theory.

....

....

....

....

31) **Revisit the Anchoring Phenomenon** How does what you learned in this investigation help explain the chemistry of ocean acidification?

....

....

....

INVESTIGATIVE PHENOMENON

GO ONLINE to Engage with real-world phenomena by watching a video and to complete a CER interactive worksheet.

How does acid rain impact the environment?

Acid-Base Equilibria

Acid rain damages forests and stone structures and can kill fish, plants, and other organisms living in bodies of water. Government regulations and modern technologies help reduce acid rain. Once you have viewed the Investigative Phenomenon video and used the claim-evidence-reasoning worksheet to draft an explanation for what you observed, answer these reflection questions about acid rain.

1 **SEP Analyze Data** The two maps show acid rain pH levels in the years 1994 and 2017. Summarize what the data show. ✏️

Comparing the pH of Rain in Different U.S. Regions

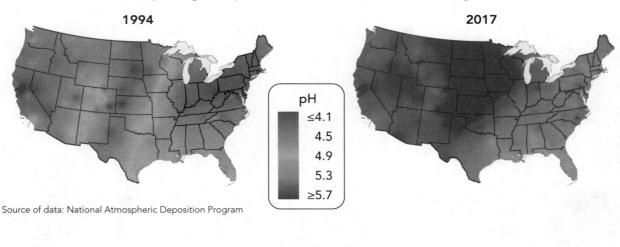

1994

2017

pH
≤4.1
4.5
4.9
5.3
≥5.7

Source of data: National Atmospheric Deposition Program

....

....

2 **SEP Obtain Information** Refer to the online "Lab pH" data for 2008 at the *National Atmospheric Deposition Program—Annual NTN Maps by Year*. Are the data shown by the 2008 map what you would expect to see? Explain. ✏️

....

....

....

Acids, Bases, and Salts

GO ONLINE to Explore and Explain the properties of acids and bases and their effects on the pH of solutions.

Properties of Acids, Bases, and Salts

The word *acid* is derived from the Latin word *acidus*, which means "tart" or "sour." The vinegar in salad dressing contains ethanoic acid, CH_3COOH. It is commonly called acetic acid. Your stomach contains hydrochloric acid, HCl, which is used to digest food.

A base has a bitter taste and feels slippery. Various solutions that contain bases are commonly referred to as alkaline solutions. Soaps are often made using the common base sodium hydroxide, NaOH.

A salt is an ionic compound that usually consists of positive metal ions and negative nonmetal ions. Salts are produced when acids and bases react with one another. Dissolved salts in solution are electrolytes. You can precipitate a salt from a solution to form a crystalline solid.

Acids, Bases, and Salts in Everyday Life Before eating a meal, most people wash their hands with soap, which is made with basic substances. During the meal, people consume foods containing various acids and salts.

Table salt is used to add more flavor to food.

Ammonia is a base that is used to clean windows.

Citrus fruits (oranges and grapefruits) and vinegar used in salad dressings contain acids.

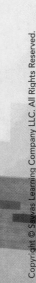

Defining Acids and Bases

Arrhenius Model of Acids and Bases There is more than one way to explain the behavior of acids and bases. The first explanation was proposed by the Swedish chemist Svante Arrhenius in 1887. In his model, acids are compounds that dissociate and form hydrogen cations, H^+, in an aqueous solution. However, in solution, the H^+ ion does not exist. Instead, a species called the **hydronium ion,** H_3O^+, forms when the dissociated H^+ ion combines with a water molecule, H_2O.

| **Hydrochloric Acid** Hydrochloric acid is actually an aqueous solution of hydrogen chloride. Hydrogen chloride forms hydronium ions, making the compound an acid.

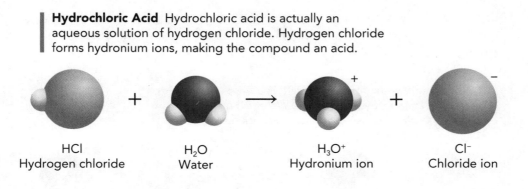

HCl	H₂O	H₃O⁺	Cl⁻
Hydrogen chloride	Water	Hydronium ion	Chloride ion

Arrhenius acids with only one hydrogen that can be ionized, such as hydrochloric acid, HCl, and nitric acid, HNO_3, are classified as monoprotic acids. The prefix *mono-* means "one," and *protic* means "proton," which is another way to describe a hydrogen cation. Carbonic acid, H_2CO_3, and sulfuric acid, H_2SO_4, are diprotic acids, as they contain two hydrogens that can be ionized. Phosphoric acid, H_3PO_4, is a triprotic acid.

An Arrhenius base is an ionic compound that releases a hydroxide ion, OH^-, when it dissociates in aqueous solution. For example, the compounds sodium hydroxide, NaOH, and potassium hydroxide, KOH, dissociate in aqueous solution to produce a metal ion and a hydroxide ion. They are both monoprotic bases. Calcium hydroxide, $Ca(OH)_2$, and magnesium hydroxide, $Mg(OH)_2$, are diprotic bases.

| **Sodium Hydroxide** Sodium hydroxide is an ionic solid that dissociates in water to form hydroxide ions, making this compound a base.

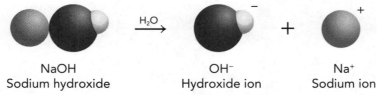

NaOH	OH⁻	Na⁺
Sodium hydroxide	Hydroxide ion	Sodium ion

(3) **Apply Concepts** Ethanoic acid, CH_3COOH, ionizes to form an ethanoate ion (CH_3COO^-) in aqueous solution. What else does it form? Is it a monoprotic acid? ✏️

Brønsted-Lowry Model of Acids and Bases According to the Arrhenius model, ammonia, NH_3, and sodium carbonate, Na_2CO_3, are not classified as bases because they do not contain at least one unit of OH in their chemical formulas. However, when you prepare solutions of NH_3 and Na_2CO_3, they react with water and produce hydroxide ions.

Johannes Brønsted and Thomas Lowry proposed a new way to define acids and bases. In their model, an acid is a hydrogen-ion donor and a base is a hydrogen-ion acceptor. For example, when ammonia and water react, a water molecule donates a hydrogen ion to an ammonia molecule. The reaction produces ammonium ions and hydroxide ions. Note that the Brønsted-Lowry model applies not just to aqueous solutions, but to any medium or phase. For instance, NH_3 and HCl are a base and an acid that can react in the gas phase.

> **Ammonia in Water** Ammonia, NH_3, is a base because it accepts hydrogen ions. Water is an acid in this example because it donates hydrogen ions.

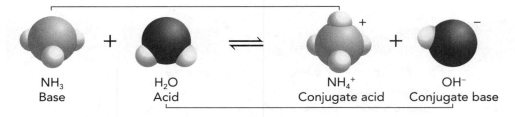

NH_3	H_2O		NH_4^+	OH^-
Base	Acid		Conjugate acid	Conjugate base

In the Brønsted-Lowry model, the products of acid-base reactions are referred to as conjugates. A **conjugate acid** is the ion or molecule formed when a base gains a hydrogen ion. A **conjugate base** is the ion or molecule that remains after an acid donates a hydrogen ion. A **conjugate acid-base pair** consists of two ions or molecules related by the loss or gain of one hydrogen ion.

Conjugate Acid-Base Pairs Conjugate acids are always paired with bases, and conjugate bases are always paired with acids. The table shows several examples, including the ammonium ion, NH_4^+, which is the conjugate acid of the base ammonia, NH_3.

Hydrogen chloride is a Brønsted-Lowry acid. The chloride ion is the conjugate base of the acid HCl.

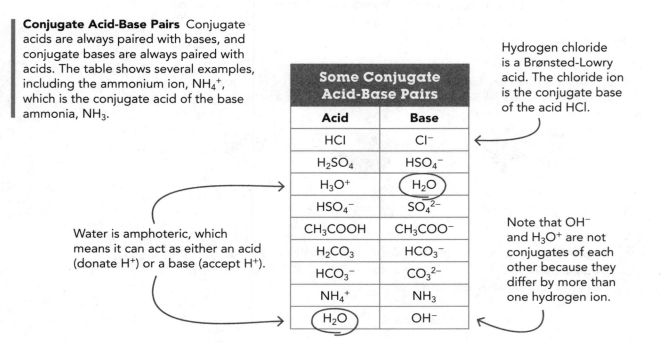

Some Conjugate Acid-Base Pairs	
Acid	**Base**
HCl	Cl^-
H_2SO_4	HSO_4^-
H_3O^+	H_2O
HSO_4^-	SO_4^{2-}
CH_3COOH	CH_3COO^-
H_2CO_3	HCO_3^-
HCO_3^-	CO_3^{2-}
NH_4^+	NH_3
H_2O	OH^-

Water is amphoteric, which means it can act as either an acid (donate H^+) or a base (accept H^+).

Note that OH^- and H_3O^+ are not conjugates of each other because they differ by more than one hydrogen ion.

Lewis Model of Acids and Bases Another model used to classify acids and bases was developed by Gilbert Lewis. Instead of donated or accepted hydrogen ions (as in the Brønsted-Lowry model), the Lewis model uses electron pairs. A **Lewis base** is a substance that donates a pair of electrons to form a covalent bond. A **Lewis acid** is a substance that accepts a pair of electrons to form a covalent bond.

▶ The Lewis model of acids and bases is the broadest of the three models.

The Lewis model extends to substances that cannot be classified as acids and bases according to either the Arrhenius or Brønsted-Lowry models.

Electron Donors and Acceptors Lewis bases donate pairs of electrons. Lewis acids accept pairs of electrons.

Electron dot structures make it easy to see that the fluoride ion and the ammonia molecule act as Lewis bases in donating electrons.

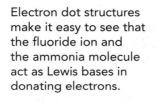

4) **SEP Construct an Explanation** When hydrogen chloride gas is added to water, the products are hydronium ions and chloride ions. Explain why, according to the Brønsted-Lowry and Lewis models, water can be described as a base in the reaction. ✏

....

....

....

5) **SEP Use Models** Use electron dot structures to model the reaction between NH_3 and BF_3. Use an arrow to show how the electron pair is donated. Identify the Lewis acid, Lewis base, and the electron pair. ✏

The Self-Ionization of Water

Pure water ionizes to a minimal extent to form hydronium ions (H_3O^+) and hydroxide ions (OH^-). The process happens because water is an amphoteric substance, and two molecules of water can react with each other, one acting as an acid and the other as a base. The process is reversible and is called the self-ionization of water.

$$H_2O(l) + H_2O(l) \rightleftharpoons H_3O^+(aq) + OH^-(aq)$$

Recall that brackets around a species means "concentration of." For example, $[H_3O^+]$ represents the concentration of hydronium ions. In pure water at 25°C, the concentration of H_3O^+ is only $1 \times 10^{-7}M$. The concentration of OH^- is also $1 \times 10^{-7}M$, as the amount of H_3O^+ ions and the amount of OH^- ions are equal in pure water. Any aqueous solution in which $[H_3O^+]$ and $[OH^-]$ are equal is a **neutral solution.**

In water or aqueous solutions at 25°C, the product of the hydronium-ion concentration and the hydroxide-ion concentration, known as the **ion-product constant for water** (K_w), equals 1.0×10^{-14}.

$$K_w = [H_3O^+] \times [OH^-] = 1.0 \times 10^{-14}$$

Reversible Reaction The self-ionization of water is a reversible ionization. The reactants are H_2O molecules, and the products are H_3O^+ and OH^- ions.

According to Le Châtelier's principle, if the system is disturbed, it will adjust to restore equilibrium. When $[H_3O^+]$ increases, $[OH^-]$ decreases. Likewise, when $[H_3O^+]$ decreases, $[OH^-]$ increases.

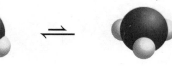

$2H_2O$
Water molecules

H_3O^+
Hydronium ion

OH^-
Hydroxide ion

SEP Use Mathematics For each given $[H_3O^+]$ or $[OH^-]$, find the corresponding $[OH^-]$ or $[H_3O^+]$ at 25°C.

$[H_3O^+] = 1.00 \times 10^{-10}M$ $[OH^-] =$ ....

$[OH^-] = 1.00 \times 10^{-4}M$ $[H_3O^+] =$ ....

$[H_3O^+] = 9.90 \times 10^{-6}M$ $[OH^-] =$ ....

Calculating pH

Instead of expressing hydronium ion concentration, $[H_3O^+]$, in molarity, the logarithmic pH scale is used to express $[H_3O^+]$. The pH of a solution is the negative logarithm of the hydronium ion concentration. Thus, every unit decrease in pH corresponds to a tenfold increase in $[H_3O^+]$. The pH is represented using the following equation.

$$pH = -\log[H_3O^+]$$

A solution with a pH of 7.0, such as pure water, is neutral.

$$pH = -\log(1 \times 10^{-7}) = 7.0$$

Summarizing pH Concepts
What are the **relationships among $[H_3O^+]$, $[OH^-]$, and pH?**

More Convenient The pH scale allows you to quantify $[H_3O^+]$ in a solution using numbers such as 3 and 12 rather than 1×10^{-3} and 1×10^{-12}. **The pH scale uses powers of ten to express $[H_3O^+]$.**

The **smaller the pH value, the more acidic** is the substance or solution.

$[H_3O^+] = [OH^-]$ for a neutral solution.

baking soda

A solution with a pH of 12.0 is one thousand times more basic than a solution with a pH of 9.0.

bleach

$[H_3O^+]$ (mol/L)	$[OH^-]$ (mol/L)	pH
1×10^{0}	1×10^{-14}	0
1×10^{-1}	1×10^{-13}	1
1×10^{-2}	1×10^{-12}	2
1×10^{-3}	1×10^{-11}	3
1×10^{-4}	1×10^{-10}	4
1×10^{-5}	1×10^{-9}	5
1×10^{-6}	1×10^{-8}	6
1×10^{-7}	1×10^{-7}	7
1×10^{-8}	1×10^{-6}	8
1×10^{-9}	1×10^{-5}	9
1×10^{-10}	1×10^{-4}	10
1×10^{-11}	1×10^{-3}	11
1×10^{-12}	1×10^{-2}	12
1×10^{-13}	1×10^{-1}	13
1×10^{-14}	1×10^{0}	14

increasing acidity

increasing basicity

lemon

A solution with a pH of 2.0 is one hundred times more acidic than a solution with a pH of 4.0.

tomato

The pH of pure water is 7. It is neutral (not acidic or basic).

The **larger the pH value, the more basic** is the substance or solution.

The pH range of 0–14 is not absolute. A solution of a strong acid or a strong base can have a pH less than 0 or greater than 14.

Writing $[H_3O^+]$ in scientific notation makes it easier to calculate pH. For example, it is easier to express $0.000010M$ as $1.0 \times 10^{-5}M$. When the coefficient in front of the power of 10 is 1, the pH is simply the negative of the exponent. The $0.000010M$ solution has $[H_3O^+] = 1.0 \times 10^{-5}M$ and a pH of 5.0. When the coefficient is a number other than 1, you can use logarithms to calculate the pH. If an acid has $[H_3O^+] = 2.0 \times 10^{-6}M$, you need to find the negative of the logarithm of 2.0×10^{-6}. A calculator will tell you that the negative of the logarithm is 5.7.

Sometimes it is useful to work with $[OH^-]$ instead of $[H_3O^+]$. Then you can use the quantity pOH, which is defined in a way similar to pH.

$$pOH = -\log[OH^-]$$

You can use pH and pOH to rewrite the K_w expression.

$$pH + pOH = 14.$$

Acidic, Neutral, and Basic Solutions A solution is acidic, neutral, or basic depending on whether its hydronium ion concentration is greater than, equal to, or less than its hydroxide ion concentration.

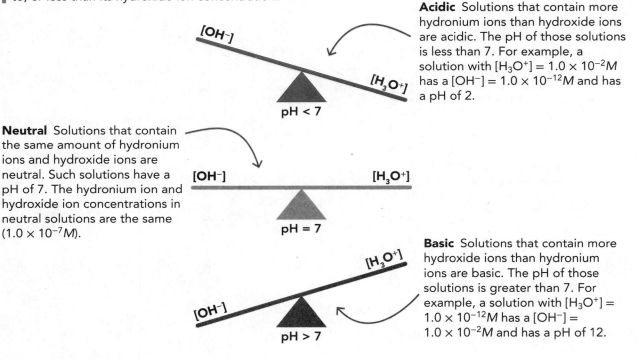

Acidic Solutions that contain more hydronium ions than hydroxide ions are acidic. The pH of those solutions is less than 7. For example, a solution with $[H_3O^+] = 1.0 \times 10^{-2}M$ has a $[OH^-] = 1.0 \times 10^{-12}M$ and has a pH of 2.

Neutral Solutions that contain the same amount of hydronium ions and hydroxide ions are neutral. Such solutions have a pH of 7. The hydronium ion and hydroxide ion concentrations in neutral solutions are the same $(1.0 \times 10^{-7}M)$.

Basic Solutions that contain more hydroxide ions than hydronium ions are basic. The pH of those solutions is greater than 7. For example, a solution with $[H_3O^+] = 1.0 \times 10^{-12}M$ has a $[OH^-] = 1.0 \times 10^{-2}M$ and has a pH of 12.

(7) **SEP Use Mathematics** Three solutions have pH values of 6, 7, and 11. How much more acidic is the pH 6 solution than the pH 7 solution if acidity is defined as $[H_3O^+]$? How much more basic is the pH 11 solution than the pH 7 solution if basicity is defined as $[OH^-]$?

Calculating pH from H_3O^+ Concentration

What is the pH of a solution with a hydronium ion concentration of $4.2 \times 10^{-10}M$?

ANALYZE List the known and the unknown.

Known	Unknown
$[H_3O^+] = 4.2 \times 10^{-10}M$	pH = ?

CALCULATE Solve for the unknown.

Start with the equation for finding pH from $[H_3O^+]$.

$$pH = -\log[H_3O^+]$$

Substitute the known $[H_3O^+]$ and use the log function on your calculator to calculate the pH.

$$pH = -\log (4.2 \times 10^{-10})$$
$$= -(-9.37675)$$
$$= 9.37675$$

Round the pH to two decimal places because the hydronium concentration has two significant figures.

$$= 9.38$$

EVALUATE Does the result make sense?

The value of the hydronium ion concentration is between $1 \times 10^{-9}M$ and $1 \times 10^{-10}M$. So, the calculated pH should be between 9 and 10, which it is.

8 What are the pH values of the following solutions, based on their H_3O^+ concentrations? ✏️

a. $[H_3O^+] = 1.4 \times 10^{-4}M$

b. $[H_3O^+] = 8.7 \times 10^{-12}M$

GO ONLINE for more practice problems.

Revisit

INVESTIGATIVE PHENOMENON

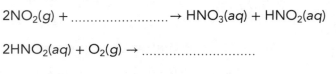

GO ONLINE to Elaborate on and Evaluate your knowledge of acids, bases, and pH by completing the peer review and engineering design activities.

In the CER worksheet you completed at the beginning of the investigation, you constructed an explanation for how acid rain can affect a forest. With a partner, reevaluate the evidence you cited in your arguments.

9 **SEP Develop Models** Rain is naturally acidic. Carbon dioxide in the atmosphere dissolves to some extent in water and reacts with it to produce a slightly acidic solution of carbonic acid:

$$CO_2(g) + H_2O(l) \rightarrow H_2CO_3(aq)$$

$$H_2CO_3(aq) + H_2O(l) \rightleftharpoons H_3O^+(aq) + HCO_3^-(aq)$$

The carbonic acid ionizes slightly, leading to rain with a pH around 5.3. Acid rain has pH levels lower than 4.3, as it contains SO_x and NO_x. Complete the equations showing how SO_3 and NO_2 produce sulfuric acid and nitric acid and contribute to rain with lower pH. *Hint:* Use the patterns you observe among the following chemical equations and the provided chemical equations for carbon dioxide. ✏️

SO_3 Reactions

$$SO_3(g) + H_2O(l) \rightarrow \text{................................}$$

$$H_2SO_4(aq) + H_2O(l)$$
$$\rightarrow \text{..........................} + HSO_4^-(aq)$$

$$\text{..........................} + H_2O(l)$$
$$\rightarrow H_3O^+(aq) + SO_4^{2-}(aq)$$

NO_2 Reactions

$$2NO_2(g) + \text{........................} \rightarrow HNO_3(aq) + HNO_2(aq)$$

$$2HNO_2(aq) + O_2(g) \rightarrow \text{.............................}$$

$$HNO_3(aq) + H_2O(l) \rightarrow H_3O^+(aq) + \text{..............................}$$

Strong and Weak Acids and Bases

 GO ONLINE to Explore and Explain the differences between strong and weak acids and bases.

Strong Acids and Bases

The classification of acids and bases as strong or weak is based on the degree to which they ionize in water. A **strong acid** is an acid that completely ionizes in aqueous solution to form hydronium ions. A useful way to represent an Arrhenius acid is as HA. Ionization of the acid HA in water yields an H_3O^+ ion and an anion A^-, as the chemical equation shows.

$$HA(s \text{ or } l \text{ or } g) + H_2O(l) \rightarrow H_3O^+(aq) + A^-(aq)$$

For a strong acid, all the acid molecules in solution become ionized. Examples of strong acids include HCl, HI, HNO_3, and H_2SO_4.

A **strong base** is a base that completely ionizes in solution to produce hydroxide ions. Most strong bases fit the Arrhenius model because they are hydroxide salts. Examples of strong bases include $NaOH$, $LiOH$, and $Ba(OH)_2$.

Ionization of Strong Acids and Bases If an acid or base is classified as strong, you know it is completely ionized in solution.

$$HCl(g) + H_2O(l) \longrightarrow H_3O^+(aq) + Cl^-(aq)$$

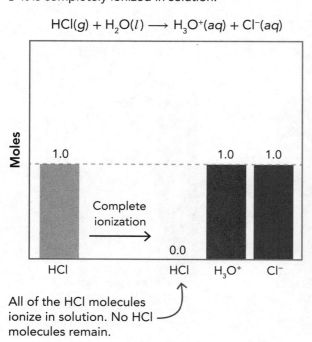

All of the HCl molecules ionize in solution. No HCl molecules remain.

$$Ba(OH)_2(s) \xrightarrow{H_2O} 2OH^-(aq) + Ba^{2+}(aq)$$

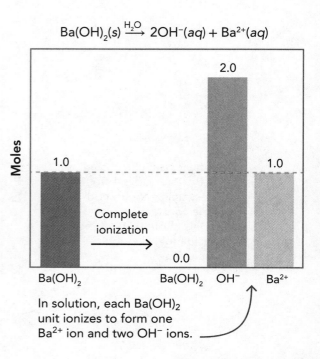

In solution, each $Ba(OH)_2$ unit ionizes to form one Ba^{2+} ion and two OH^- ions.

Weak Acids

The Nature of Weak Acids A **weak acid** is an acid that ionizes only partially in solution to produce hydronium ions. The ionization of a weak acid yields the same products as a strong acid. However, in the ionization equation, an unequal equilibrium arrow is used to show that the ionization process does not go very far to the right.

$$HA(aq) + H_2O(l) \rightleftharpoons H_3O^+(aq) + A^-(aq)$$

Weak acids are more common than strong acids. A few examples are hydrofluoric acid (HF), ethanoic acid (CH_3COOH), and carbonic acid (H_2CO_3). All weak acids partially ionize in solution, but each ionizes to a different degree.

Ionization of Weak Acids
The bar graphs show the extent of ionization for two weak acids. Different weak acids ionize to different extents, but neither ionizes fully.

The first ionization constant for oxalic acid is 5.6×10^{-2}. About 15% of the acid molecules ionize in solution.

The ionization constant for ethanoic acid is 1.8×10^{-5}, less than a thousandth of the constant for oxalic acid. Only about 0.3% of the acid molecules ionize in solution.

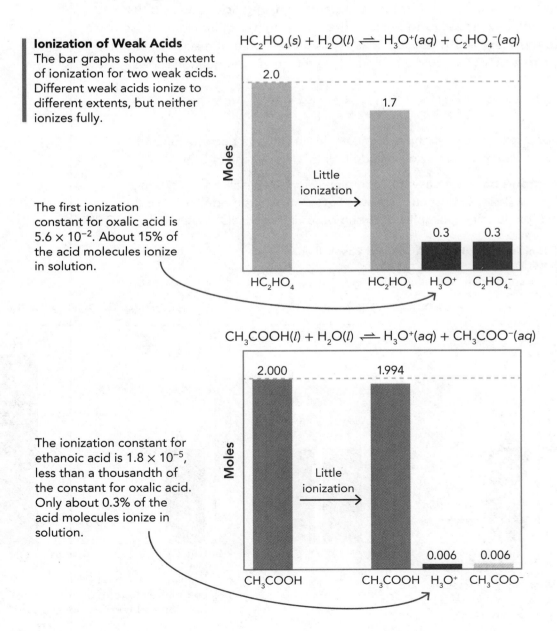

$$HC_2HO_4(s) + H_2O(l) \rightleftharpoons H_3O^+(aq) + C_2HO_4^-(aq)$$

$$CH_3COOH(l) + H_2O(l) \rightleftharpoons H_3O^+(aq) + CH_3COO^-(aq)$$

Acid Ionization Constants You have written the ion product constant K_w for the self-ionization of water. In a similar way, you can write an acid ionization constant, sometimes called a dissociation constant, K_a, for a weak acid. The K_a expression has this form:

$$K_a = \frac{[H_3O^+] \times [A^-]}{[HA]}$$

The value of K_a tells you how far to the right the ionization process goes. Based on what you know about weak acids, you can predict that K_a values should be quite small. The numerator of the fraction is small because the acid does not ionize completely, and the denominator is large in comparison. Each weak acid has a characteristic K_a value. Diprotic and triprotic weak acids have a different K_a value for each ionization. The succeeding K_a values for such acids grow smaller.

The Range of K_a Values For weak acids, K_a values are small numbers. Each acid has its own value.

A larger negative exponent means a smaller number and, therefore, a smaller K_a (less ionization).

Ionization Constants of Weak Acids		
Acid	**Chemical equation for ionization**	**K_a (25°C)**
Phosphoric acid	$H_3PO_4(aq) + H_2O(l) \rightleftharpoons H_3O^+(aq) + H_2PO_4^-(aq)$	7.5×10^{-3}
	$H_2PO_4^-(aq) + H_2O(l) \rightleftharpoons H_3O^+(aq) + HPO_4^{2-}(aq)$	6.2×10^{-8}
	$HPO_4^{2-}(aq) + H_2O(l) \rightleftharpoons H_3O^+(aq) + PO_4^{3-}(aq)$	4.8×10^{-13}
Citric acid	$H_3C_6H_5O_7(aq) + H_2O(l) \rightleftharpoons H_3O^+(aq) + H_2C_6H_5O_7^-(aq)$	7.4×10^{-4}
	$H_2C_6H_5O_7^-(aq) + H_2O(l) \rightleftharpoons H_3O^+(aq) + HC_6H_5O_7^{2-}(aq)$	1.7×10^{-5}
	$HC_6H_5O_7^{2-}(aq) + H_2O(l) \rightleftharpoons H_3O^+(aq) + C_6H_5O_7^{3-}(aq)$	4.0×10^{-7}
Benzoic acid	$C_6H_5COOH(aq) + H_2O(l) \rightleftharpoons H_3O^+(aq) + C_6H_5COO^-(aq)$	6.3×10^{-5}
Ethanoic acid	$CH_3COOH(aq) + H_2O(l) \rightleftharpoons H_3O^+(aq) + CH_3COO^-(aq)$	1.8×10^{-5}
Carbonic acid	$H_2CO_3(aq) + H_2O(l) \rightleftharpoons H_3O^+(aq) + HCO_3^-(aq)$	4.3×10^{-7}
	$HCO_3^-(aq) + H_2O(l) \rightleftharpoons H_3O^+(aq) + CO_3^{2-}(aq)$	4.8×10^{-11}

10 **SEP Use Math** Use the information in the table to write the K_a expression for each of the ionizations of carbonic acid. ✏️

Weak Bases

The Nature of Weak Bases A **weak base** reacts with water to produce hydroxide ions in solution, but the quantity of ions produced is relatively small because the formation of reactants is favored.

▶ Unlike most strong bases that dissolve to form hydroxide ions in solution, weak bases react with water to produce hydroxide ions in solution.

A useful way to represent a base is as B. The reaction of a weak base (B) with water yields a cation (BH^+) and an OH^- ion.

$$B(aq) + H_2O(l) \rightleftharpoons BH^+(aq) + OH^-(aq)$$

There are many weak bases. A few examples are ammonia (NH_3), pyridine (C_5H_5N), and the carbonate anion (CO_3^{2-}). All weak bases react with water to produce OH^- ions in solution, but each base reacts with water to a different degree.

Strong Base vs. Weak Base Not only do strong and weak bases differ in how much they affect pH through the production of OH^- ions, they also generally produce OH^- ions through different processes.

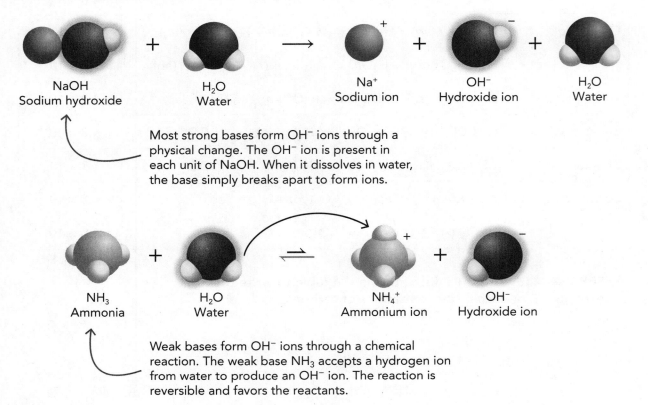

NaOH
Sodium hydroxide

+

H_2O
Water

→

Na^+
Sodium ion

+

OH^-
Hydroxide ion

+

H_2O
Water

Most strong bases form OH^- ions through a physical change. The OH^- ion is present in each unit of NaOH. When it dissolves in water, the base simply breaks apart to form ions.

NH_3
Ammonia

+

H_2O
Water

$\rightleftharpoons$

NH_4^+
Ammonium ion

+

OH^-
Hydroxide ion

Weak bases form OH^- ions through a chemical reaction. The weak base NH_3 accepts a hydrogen ion from water to produce an OH^- ion. The reaction is reversible and favors the reactants.

Bases in Synthesis Pyridine is a base commonly used in synthesizing organic compounds.

Base Ionization Constants When a substance reacts as a base, it is convenient to have a straightforward way to describe how far to the right the reaction goes. The base ionization (or dissociation) constant K_b does just that. The K_b expression has this form:

$$K_b = \frac{[BH^+] \times [OH^-]}{[B]}$$

You can predict that, for a weak base, K_b values should be quite small. The numerator of the fraction is small because the reaction does not go very far to the right, and the denominator is large in comparison. Each weak base has a characteristic K_b value.

The Range of K_b Values For weak bases, K_b values are small numbers. Each base has its own value.

Each K_b value describes how far to the right the reaction goes when the base reacts with water to produce OH^- ions.

Ionization Constants of Weak Bases		
Base	**Chemical equation for ionization**	**K_b (25°C)**
Carbonate ion	$CO_3^{2-}(aq) + H_2O(l) \rightleftharpoons OH^-(aq) + HCO_3^-(aq)$	1.8×10^{-4}
	$HCO_3^-(aq) + H_2O(l) \rightleftharpoons OH^-(aq) + H_2CO_3^-(aq)$	1.5×10^{-11}
Ammonia	$NH_3(aq) + H_2O(l) \rightleftharpoons OH^-(aq) + NH_4^+(aq)$	1.8×10^{-5}
Hydrazine	$N_2H_4(aq) + H_2O(l) \rightleftharpoons OH^-(aq) + N_2H_5^+(aq)$	1.3×10^{-6}
Pyridine	$C_5H_5N(aq) + H_2O(l) \rightleftharpoons OH^-(aq) + C_5H_5NH^+(aq)$	1.7×10^{-9}

(11) **SEP Use Math** Use the information in the table to write the K_b expression for ammonia, NH_3. 🖊

Calculating pH for Weak Acids and Bases

You can use K_a and K_b expressions (and what you know about stoichiometry) to estimate the pH of monoprotic weak acid and weak base solutions. To find the pH of a weak acid solution, you first need to solve the K_a expression for $[H_3O^+]$. You can then use that value in the equation $pH = -\log [H_3O^+]$. Each mole of a monoprotic weak acid that ionizes produces 1 mole of H_3O^+ ions and 1 mole of the acid's conjugate base. Therefore, in solution, the concentration of H_3O^+ ions equals the concentration of the conjugate base, allowing you to substitute the variable x for both concentrations. The initial concentration of the acid, represented as C, can be substituted in the denominator because it is very close to the concentration of the acid after ionization. By making those three substitutions, you can write

$$K_a = \frac{[H_3O^+] \times [A^-]}{[HA]} = \frac{x^2}{C}$$

Then you can solve for $[H_3O^+]$, or x, algebraically.

Citric Acid is a triprotic acid, so it has three K_a values (one for each ionization). In most cases, you can estimate the pH of a diprotic or triprotic acid using only the first K_a value and the ionization expression.

$K_{a1} = 7.4 \times 10^{-4}$

$K_{a2} = 1.7 \times 10^{-5}$

$K_{a3} = 4.0 \times 10^{-7}$

(12) **CCC Cause and Effect** Describe the relationships between pH, the concentration of H_3O^+ or OH^- ions, and the extent to which the weak acid or base ionizes. 🖊

....

....

....

....

Estimating pH of a Weak Acid Solution

Estimate the pH of a 0.100M solution of citric acid. The acid ionization constant for the first ionization is 7.4×10^{-4}. Assume you can estimate the pH using only the first ionization constant.

ANALYZE List the knowns and the unknown.

Knowns	Unknown
$K_a = 7.4 \times 10^{-4}$	pH = ?
$C = 0.100M$	

CALCULATE Solve for the unknown.

Start with the equation.	$K_a = \dfrac{x^2}{C}$

Substitute the known values for C and K_a.	$7.4 \times 10^{-4} = \dfrac{x^2}{0.100M}$

Solve the equation for x. First, multiply each side by the concentration. Then, take the square root of each side.

$x^2 = 7.4 \times 10^{-4} \times 0.100M$

$x^2 = 7.4 \times 10^{-5}$

$x = 8.6 \times 10^{-3}$

Use the equation for finding pH from $[H_3O^+]$. Remember, x equals $[H_3O^+]$.

$pH = -\log [H_3O^+] = -\log x$

$pH = -\log (8.6 \times 10^{-3})$

$pH = -(-2.07)$

$pH = 2.07$

EVALUATE Does the result make sense?

The value of the hydronium-ion concentration is close to $1 \times 10^{-2}M$. Therefore, the calculated pH should be close to 2.

(13) Estimate the pH of vinegar, which is a 0.100M aqueous solution of ethanoic acid. Use the K_a value from the Ionization Constants of Weak Acids table. ✏

GO ONLINE for more practice problems.

Strength vs. Concentration

Two factors affect the pH of a solution—strength and concentration. The strength of an acid or base (whether it is strong or weak) determines how far to the right the ionization process goes. The concentration of the acid or base solution determines how many moles of acid or base are present in a volume of solution. The two factors work together to affect the pH of a solution.

Factors That Affect pH

How do an acid's strength and concentration affect pH?

Ionization of Acids In a solution of a strong acid, the acid fully ionizes and produces one H_3O^+ ion for each acid molecule. In a weak acid solution, very few acid molecules form H_3O^+ ions, so there is a smaller change in pH. (The amount of ionization for the weak acid is exaggerated in this figure.)

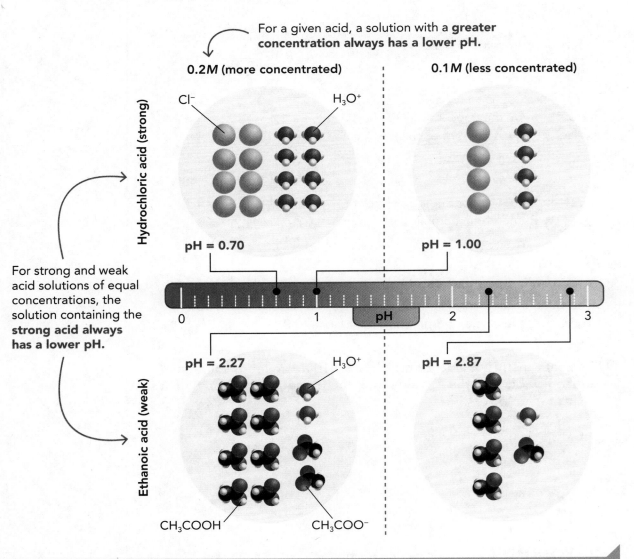

For a given acid, a solution with a **greater concentration always has a lower pH.**

0.2*M* (more concentrated)   0.1*M* (less concentrated)

Cl⁻ H_3O^+

Hydrochloric acid (strong)

pH = 0.70   pH = 1.00

For strong and weak acid solutions of equal concentrations, the solution containing the **strong acid always has a lower pH.**

0   1   pH   2   3

pH = 2.27 H_3O^+ pH = 2.87

Ethanoic acid (weak)

CH_3COOH CH_3COO^-

(14) **CCC Scale, Proportion, and Quantity** Explain why strength and concentration are distinct qualities that are not related. ✏️

....

....

....

....

Revisit

INVESTIGATIVE PHENOMENON

📶

GO ONLINE to Elaborate on and Evaluate your knowledge of strong and weak acids and bases by completing the peer review and data analysis activities.

In the CER worksheet you completed at the beginning of the investigation, you constructed an explanation for how acid rain can affect a forest. Work with a partner to reevaluate the evidence you cited in your arguments.

(15) **CCC Patterns** Burning fossil fuels releases carbon dioxide and oxides of sulfur and nitrogen into the atmosphere. These three substances form carbonic acid, sulfuric acid, and nitric acid, respectively. Based on what you have studied in this Experience, what important difference is there between acids formed from carbon dioxide and those formed from sulfur and nitrogen oxides? ✏️

....

....

....

....

....

Reactions of Acids and Bases

GO ONLINE to Explore and Explain neutralization reactions and acid-base titrations.

Acid-Base Neutralization Reactions

A reaction in which an acid and a base in an aqueous solution produce a salt and water is called a **neutralization reaction.** Such a reaction can be written with this general form:

$$Acid + Base \rightarrow Salt + Water$$

A neutralization reaction is complete when both reactants are entirely consumed. When a strong acid such as HCl reacts with a strong base such as KOH, a salt solution with a neutral pH results.

$$HCl(aq) + KOH(aq) \rightarrow KCl(aq) + H_2O(l)$$

However, other types of neutralization reactions do not generally result in neutral solutions.

Increasing the pH of a Lake A lake can be made less acidic by adding a base such as lime, $Ca(OH)_2$, to it. The dusty cloud contains lime, which dissolves in the lake, releasing OH^- ions. The OH^- ions react with H_3O^+ ions in the lake to form water and reduce the lake's acidity, moving the pH closer to neutral.

Mole Ratios in Acid-Base Reactions

How do you **determine mole ratios** in neutralization reactions?

Identifying Mole Ratios The ratio between the numbers of moles of substances involved in a reaction is called the mole ratio. **Use the coefficients in the balanced chemical equation to identify the mole ratio of one substance to another.**

Balancing H_3O^+ and OH^- When ionized, a monoprotic acid, such as HCl, forms one H_3O^+ ion in solution. The diprotic acid H_2SO_4 forms two H_3O^+ ions when ionized. In each case, **an equivalent number of OH^- ions are needed to neutralize the H_3O^+ ions.**

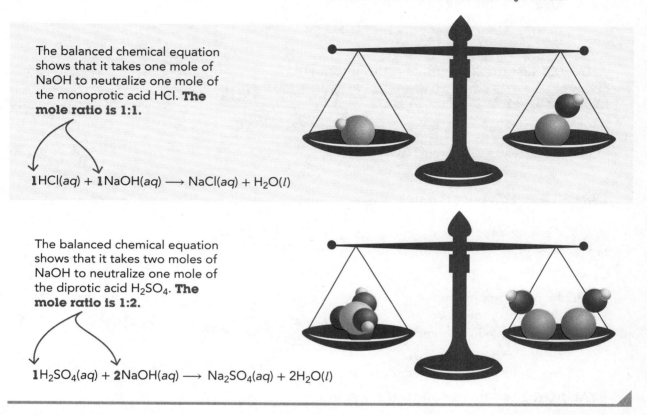

The balanced chemical equation shows that it takes one mole of NaOH to neutralize one mole of the monoprotic acid HCl. **The mole ratio is 1:1.**

$$\mathbf{1}HCl(aq) + \mathbf{1}NaOH(aq) \longrightarrow NaCl(aq) + H_2O(l)$$

The balanced chemical equation shows that it takes two moles of NaOH to neutralize one mole of the diprotic acid H_2SO_4. **The mole ratio is 1:2.**

$$\mathbf{1}H_2SO_4(aq) + \mathbf{2}NaOH(aq) \longrightarrow Na_2SO_4(aq) + 2H_2O(l)$$

---

(16) **CCC Cause and Effect** Shown here is a balanced equation for the neutralization reaction of hydrochloric acid and calcium hydroxide.

$$2HCl(aq) + Ca(OH)_2(aq) \rightarrow CaCl_2(aq) + 2H_2O(l)$$

Explain what happens if you add 2 moles or 0.5 moles of $Ca(OH)_2$ to a solution containing 2 moles of HCl. ✏

....

....

....

....

Finding the Moles Needed for Neutralization

The term *neutralization* is used to describe both the reaction type and the point at which a neutralization reaction is complete. How many moles of sulfuric acid are required to neutralize 0.50 mol of sodium hydroxide? The chemical equation for the reaction is

$$H_2SO_4(aq) + 2NaOH(aq) \rightarrow Na_2SO_4(aq) + 2H_2O(l)$$

ANALYZE List the knowns and the unknown.

Knowns	Unknown
mol NaOH = 0.50 mol	mol H_2SO_4 = ? mol
1 mol H_2SO_4 reacts with 2 mol NaOH	

CALCULATE Solve for the unknown.

Write the mole ratio of acid to base as a conversion factor.

$$\text{mole ratio} = \frac{1 \text{ mol } H_2SO_4}{2 \text{ mol NaOH}}$$

Multiply the number of moles of NaOH by the conversion factor to determine the number of moles of H_2SO_4.

$$0.50 \text{ mol NaOH} \times \frac{1 \text{ mol } H_2SO_4}{2 \text{ mol NaOH}} = 0.25 \text{ mol } H_2SO_4$$

EVALUATE Does the result make sense?

Because the mole ratio of H_2SO_4 to NaOH is 1:2, the number of moles of H_2SO_4 should be half the number of moles of NaOH.

(17) **The neutralization reaction of potassium hydroxide and sulfuric acid is as follows:**

$$2KOH(aq) + H_2SO_4(aq) \rightarrow K_2SO_4(aq) + 2H_2O(l)$$

Use the equation to calculate how many moles of KOH are needed to neutralize 0.45 mol of H_2SO_4. ✏

GO ONLINE for more practice problems.

Salt Solutions and Salt Hydrolysis

Salt Hydrolysis Recall that a salt is one of the products of a neutralization reaction. The acid contributes an anion and the base contributes a cation. **Salt hydrolysis** is a process in which the cations or anions of a dissociated salt accept hydrogen ions from water or donate hydrogen ions to water.

Consider $NaCH_3COO$, the salt of a weak acid and a strong base. In solution, the salt is completely ionized, forming ethanoate ions (CH_3COO^-) and sodium ions (Na^+). The ethanoate ion is a Brønsted-Lowry base, which means it is a hydrogen ion acceptor. At equilibrium, the reactants are favored in the reversible reaction. Therefore a solution of $NaCH_3COO$ is only slightly basic.

$$CH_3COO^-(aq) + H_2O(l) \rightleftharpoons CH_3COOH(aq) + OH^-(aq)$$

Similarly, the salt of a weak base and a strong acid forms an acidic solution, because the conjugate acid donates a hydrogen ion to a water molecule. In contrast, a strong acid or base ionizes completely, and the reverse reaction happens only to a negligible degree. As a result, the conjugate base of a strong acid does not have appreciable basic properties, and the conjugate of a strong base does not have appreciable acidic properties.

(18) **SEP Use Models** Use a chemical equation to explain how the carbonate ions in Mono Lake contribute to its alkalinity. ✏️

....

....

Mono Lake Due to high concentrations of salts that contain carbonates, the lake is alkaline with a pH close to 10. The calcium carbonate formations in the lake are called tufa towers.

Qualitative Determination of pH When they are in solution, the anion and the cation of a salt separate, and each ion acts independently with the water molecules in the solution. Some ions react with water molecules in a way that changes the pH of a solution. For example, the cation NH_4^+ is the conjugate acid of a weak base. It is a Brønsted-Lowry acid that reacts with water to form hydronium ions, making the solution acidic. The anion F^-, the conjugate base of a weak acid, reacts with water to form hydroxide ions, making the solution basic. Such ions are called acidic cations and basic anions, respectively. Other cations (such as Na^+) or anions (such as Cl^-) do not interfere with pH. They are called neutral ions.

◼ **The acid-base properties of the ions that make up a salt determine whether a solution of that salt is acidic, neutral, or basic.**

When one or both ions that form a salt are neutral, the prediction is simple. When the cation is acidic and the anion is basic, predicting the pH of a solution requires more information. The pH of such solutions depend on the relative acid-base strengths of the cation and anion.

Neutral cation + **neutral** anion = **neutral** solution
Example: NaCl solution

Acidic cation + **neutral** anion = **acidic** solution
Example: NH_4Cl solution

Neutral cation + **basic** anion = **basic** solution
Example: NaF solution

Acidic cation + **basic** anion = varies
Example: NH_4CN solution

The Effect of Ions on pH		
Ion Type	**How It Affects pH**	**Examples**
Conjugate base of a strong acid or a spectator ion	No effect; results in a **neutral** solution	Cl^-, Br^-, I^-, NO_3^-, Na^+, K^+, Mg^{2+}
Conjugate base of a weak acid	Hydrolyzes; results in a **basic** solution	CH_3COO^-, HCO_3^-, F^-, CN^-
Conjugate acid of a weak base	Hydrolyzes; results in an **acidic** solution	NH_4^+, $C_5H_5NH^+$

(19) **SEP Analyze Data** Use the table to predict whether NH_4Br will form an acidic, neutral, or basic solution. Explain. 🖉

....

....

....

Using the Conjugate-Seesaw Analogy You can think about the relative strengths of the ions that make up a salt and the acid and base that formed the salt as being like objects on seesaws. As with a seesaw, the closer to the ground is one side, the farther from the ground is the other side. When an acid is very strong (at the bottom of the seesaw), the conjugate base is so weak (at the top of the seesaw) that it has no effect on pH. The analogy is appropriate because the strength of an acid and its conjugate base or a base and its conjugate acid are balanced in exactly the same way $[H_3O^+]$ and $[OH^-]$ are balanced with reference to K_w.

How Ions Affect pH

How can you tell whether a salt solution is acidic, basic, or neutral?

Consider the Conjugates You can use conjugate seesaws to predict whether a salt solution is acidic, basic, or neutral. **The stronger an acid or base, the weaker is its conjugate. The weaker an acid or base, the stronger is its conjugate.**

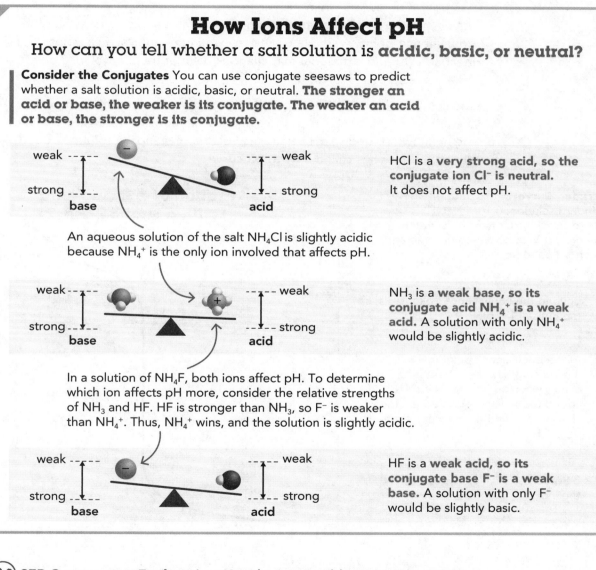

HCl is a **very strong acid**, so the conjugate ion Cl⁻ is neutral. It does not affect pH.

An aqueous solution of the salt NH_4Cl is slightly acidic because NH_4^+ is the only ion involved that affects pH.

NH_3 is a **weak base, so its conjugate acid NH_4^+ is a weak acid.** A solution with only NH_4^+ would be slightly acidic.

In a solution of NH_4F, both ions affect pH. To determine which ion affects pH more, consider the relative strengths of NH_3 and HF. HF is stronger than NH_3, so F⁻ is weaker than NH_4^+. Thus, NH_4^+ wins, and the solution is slightly acidic.

HF is a **weak acid, so its conjugate base F⁻ is a weak base.** A solution with only F⁻ would be slightly basic.

20 **SEP Construct an Explanation** Use the irreversible ionization equation of HCl gas in water and the Brønsted-Lowry model of acids and bases to explain why the Cl⁻ ion is such a weak base that it can be considered a neutral ion. ✏️

....

....

Acid-Base Titrations

An important method for investigating the interactions of acids and bases is a **titration,** in which a volume of a solution of known concentration is added to a solution of known volume but unknown concentration. The solution of known concentration, called the standard solution, is added in small measured increments until the neutralization reaction is complete. The unknown concentration can then be calculated from the number of moles in the added volume of the standard solution.

Neutralization occurs when the numbers of moles of H_3O^+ and OH^- are equal, and the point in a titration where neutralization occurs is called the **equivalence point.** A simple way to tell when the equivalence point is reached is to add a material that changes color at the equivalence point, called an acid-base indicator.

You can also estimate the equivalence point by following the change in the unknown solution's pH as the standard solution is added. The graph of the unknown solution's pH versus the volume of standard solution added during a titration is called a **titration curve.**

Titration Curve In this titration, the standard solution, 0.10*M* NaOH, is slowly added to 50.0 mL of an HCl solution. The pH of the solution is measured and recorded periodically.

Beyond the equivalence point (pH > 8), the indicator is blue.

At the equivalence point (pH = 7), the indicator is green. Neutralization occurs when 50.0 mL of NaOH is added to the flask. The titration data allow you to find the concentration of HCl, 0.10*M*.

Below the equivalence point (pH < 6), the indicator is yellow.

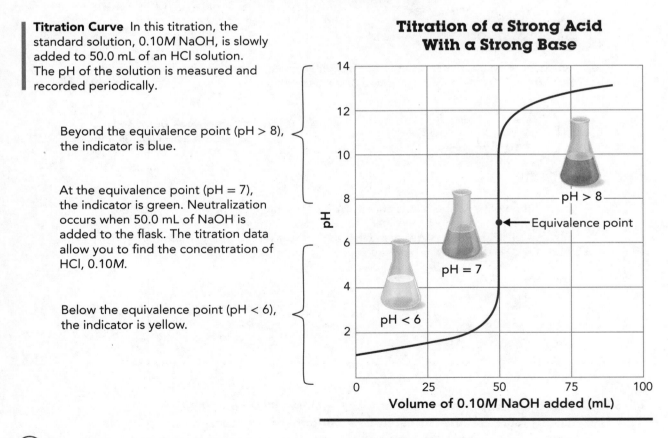

Titration of a Strong Acid With a Strong Base

21) **SEP Use Mathematics** How many milliliters of 0.450*M* HCl will neutralize 25.0 mL of 1.00*M* KOH?

Titrations and pH Curves

The shape of the titration curve not only makes it possible to determine the equivalence point in the titration but also allows you to select a suitable indicator. When NaOH is titrated with HCl, the curve is the mirror image of the strong acid–strong base titration, with pH decreasing throughout the titration. The reaction produces a neutral salt, and the equivalence point is at pH = 7.

When a weak acid such as CH_3COOH is titrated with a strong base such as NaOH, the curve shows pH increasing. The salt produced in the reaction is $NaCH_3COO$. Recall that Na^+ does not affect pH, and CH_3COO^-, the conjugate base of a weak acid, reacts with water molecules to increase the pH. Thus, the equivalence point is at a pH greater than 7, at pH = 9.

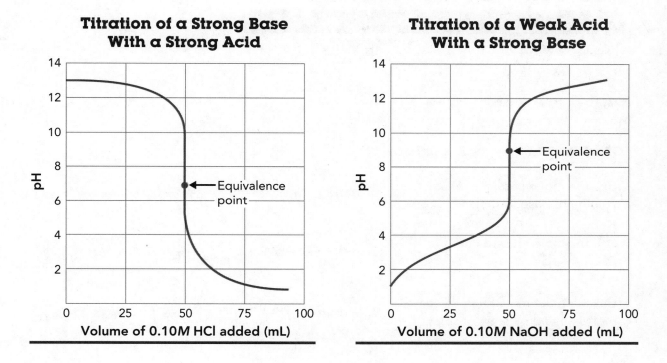

Titration of a Strong Base With a Strong Acid

Titration of a Weak Acid With a Strong Base

22) **SEP Interpret Data** Use the titration curves and your knowledge of conjugate acid and base behavior to predict whether the titration of a weak base with a strong acid would have an equivalence point greater than or less than 7. Explain your reasoning. ✎

....

....

....

....

Determining the Concentration by Titration

A 25-mL sample of a solution containing an unknown concentration of H_2SO_4 was titrated with a standard solution of $1.0M$ NaOH. If 18 mL of the NaOH solution was required to reach the equivalence point, what was the concentration of H_2SO_4 in the unknown solution? The chemical equation for the reaction is

$$H_2SO_4(aq) + 2NaOH(aq) \rightarrow Na_2SO_4(aq) + 2H_2O(l)$$

ANALYZE List the knowns and the unknown.

Knowns	Unknown
$[NaOH] = 1.0M$	$[H_2SO_4] = ?M$
$V_{NaOH} = 18$ mL $= 0.018$ L	
$V_{H_2SO_4} = 25$ mL $= 0.025$ L	

CALCULATE Solve for the unknown.

Use the molarity to convert the volume of base to moles of base.	$0.018 \text{ L NaOH} \times \dfrac{1.0 \text{ mol NaOH}}{1 \text{ L NaOH}} = 0.018 \text{ mol NaOH}$
Use the mole ratio to find the moles of acid.	$0.018 \text{ mol NaOH} \times \dfrac{1 \text{ mol } H_2SO_4}{2 \text{ mol NaOH}} = 0.0090 \text{ mol } H_2SO_4$
Calculate the molarity by dividing moles of acid by liters of solution.	$\text{molarity} = \dfrac{\text{mol of solute}}{\text{L of solution}} = \dfrac{0.0090 \text{ mol}}{0.025 \text{ L}} = 0.36M \ H_2SO_4$

EVALUATE Does the result make sense?

If the acid had the same molarity as the base ($1.0M$), 50 mL of base would neutralize 25 mL of acid. Because the volume of base is much less than 50 mL, the molarity of the acid must be much less than $1.0M$.

23 What is the molarity of a solution of H_3PO_4 if 10.2 mL is neutralized by 53.5 mL of $0.20M$ KOH? ✏️

GO ONLINE for more practice problems.

INVESTIGATIVE PHENOMENON

GO ONLINE to Elaborate on and Evaluate your knowledge of neutralization reactions and acid-base titrations by completing the peer review and data analysis activities.

In the CER worksheet you completed at the beginning of the investigation, you constructed an explanation for how acid rain can affect a forest. With a partner, reevaluate your arguments.

(24) **SEP Construct an Explanation** Some lakes in Illinois are alkaline. The average pH of those lakes is 8 to 9 because the rock formations that surround the lakes contain high levels of calcium carbonate. Use chemical equations to explain how calcium carbonate neutralizes the acidity of rain containing HNO_3 and H_2SO_4. ✏

....

....

....

....

....

....

Buffers and Equilibria

 GO ONLINE to Explore and Explain how the components of a buffer system work together to maintain pH.

Example of a Buffer System

A solution in which pH remains relatively constant when small amounts of acid or base are added is called a **buffer.** Because buffers resist pH changes by neutralizing added acids or bases, they are important in biological systems. For example, the pH of human blood needs to be kept close to 7.4 because many of the chemical reactions that take place in cells are sensitive to slight changes in pH. To maintain that pH, blood contains a buffer system consisting of a mixture of carbonic acid and its conjugate base, hydrogen carbonate ion. The system ensures that the pH of the blood remains relatively constant.

When blood pH is less than 7.35, a condition called acidosis occurs. It is often caused by too much CO_2 in the blood, which dissolves in water to produce carbonic acid and increase the amount of H_3O^+. Treatment often includes infusing a solution with hydrogen carbonate ions into the blood. The hydrogen carbonate ion reduces acidity because it is the conjugate base of carbonic acid. As a base, it can react with the additional H_3O^+ in the blood. When blood pH is greater than 7.45, the opposite condition, alkalosis, occurs. It is often caused by too little CO_2 or H_3O^+ in the blood. Treatment may involve breathing in and out of a paper bag.

Balancing Blood pH When a person hyperventilates, the increase in the amount of CO_2 exhaled effectively lowers the amount of carbonic acid in the blood. Removing acid from the blood increases pH. Using a paper bag to re-breathe the exhaled CO_2 helps the body bring blood pH levels back to normal.

Breathing into a paper bag ensures that the exhaled CO_2 is breathed back in.

Buffer Solutions

How Buffers Work Buffer systems consist of either a weak acid and its conjugate base or a weak base and its conjugate acid. They can react with H_3O^+ and OH^- ions. Buffer solution components work together to keep the pH relatively constant no matter which ions (H_3O^+ or OH^-) are added.

▶ **In general, adding acids or bases to a buffered solution results in only a small change in pH.**

One example of a buffer system is a solution of ethanoic acid (weak acid) and the ethanoate ion (conjugate base). The system can be used to show how a buffer works. When you add acid to the buffer solution, the ethanoate ions (CH_3COO^-) act like a H_3O^+ "sponge." When you add a base, the ethanoic acid (CH_3COOH) molecules act like an OH^- "sponge."

Adding acid: $CH_3COO^-(aq) + H_3O^+(aq) \rightleftharpoons CH_3COOH(aq) + H_2O(l)$

Adding base: $CH_3COOH(aq) + OH^-(aq) \rightleftharpoons CH_3COO^-(aq) + H_2O(l)$

In each case, the reverse reaction happens but is minimal, and therefore the change in pH is very slight.

Buffer Solutions Explained In this buffer solution, the acid is HA, and the conjugate base is the anion A^-. The concentration of HA increases when an acid is added to the solution, while the concentration of A^- decreases. The reverse occurs when a base is added to the solution.

When HCl is added to the solution, the anion reacts with the hydronium ion:
$A^-(aq) + H_3O^+(aq) \rightleftharpoons HA(aq) + H_2O(l)$
There is very little change in pH.

When NaOH is added to the solution, the acid reacts with the hydroxide ion:
$HA(aq) + OH^-(aq) \rightleftharpoons A^-(aq) + H_2O(l)$
There is very little change in pH.

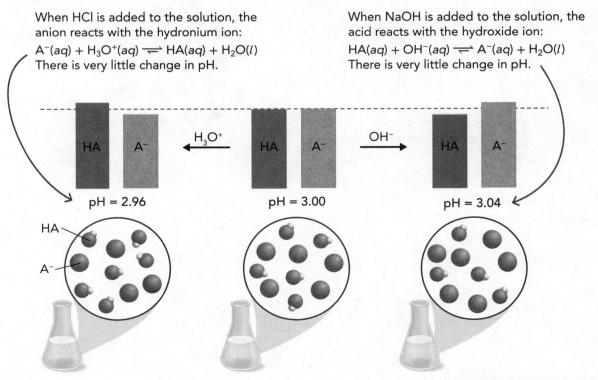

Buffer Solutions and Equilibrium Buffers work by applying Le Châtelier's principle to weak acid equilibrium. Consider the ethanoic acid–ethanoate ion buffer system again. When an acid is added to the buffer, the equilibrium is disturbed by the increase in the concentration of hydronium ions. The disturbance pushes the reaction in the direction of the products and results in a new equilibrium with a lower concentration of hydronium ions and a higher concentration of products.

$$CH_3COO^-(aq) + H_3O^+(aq) \rightleftharpoons CH_3COOH(aq) + H_2O(l)$$

When hydroxide ions are added, the equilibrium is disturbed by the increase in the concentration of hydroxide ions. The disturbance causes the reaction to shift away from hydroxide ion and in the direction of the products.

$$CH_3COOH(aq) + OH^-(aq) \rightleftharpoons CH_3COO^-(aq) + H_2O(l)$$

Again, a new equilibrium is established with a lower concentration of hydroxide ions and a higher concentration of products.

Making an Acidic Buffer When a weak acid, CH_3COOH, and a salt of its conjugate base, such as $NaCH_3COO$, are added to water, the species in the solution are CH_3COOH, H_3O^+, CH_3COO^-, and Na^+.

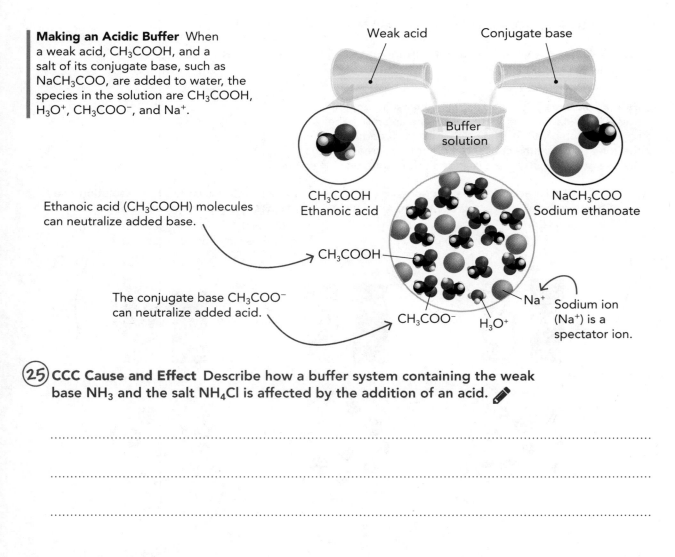

Weak acid

Conjugate base

Buffer solution

CH_3COOH
Ethanoic acid

$NaCH_3COO$
Sodium ethanoate

Ethanoic acid (CH_3COOH) molecules can neutralize added base.

The conjugate base CH_3COO^- can neutralize added acid.

CH_3COOH

CH_3COO^-

H_3O^+

Na^+

Sodium ion (Na^+) is a spectator ion.

㉕ **CCC Cause and Effect** Describe how a buffer system containing the weak base NH_3 and the salt NH_4Cl is affected by the addition of an acid. ✎

....

....

....

Buffer Capacity and Range

For a buffer to be effective, it should be able to neutralize added acids and bases, while keeping the pH relatively constant. However, there are limits to how much acid or base a buffer can neutralize before a drastic change in pH happens. **Buffer capacity** is a measure of the amount of acid or base that may be added to a buffer system before a significant change in pH happens. The effectiveness of a buffer depends on the concentration of the buffer components. **Buffer range** is the overall pH range in which a buffer system is effective at maintaining a relatively constant pH.

Concentration and Buffers
Increasing the concentration of the buffer components increases buffer capacity. A highly concentrated buffer can neutralize more acid or base than a dilute buffer.

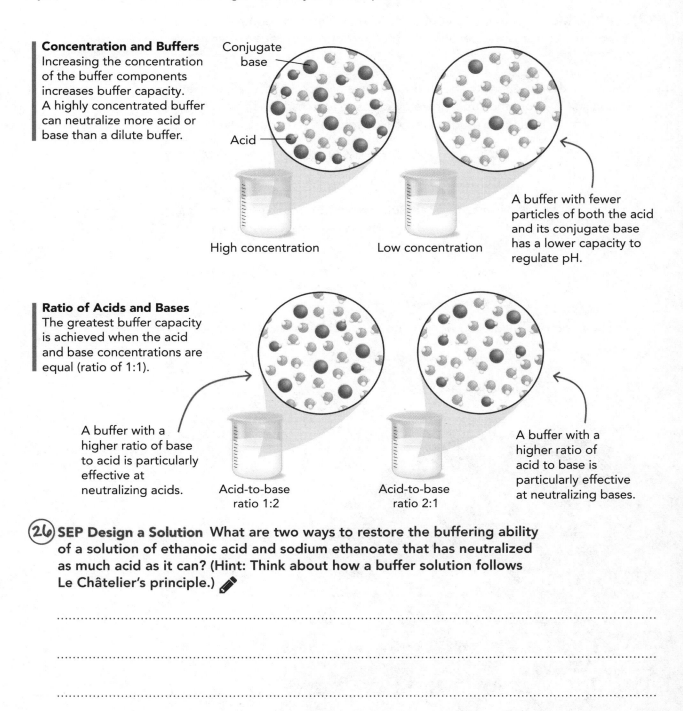

Conjugate base

Acid

High concentration

Low concentration

A buffer with fewer particles of both the acid and its conjugate base has a lower capacity to regulate pH.

Ratio of Acids and Bases
The greatest buffer capacity is achieved when the acid and base concentrations are equal (ratio of 1:1).

A buffer with a higher ratio of base to acid is particularly effective at neutralizing acids.

Acid-to-base ratio 1:2

Acid-to-base ratio 2:1

A buffer with a higher ratio of acid to base is particularly effective at neutralizing bases.

26 **SEP Design a Solution** What are two ways to restore the buffering ability of a solution of ethanoic acid and sodium ethanoate that has neutralized as much acid as it can? (Hint: Think about how a buffer solution follows Le Châtelier's principle.) ✏️

....

....

....

GO ONLINE to Elaborate on and Evaluate your knowledge of buffers by completing the class discussion and writing activities.

In the CER worksheet you completed at the beginning of the investigation, you constructed an explanation for how acid rain can affect a forest. With a partner, reevaluate your arguments.

(27) **SEP Use Models** In waters with underlying calcium carbonate rocks, an important buffer is the carbon dioxide–hydrogen carbonate–carbonate system.

Complete the equations to show how the system works. At the air-and-water interface, CO_2 from the atmosphere dissolves to form carbonic acid. Carbonic acid reacts with water to produce an acidic hydrogen carbonate solution.

$$CO_2(g) + H_2O(l) \rightleftharpoons H_2CO_3(aq)$$

$$H_2CO_3(aq) + H_2O(l) \rightleftharpoons \text{\dotfill}$$

At the rock-and-water interface, calcium carbonate dissolves to produce calcium ions and carbonate ions. The carbonate ion reacts with water to produce a basic hydrogen carbonate solution.

$$CaCO_3(s) + H_2O(l) \rightleftharpoons Ca^{2+}(aq) + CO_3^{2-}(aq) + H_2O(l)$$

$$CO_3^{2-}(aq) + H_2O(l) \rightleftharpoons \text{\dotfill}$$

The hydrogen carbonate ion works to neutralize either an acid or a base.

$$HCO_3^-(aq) + H_3O^+(aq) \rightleftharpoons \text{\dotfill}$$

$$HCO_3^-(aq) + OH^-(aq) \rightleftharpoons \text{\dotfill}$$

ASSESSMENT

 GO ONLINE to Evaluate what you learned about acid-base reactions and equilibria by using the available assessment resources.

In the Performance-Based Assessment, you conducted a quantitative analysis of substances involved in acid rain. Wrap up your analysis by answering the following questions.

28) **SEP Apply Scientific Reasoning** You tested three samples of acids. Which acid is likely to be most damaging to buildings and the biosphere? The least damaging? Explain.

....

....

....

29) **Connect to Science and Society** In recent decades, efforts have been made to reduce emissions that contribute to acid rain. Based on your measurements, which sort of emissions should be targeted to give the greatest reduction in atmospheric acidity? Is it possible to get rid of all acid-contributing emissions?

....

....

....

....

....

....

30) **Revisit the Anchoring Phenomenon** Recall the pollution image that introduced Storyline 4. How does what you learned in this investigation relate to that image and help explain how Earth's water resources can become increasingly acidic?

....

....

....

....

....

GO ONLINE to Engage with real-world phenomena by watching a video and to complete a CER interactive worksheet.

What is happening to the world's coral reefs?

Ocean Acidification

Coral reefs need three things to thrive: warm water temperatures, good light levels, and the chemical building blocks of a mineral called aragonite ($CaCO_3$) that can be extracted from seawater and used to build skeletons. Without these three things, the appearance and health of coral reefs change. Once you have viewed the Investigative Phenomenon video and worked on a first draft of a claim-evidence-reasoning exercise to explain what is happening to the world's coral reefs, discuss with a partner the following questions.

1) **CCC Energy and Matter** Identify at least three ways that you think rising global temperatures could alter the three parameters that coral reefs need to survive.

....

....

....

....

....

2) **CCC Cause and Effect** Corals thrive in clear water that sunlight can penetrate. How might algal blooms affect the clarity of water and thus affect the health of coral ecosystems?

....

....

....

....

....

Ocean pH Levels

 **GO ONLINE** to Explore and Explain ocean pH and acidification.

Carbon Dioxide and Ocean pH

The ocean and atmosphere maintain an equilibrium of their concentrations of carbon dioxide (CO_2). If the system is disrupted, there will be a net flow of carbon between the two reservoirs until equilibrium is restored. Atmospheric CO_2 has been increasing due to the human combustion of fossil fuels, so CO_2 is increasingly being driven into the ocean.

The equilibrium between the atmosphere and ocean has been a helpful counterbalancing feedback that has slowed the rate at which carbon dioxide has increased in the atmosphere. Roughly 30% of the carbon dioxide humans have released has gone into the ocean, lessening the potential greenhouse gas forcing on atmospheric temperature. However, the increased carbon dioxide absorption is dropping ocean pH and making the ocean increasingly acidic.

Correlation between Carbon Dioxide and pH Atmospheric CO_2, oceanic CO_2, and ocean acidity were measured at stations in Hawaii. Atmospheric CO_2 is shown in parts per million (ppm); seawater pCO_2 is the partial pressure of CO_2 gas in solution, expressed in microatmospheres (μatm). As CO_2 concentrations in the atmosphere and ocean have increased, ocean pH has gone down.

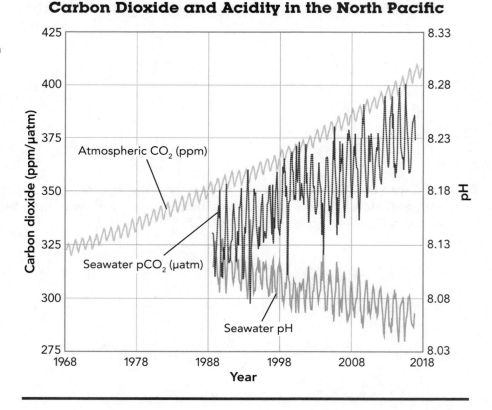

Carbon Dioxide and Acidity in the North Pacific

Atmospheric CO_2 (ppm)

Seawater pCO_2 (μatm)

Seawater pH

A series of chemical reactions in seawater results in a greater number of free hydrogen ions (H⁺), which increases the acidity of the water. First, a carbon dioxide molecule reacts with water to form carbonic acid. Then, the carbonic acid molecule ionizes to form a free H^+ ion and a hydrogen carbonate ion. The hydrogen carbonate ion then ionizes further, releasing another H^+ ion and a carbonate ion.

⬛ **A cause-and-effect relationship exists between carbon dioxide levels and ocean pH. An increase in dissolved carbon dioxide drives a set of chemical reactions that result in increased ocean acidity.**

Acid-Forming Reactions in Seawater Adding carbon dioxide to the ocean makes seawater more acidic. One dissolved carbon dioxide molecule may react with water to release two free H^+ ions.

$$CO_2 \; + \; H_2O \; \longrightarrow \; H_2CO_3 \; \longrightarrow \; H^+ \; + \; HCO_3^-$$

The dissolution of atmospheric carbon dioxide (CO_2) in ocean water **forms carbonic acid** (H_2CO_3).

Carbonic acid ionizes to form hydrogen carbonate (HCO_3^-) and free hydrogen (H^+) ions, **lowering the pH** of the solution.

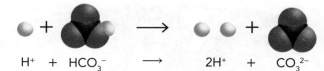

$$H^+ \; + \; HCO_3^- \; \longrightarrow \; 2H^+ \; + \; CO_3^{2-}$$

Hydrogen carbonate ions ionizes further to form carbonate ions (CO_3^{2-}) and more free hydrogen ions, **further lowering pH.**

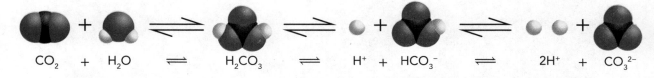

$$CO_2 \; + \; H_2O \; \rightleftharpoons \; H_2CO_3 \; \rightleftharpoons \; H^+ \; + \; HCO_3^- \; \rightleftharpoons \; 2H^+ \; + \; CO_3^{2-}$$

In a system of dynamic equilibrium, **the direction of the chemical reaction can shift** depending on the relative concentrations of reactants and products.

The system continually shifts between higher or lower pH depending on the amount of carbon dioxide and carbonate and hydrogen carbonate ions in the seawater.

(3) **CCC Stability and Change** Describe what will happen to the flow of these reactions if carbonate ions are continuously removed from the system by marine organisms that use the ions to make calcium carbonate shells. ✏️

....

....

....

Geographic Ocean pH Variation

Factors Influencing pH Ocean pH varies significantly around the world. Several factors influence horizontal and vertical variance in pH levels. Latitude and ocean currents affect water temperature and salinity. Warmer water and less saline waters have lower pH. The influx of fresh water near coastal areas and upwelling of deep currents make waters more acidic. Runoff of fertilizers from agriculture can lead to algal blooms, which then decay by bacterial respiration that increases CO_2 and lowers pH.

In general, tropical and temperate oceans, where coral reefs grow, have fairly stable pH levels of about 8.05–8.15, though the mid-Pacific varies greatly with El Niño/La Niña oscillations. In polar regions, pH levels rise in the summertime as massive plankton blooms absorb carbon dioxide and fall in the dark winters when the plankton die off. In general, the Indian Ocean is the most acidic ocean basin.

Global pH Variations Ocean pH levels are not constant. pH values vary laterally, vertically, seasonally, and with time in the same location.

Upwelling water from the deep ocean brings dissolved ions and carbon dioxide to surface waters, lowering the pH.

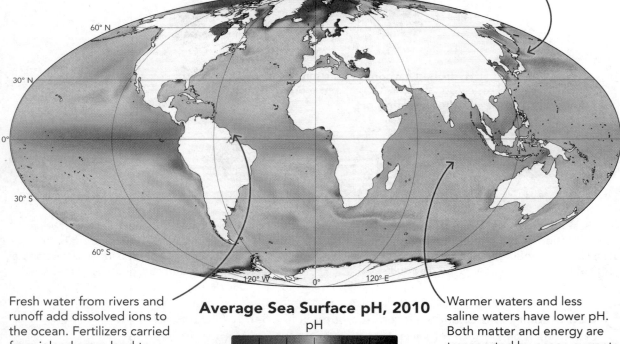

Average Sea Surface pH, 2010

pH

7.7 7.8 7.9 8.0 8.1 8.2 8.3

Data from: NOAA

Fresh water from rivers and runoff add dissolved ions to the ocean. Fertilizers carried from inland areas lead to algal blooms that cause a decrease in ocean pH when the algae die and decay.

Warmer waters and less saline waters have lower pH. Both matter and energy are transported by ocean currents between the equatorial regions and the poles.

Vertical pH Variations As depth increases, water temperature generally decreases and the amount of dissolved carbon dioxide generally increases. More dissolved CO_2 drives the formation of carbonic acid, which means more H^+ ions in solution. As a result, ocean pH generally decreases with depth.

In many coastal regions, surface currents flow parallel to or away from the coastline. Where deep currents encounter seamounts or continental shelves, the acidic deep waters are diverted upward, lowering the pH of surface waters near the coast. While this is a natural process, the significant increase in ocean acidity due to human activities has increased ocean acidity of coastal waters, where most marine life exists, faster than natural processes can buffer the change.

(4) **CCC Patterns** Coastal upwelling brings CO_2-rich, low-pH waters toward the surface. Based on the contours for the partial pressure of CO_2, or pCO_2, and pH, draw on one of the contours what you expect the pattern of ocean flow to be. ✎

pCO₂ with Depth off Point St. George, California, 2007

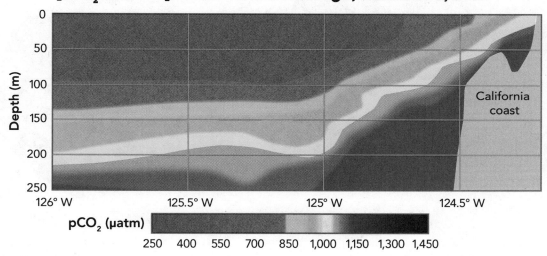

pCO₂ (μatm)

250 400 550 700 850 1,000 1,150 1,300 1,450

pH with Depth off Point St. George, California, 2007

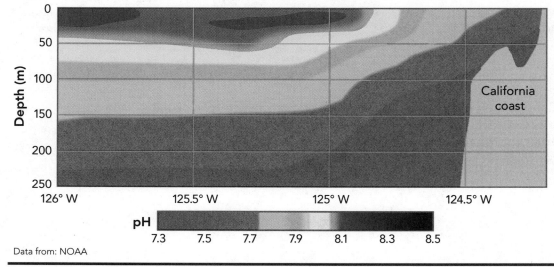

pH

7.3   7.5   7.7   7.9   8.1   8.3   8.5

Data from: NOAA

Ocean Salinity

The world's rivers carry salt to the ocean, making seawater saline, or salty. The amount of dissolved salts in water is described as the water's **salinity.** Salt plays critical roles in controlling ocean chemistry and biology. It also controls the pattern of deep ocean currents, because salty water is dense and will sink. In the North Atlantic, water is both cold and salty, making it especially dense. The sinking of this dense water helps to drive the global circulation of deepwater currents.

Ocean Surface Salinity Variations Ocean salinity varies significantly by location. Salinity is affected by air and ocean temperature, evaporation and precipitation rates, and freshwater influx.

The dry latitudes about 30° north and south of the equator have high evaporation rates. Because salts do not leave the ocean with evaporated water, ocean salinity is high in these regions.

Melting of ice in Antarctica adds fresh water to the ocean, which lowers salinity. Melting of ice in Greenland also lowers salinity.

Sea Surface Salinity, 2005–2017
(practical salinity units, PSU)

| 31 | 32 | 33 | 34 | 35 | 36 |

Data from: NOAA

Tropical regions have high evaporation rates but also high precipitation rates, which adds fresh water to the ocean and lowers salinity.

(5) **SEP Construct an Explanation** Rivers carry about 4 billion tons of salt to the ocean each year, and evaporated water does not contain salt. Construct an explanation for why the mean ocean salinity has stayed roughly constant over Earth's history. ✎

....

....

....

Ocean Alkalinity

Total alkalinity (TA) is the sum of excess ions in the water that could absorb H^+ ions. Mostly these ions are hydrogen carbonate (HCO_3^-) and carbonate (CO_3^{2-}). Other ions include hydrogen sulfate (HSO_4^-), hydroxide (OH^-), and phosphates (PO_4^{3-}). These ions all accept extra protons, removing the protons from the seawater. Thus, the alkalinity of the ocean buffers the acidification. The total alkalinity of seawater is not the same thing as the basicity, which is simply a measure of how high the pH is.

> **Ocean Surface Alkalinity Variations** Water with high alkalinity resists acidification by absorbing H^+ ions. The alkalinity itself is not affected by the addition of carbon dioxide.

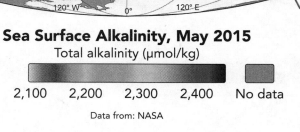

Alkalinity is higher where evaporation rates are high and where organisms break down compounds in the absence of oxygen as a result of reducing sulfates or denitrification.

Sea Surface Alkalinity, May 2015
Total alkalinity (μmol/kg)

2,100   2,200   2,300   2,400   No data

Data from: NASA

Regions of freshwater inflow, from heavy rainfall, rivers, or the melting of ice, have lower alkalinity.

6 **SEP Explain Phenomena** The map shows two regions in the Atlantic Ocean that have very high alkalinity. Construct an explanation for why these two regions have high alkalinity. 🖉

....

....

....

Le Châtelier's Principle and Future Ocean pH

The addition of CO_2 to the ocean is disrupting the ocean carbon system, driving the equations for carbon and bicarbonate dissolution toward an increase in carbonate and H^+ ions, increasing acidity. This is an example of Le Châtelier's principle: ocean pH had been fairly stable, but human-released CO_2 is driving that system toward a new equilibrium. Where that equilibrium ends up depends largely on how much CO_2 humans release in the future.

Surface Temperature and pH Projections The Intergovernmental Panel on Climate Change (IPCC) modeled different scenarios of greenhouse gas concentrations called Representative Concentration Pathways (RCPs). In the RCP2.6 model, humans drastically reduce CO_2 emissions in the year 2020. In the RCP8.5 model, humans continue to release CO_2 at high rates.

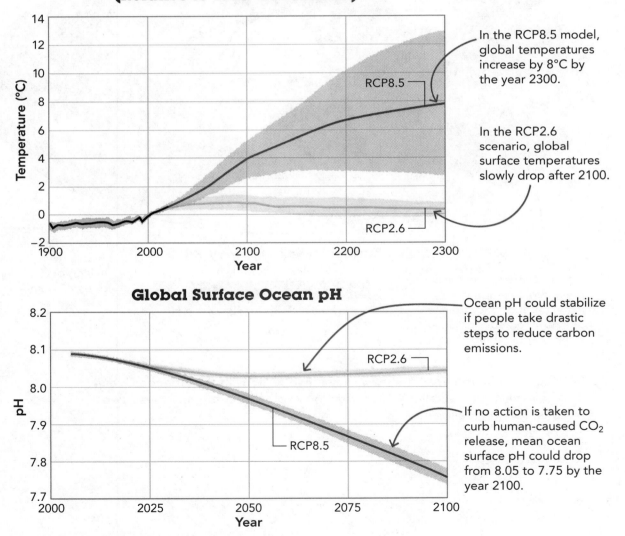

Global Average Surface Temperature Change (Relative to 1986–2005 mean)

In the RCP8.5 model, global temperatures increase by 8°C by the year 2300.

In the RCP2.6 scenario, global surface temperatures slowly drop after 2100.

Global Surface Ocean pH

Ocean pH could stabilize if people take drastic steps to reduce carbon emissions.

If no action is taken to curb human-caused CO_2 release, mean ocean surface pH could drop from 8.05 to 7.75 by the year 2100.

Data from: Intergovernmental Panel on Climate Change

7. **CCC Stability and Change** Summarize how Le Châtelier's principle can be applied to describe the dynamic equilibrium between carbon dioxide concentrations in the atmosphere, alkalinity, and ocean pH. ✏️

....

....

....

....

Revisit

INVESTIGATIVE PHENOMENON

GO ONLINE to Elaborate and Evaluate your knowledge of the effects of a changing ocean pH by completing the class discussion and data analysis activities.

In the CER worksheet, you drafted a scientific argument to explain what is happening to the world's coral reefs. With a partner, reevaluate the evidence cited in your arguments.

8. **CCC Cause and Effect** Most corals are adapted to survive in tropical, subtropical, and temperate oceans. Based on patterns of alkalinity and salinity in the oceans, why are corals threatened by changes in ocean pH? ✏️

....

....

....

....

....

The Ocean as a Carbon Sink

GO ONLINE to Explore and Explain how carbon dioxide is exchanged between the ocean and atmosphere.

Ocean–Atmosphere Carbon Dioxide Exchange

Roughly 80 gigatons of carbon—that's 80 billion tons—is exchanged each year between the atmosphere and the ocean surface layer. The increase in atmospheric carbon from preindustrial levels means that more carbon dioxide is exchanged between the ocean surface and atmosphere each year. However, the cycling of carbon between the ocean and atmosphere is more complicated than a simple gas exchange at the ocean surface.

Marine Organisms Are Carbon Reservoirs Carbon in the ocean cycles through both inorganic and organic pathways. **Carbon reservoirs** are components of the Earth system in which carbon is stored. The ocean is sometimes called a carbon sink, or carbon storage area, because of the large amount of carbon stored in ocean carbon reservoirs. Although only about 6 Gt of carbon (GtC) exists within marine life at any given time, due to the short life span of plankton, over eight times that amount cycles through the marine biosphere each year.

Ocean Plankton Most of the carbon in ocean organisms is in the form of calcium carbonate ($CaCO_3$) shells of single-celled plankton, such as coccolithophores. About 50 Gt of carbon is consumed each year by marine life to make their shells and skeletons.

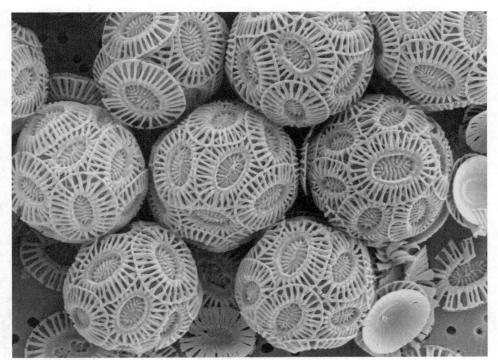

Ocean–Atmosphere Carbon Reservoirs and Rates This image shows the sizes of carbon reservoirs (boxed labels) in gigatons of carbon (GtC) and carbon fluxes and rates (arrows) in gigatons of carbon per year (GtC/yr). The values for human inputs reflect how human activities affect reservoirs and rates.

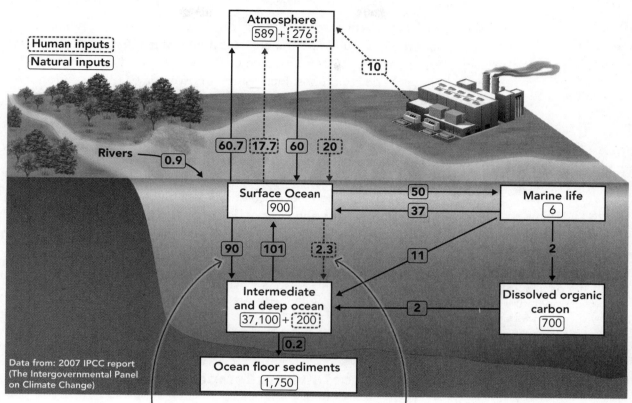

Data from: 2007 IPCC report (The Intergovernmental Panel on Climate Change)

Carbon flows between reservoirs at different rates. Carbon from the surface ocean enters the deep ocean at a natural rate of 90 GtC/yr.

Human activity has increased the amount of carbon in the surface ocean, which increased the rate of flux into the intermediate and deep ocean by 2.3 GtC/yr.

Deep Ocean Carbon Cycling Carbon doesn't stay in the surface ocean layer for long. About one tenth of it sinks down into the intermediate and deeper ocean, where it remains for hundreds or thousands of years. Thus, the deep ocean holds most of the ocean's carbon. Because of the carbon exchange between the ocean and atmosphere, the human contributions to atmospheric carbon are changing the dynamics of the ocean carbon cycle. An additional 2.3 GtC is added to the deeper ocean each year, making the deep ocean increasingly more acidic.

9 **SEP Analyze Data** Most carbon sediment accumulation on the seafloor is in the form of calcium carbonate. These sediments largely become the sedimentary rock limestone. Using the rate of carbon accumulation on the seafloor and the atomic mass of calcium carbonate (100.1 g/mol), compute the mass of new limestone that is generated each year (in tons). ✏️

Temperature, Pressure, and the Carbonate Compensation Depth

The rate of a chemical reaction and its equilibrium point vary as a function of temperature, pressure, and the concentrations of reactants and products. These dependencies affect how ocean CO_2 levels respond to changing global atmospheric conditions. Increasing atmospheric CO_2 concentrations are driving carbon into the ocean, but they also create feedbacks that affect what becomes of that carbon.

Warmer atmospheric temperatures have led to warmer oceans. Near the ocean surface, this process can drive some dissolved carbon dioxide gas out of the ocean and into the atmosphere. However, deeper in the ocean this process drives the chemical dissolution reaction of CO_2 toward an increase in carbonate ions and H^+ ions, lowering the pH and making the ocean more acidic.

Temperature and CO_2 Solubility The solubility of carbon dioxide in water decreases with increasing temperature. An increase in ocean temperature decreases the amount of CO_2 gas that can stay dissolved within the seawater.

Cold water holds carbonation better than warm water does.

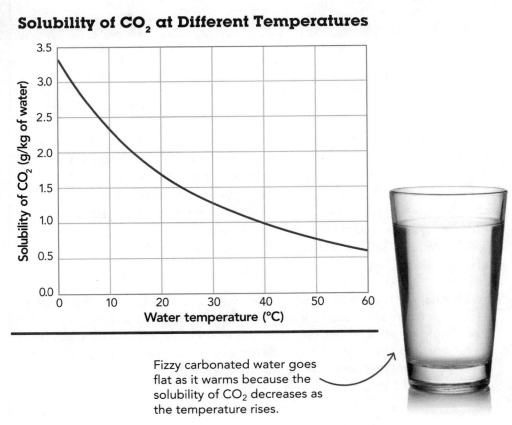

Solubility of CO$_2$ at Different Temperatures

Fizzy carbonated water goes flat as it warms because the solubility of CO_2 decreases as the temperature rises.

The solubility of CO_2 in water is also affected by pressure: higher pressures—found at deeper depths—allow more carbon dioxide to be dissolved within the water. In the ocean, calcium carbonate ($CaCO_3$) becomes increasingly unstable with increasing pressure. Below a certain depth, called the **carbonate compensation depth** or CCD, the $CaCO_3$ shells of organisms dissolve into Ca^{2+} and hydrogen carbonate ions.

Carbonate Compensation Depth
How does **CaCO₃ solubility** change with **depth**?

Dissolved vs. Deposited Calcareous Sediments Sediments that contain $CaCO_3$ are called calcareous sediments. The relative amount of calcium carbonate that is stored in sediments or dissolved in seawater varies with depth.

Carbonate shells of dead marine organisms **begin to dissolve as they fall** from the surface.

The rate of **dissolution increases** significantly at about 3,000 m.

Carbonate compensation depth (CCD)

Depth (m)

Percentage of $CaCO_3$ in sediments

Increasing rate of $CaCO_3$ dissolution

Temperature decreases and pressure increases with depth. **These factors affect the rate of dissolution.**

Pressure

Temperature

Below the CCD, **carbonate shells dissolve completely.** Therefore, limestones form at depths above the CCD, and sediments deposited below the CCD are siliceous.

Deep ocean waters have very low temperatures and very high pressures, both of which favor **high levels of dissolved CO₂ and low levels of solid carbonate.**

(10) **CCC Stability and Change** The solubility of carbon dioxide within liquid magma also increases with pressure. Explain how this could contribute to the explosive nature of some volcanic eruptions. ✏️

....

....

....

Biogenic Carbon

The inorganic and organic chemical reactions involving ocean carbon provide a complex set of cycles. Though they are closely linked, these cycles are often separated out into two parts: a largely inorganic solubility carbon pump and an organic biological carbon pump. The solubility pump takes dissolved surface carbon and brings it into the deep, vast reservoir of dissolved carbon. The biologic pump takes that dissolved carbon and builds organic material from it when currents return it toward the surface.

Solubility Carbon Pump Inorganic chemical reactions begin with the influx of carbon into the ocean in the form of atmospheric CO_2 and the dissolved Ca^+ and CO_3^{2-} ions of weathered continental rock.

Carbon dioxide and water combine to form carbonic acid, which ionizes into hydrogen carbonate and hydrogen ions.

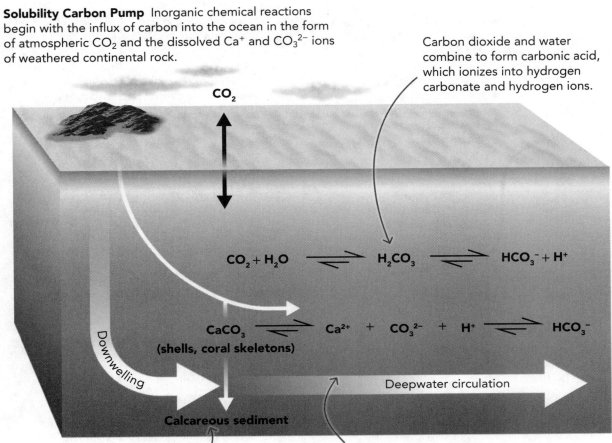

$$CO_2 + H_2O \rightleftharpoons H_2CO_3 \rightleftharpoons HCO_3^- + H^+$$

$$CaCO_3 \rightleftharpoons Ca^{2+} + CO_3^{2-} + H^+ \rightleftharpoons HCO_3^-$$

(shells, coral skeletons)

Downwelling

Calcareous sediment

Deepwater circulation

Calcium carbonate crystals and shells eventually fall to the ocean floor, forming calcareous sediment.

Cold, carbon-rich surface water sinks deep into the ocean. Currents carry it thousands of kilometers before it resurfaces through upwelling. This can take hundreds of years.

Ocean Currents The solubility and biologic carbon pumps are closely connected with the deep ocean currents that move water around Earth's ocean basins. As currents drop below the carbonate compensation depth (CCD), carbonate particles dissolve into hydrogen carbonate ions. These ions are able to form solid carbonate again once the water rises back above the CCD in areas of upwelling.

Carbon in the Marine Biosphere The base of the food web of the marine biosphere is single-celled phytoplankton, which consume CO_2 and water to make organic molecules such as glucose ($C_6H_{12}O_6$). Phytoplankton use the energy from sunlight, so they live in the shallow ocean. All life forms require carbon, but some phytoplankton such as coccolithophores also use carbon to build calcium carbonate shells. The phytoplankton are eaten by zooplankton, which also usually have carbonate shells or skeletons. The plankton are eaten by successively larger organisms, and the carbon moves up the food chain.

Biologic Carbon Pump Organic chemical reactions use CO_2 from the atmosphere and dissolved carbon from weathered land rocks. They also draw heavily upon the upwelling of deep ocean currents, which carry dissolved carbon back toward the surface.

Marine organisms use Ca^{2+} and CO_3^{2-} ions from weathered rock to build their shells. The shells eventually fall toward the ocean floor.

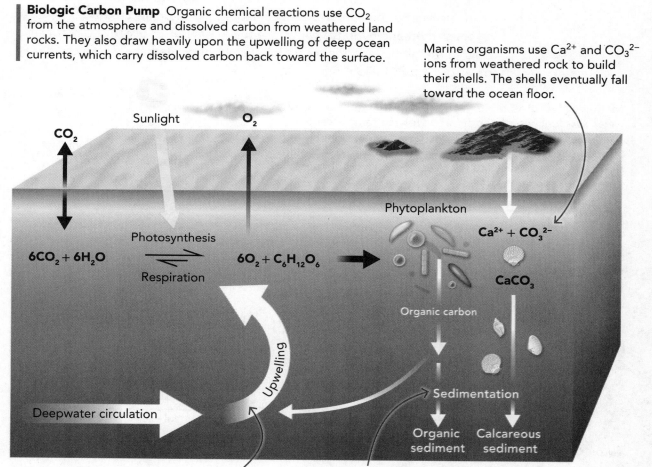

Sunlight

CO_2

O_2

Phytoplankton

$Ca^{2+} + CO_3^{2-}$

Photosynthesis

$6CO_2 + 6H_2O$ ⇌ $6O_2 + C_6H_{12}O_6$

Respiration

$CaCO_3$

Organic carbon

Upwelling

Sedimentation

Deepwater circulation

Organic sediment   Calcareous sediment

Decomposition of dead organisms and dissolution of shells contribute ions and nutrients that are brought to the surface by upwelling and are used by organisms at the surface.

Most of the carbonate sediment from dead organisms becomes part of the dissolved carbon within the deepwater circulation. Above the CCD, these shells form calcareous sediments.

11. **SEP Use a Model to Evaluate** What would happen to the annual rates of limestone precipitation in the ocean if the ocean water were to become much warmer and more acidic? (Hint: First describe what will happen to the CCD.) ✏️

....

....

....

Methane Hydrates

Methane Gas Deposits Methane (CH_4) gas is formed by bacteria in seafloor sediments. When the methane rises through the seafloor sediments, it reacts with water in the sediments if the conditions are correct. The resulting frozen combinations of methane and water are called **methane hydrates.** These methane ices are stable at temperatures warmer than water ice is usually stable. They are abundant on land within the frozen permafrost of the Arctic tundra and are extremely abundant in shallow marine offshore sediments. Seismic imaging has identified the occurrence of layers of methane hydrates within the top kilometer of ocean sediments all around the globe, and the total global amount of methane within them may be as great as 8 trillion tons.

Methane Hydrate Stability The stability of methane hydrates varies as a function of depth (pressure) and temperature. The frozen hydrates are stable at higher pressures and lower temperatures. Methane hydrates are located by seismic ships that send seismic waves to the ocean floor. Hydrophones detect the reflected waves.

The hydrothermal gradient line shows that water temperature decreases with depth below the ocean surface.

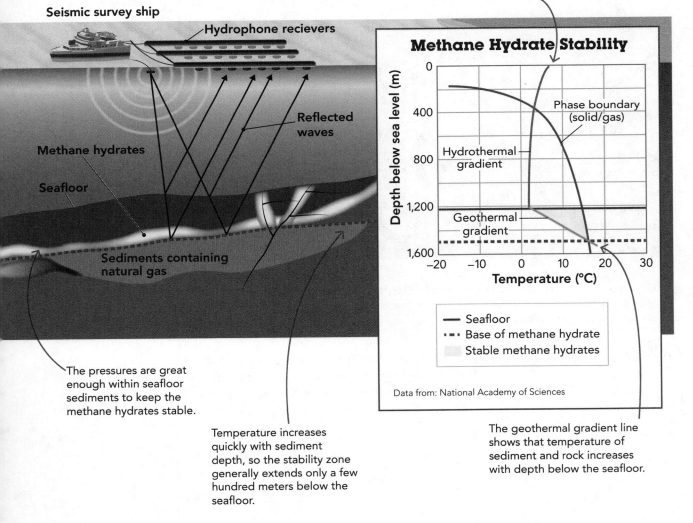

Seismic survey ship

Hydrophone recievers

Reflected waves

Methane hydrates

Seafloor

Sediments containing natural gas

The pressures are great enough within seafloor sediments to keep the methane hydrates stable.

Temperature increases quickly with sediment depth, so the stability zone generally extends only a few hundred meters below the seafloor.

The geothermal gradient line shows that temperature of sediment and rock increases with depth below the seafloor.

Methane Hydrate Stability

Depth below sea level (m): 0, 400, 800, 1,200, 1,600

Temperature (°C): −20, −10, 0, 10, 20, 30

Phase boundary (solid/gas)

Hydrothermal gradient

Geothermal gradient

— Seafloor
- - - Base of methane hydrate
Stable methane hydrates

Data from: National Academy of Sciences

Feedbacks with Global Warming Climate change will impact the stability zone of offshore methane gas hydrates. Rising sea levels and the resulting higher pressure favor methane stability. However, warming ocean temperatures are beginning to raise the lower boundary of the frozen methane hydrate, releasing methane gas into the ocean and atmosphere.

◗ **Because methane is a greenhouse gas, a positive feedback loop exists between global warming and the release of methane gas from hydrates.**

⑫ **CCC Stability and Change** Would you expect the thickness of the methane hydrate stability zone to be thicker or thinner for deeper ocean locations compared to shallow ocean locations? Explain. ✐

....

....

....

....

Revisit

INVESTIGATIVE PHENOMENON

GO ONLINE to Elaborate on and Evaluate your knowledge of the exchange of carbon between the ocean and atmosphere by completing the peer review and writing activities.

In the CER worksheet, you drafted a scientific argument to explain what is happening to the world's coral reefs. With a partner, reevaluate the evidence cited in your arguments.

⑬ **SEP Identify Patterns** Explain two different pathways carbon can take to enter the ocean to become available for marine life. ✐

....

....

....

....

....

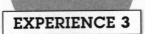
The Ocean and Climate Change

GO ONLINE to Explore and Explain how the ocean influences Earth's climate.

Ocean Surface Currents

Ocean water plays a large role in regional climate patterns. One reason for this is the high specific heat of water, which allows water to store a lot of thermal energy. This energy can be transferred to the atmosphere along the surface of the ocean. **Ocean surface currents** are areas of ocean water that flow steadily in a particular direction close to the ocean's surface. As these currents move water across the globe, they also redistribute thermal energy, affecting regional atmospheric patterns.

Currents within ocean basins largely take the form of rotating spirals called gyres that spin clockwise in the Northern Hemisphere and counterclockwise in the Southern Hemisphere. Gyres often bring warm water toward the poles along the west sides of the ocean basins and return cold water back toward the equator along the east sides of the basins.

Large-scale Surface Ocean Currents This map shows a simplified representation of the main surface ocean currents. The currents are mostly separated among the Pacific, Atlantic, and Indian Ocean basins, and connected only around Antarctica (and by a few narrow straits).

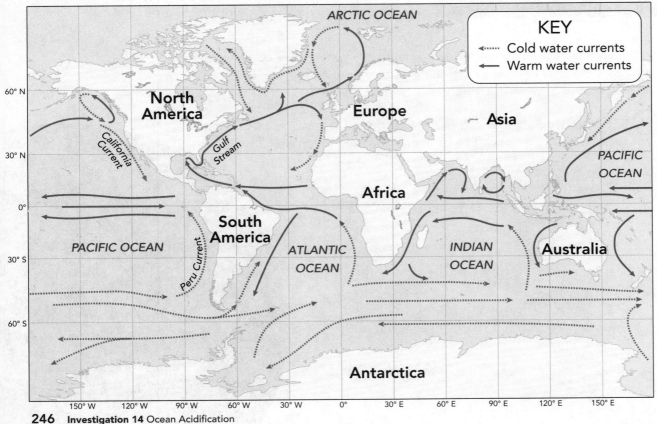

Small-scale Surface Ocean Currents This graphic representation shows the actual pattern of surface ocean currents in the mid-Atlantic in November 2005. Note how currents take the form of many small gyres, within the overall pattern of the large North Atlantic gyre.

The strong narrow current coming out of the Gulf of Mexico and snaking up the eastern U.S. coast is the Gulf Stream.

Surface ocean current patterns are determined by a combination of continental outlines, deep ocean currents, and surface winds. Because winds are always shifting in direction and strength, the exact patterns of surface currents are variable over periods of days, months, years, decades, centuries, and even longer. Surface currents may look very different during ocean storms than during periods of calm winds.

Surface currents can also change over Ice Age cycles. Currently, the Atlantic and Pacific Ocean basins are connected across the Arctic Sea through the Bering Strait (next to Alaska), and the Indian and Pacific Ocean basins are connected through Indonesia. However, during the last Ice Age, when sea levels were about 125 m lower, these shallow straits were all above sea level and the ocean basins were even more cut off from each other.

(14) **CCC Energy and Matter** The coasts of central New Jersey and northern California both share the same latitude, about 40° north. However, if you went swimming in the summer you would likely find the water in New Jersey comfortably warm but the water in northern California uncomfortably cold. Use the ocean surface currents map to explain why this would be so. ✎

....

....

....

Coriolis Effect

The patterns of clockwise rotation in ocean current gyres in the Northern Hemisphere and counterclockwise rotation in gyres in the Southern Hemisphere are a result of the Coriolis effect. The **Coriolis effect** describes the curved path that an object takes when it moves in a straight line across a rotating object perpendicular to the axis of rotation.

On Earth, the Coriolis effect causes ocean water, air, and even liquid iron in the outer core to move in curved paths as each substance travels north or south. Because ocean water is trapped within ocean basins, the result is a connecting set of rotating gyres.

Coriolis Model Currents traveling toward or away from the equator are redirected by the rotation of Earth.

North Pole

In this model, the arrow represents an air or ocean current traveling south from the North Pole.

Expected path

Actual path

While the arrow is in motion, Earth rotates to the east. Because the circumference of Earth is greater at the equator than at the pole, the equator rotates faster than the pole.

N
W   E
S

Equator

Earth's rotation

The Coriolis effect is reversed in the Southern Hemisphere. An ocean or air current traveling from the South Pole toward the equator would again veer toward the west, but that would result in a leftward or counterclockwise motion.

In the reference frame of the rotating Earth, the arrow has followed a curved path, veering to the right and missing the target. The same clockwise-curving path to the right would result if the arrow was shot from the equator toward the pole.

(15) **SEP Use Models** Use the model of a flying arrow to explain why the Coriolis effect is smallest near the equator. ✏

....

....

....

....

Deep Ocean Currents

Connected to surface ocean currents from below is a complex network of deep ocean currents. **Deep ocean currents** are subsurface patterns of ocean circulation that move water within and among the ocean basins. Unlike surface currents, deep currents are driven by differences in density.

The density of water depends on its temperature and salinity. An increase in temperature means a decrease in density, so warmer water resists sinking. An increase in salinity, on the other hand, means an increase in density, so salty water sinks more easily. In general, colder and denser water near the poles sinks while warmer water near the equator rises. Water moves slowly through the system, taking centuries or even millennia before returning to the surface.

Sinking Polar Water This simplified diagram of deep ocean currents shows some of the horizontal and vertical patterns.

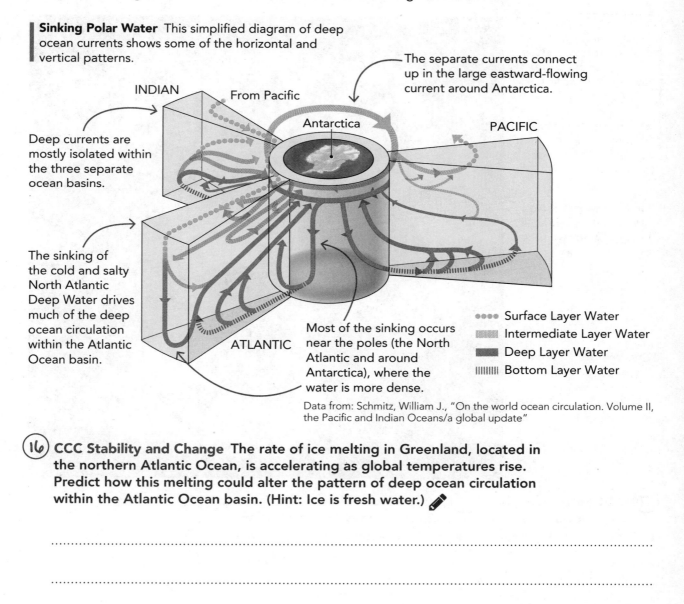

The separate currents connect up in the large eastward-flowing current around Antarctica.

INDIAN   From Pacific

Antarctica   PACIFIC

Deep currents are mostly isolated within the three separate ocean basins.

The sinking of the cold and salty North Atlantic Deep Water drives much of the deep ocean circulation within the Atlantic Ocean basin.

ATLANTIC

Most of the sinking occurs near the poles (the North Atlantic and around Antarctica), where the water is more dense.

···· Surface Layer Water
▨▨▨ Intermediate Layer Water
▬▬ Deep Layer Water
||||| Bottom Layer Water

Data from: Schmitz, William J., "On the world ocean circulation. Volume II, the Pacific and Indian Oceans/a global update"

16 **CCC Stability and Change** The rate of ice melting in Greenland, located in the northern Atlantic Ocean, is accelerating as global temperatures rise. Predict how this melting could alter the pattern of deep ocean circulation within the Atlantic Ocean basin. (Hint: Ice is fresh water.) 🖉

....

....

....

Ocean Heat Reservoirs

As surface waters are warmed by the atmosphere, deep ocean currents carry the heat below the surface. In this way, the ocean is like a giant battery, storing massive amounts of thermal energy, and ocean currents are like electric currents, carrying energy around the globe to power atmospheric systems.

By storing heat from the atmosphere, the ocean acts as a buffer for global warming and delays climate change. Eventually, currents will carry the warm water to the surface again, raising atmospheric temperatures. Current warming is partly reduced by the upwelling of ancient, colder water that sank into the deep ocean during the Little Ice Age, from 1250–1850 CE.

Warming Ocean The "shells" on these globes represent cross-sections of the upper layer of the Pacific (left) and Atlantic (right) oceans indicating temperature changes at different depths for a succession of decades.

Blue represents cooler temperatures, while red represents warmer temperatures.

Over the past several decades, the surface ocean has warmed and heat has moved deeper into the ocean.

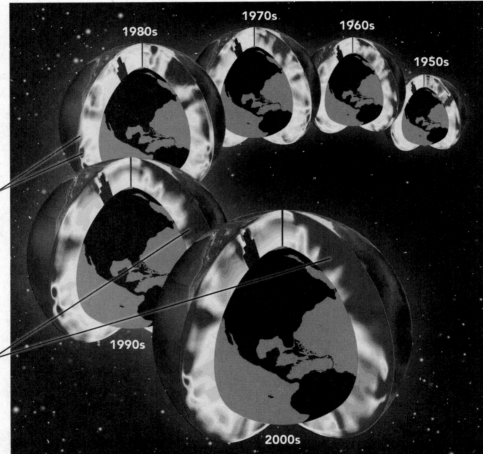

17 **CCC Patterns** Is the overall temperature of the ocean increasing or decreasing? Has the rate at which ocean temperature is changing increased, decreased, or stayed the same? Explain your answer. ✎

....

....

....

Calculate the Heat Carried by the Gulf Stream

The Gulf Stream carries warm water from the Gulf of Mexico to the Arctic Sea. The current is about 100 km wide and 1 km deep, and flows at a rate of about 1 m/s, resulting in a volumetric flow rate of 1×10^8 m^3/s. The water in the Gulf Stream is about 10°C warmer than surrounding water. Assuming a specific heat of seawater of about 4,000 J/m^3·°C, calculate how many terawatts of power the Gulf Stream carries. (Note: 1 terawatt (TW) = 10^{12} watts = 10^{12} J/s.)

Analyze List the knowns and unknowns.

Knowns	Unknown
volumetric flow rate = 1×10^8 m^3/s	Power = ? TW
$\Delta T = +10°C$	
Specific heat of seawater = 4,000 J/m^3·°C	

Calculate Solve for the unknown.

Analyze the units of the given measurements to derive an equation that converts the flow rate (m^3/s) into an energy transfer rate (J/s).

Power = flow rate × volumetric heat capacity × ΔT
= (m^3/s) × J/m^3·°C × °C = J/s

Substitute the knowns into the equation and solve.

Power = 1×10^8 m^3/s × 4,000 J/m^3·°C × 10°C
= 4×10^{12} J/s × $\frac{1\ TW}{10^{12}\ J/s}$ = 4 TW

Evaluate Does the result make sense?

A huge volume of warm water flows through the Gulf Stream, so it makes sense that it would transport a significant amount of thermal energy.

18) **CCC Scale, Proportion, and Quantity** The Kuroshio Current is a warm-water current that flows northward along the coast of Japan. It flows at a rate of 40,000,000 m^3/s, and its temperature difference is the same as the Gulf Stream's. Calculate the power, in TW, of the Kuroshio Current. ✏️

GO ONLINE for more practice problems.

Ocean Thermoclines

The ocean is divided into horizontal temperature layers, with a warm layer near the surface and a cold layer below. A **thermocline** marks the transition zone between the upper and lower water layers. It is steeper in tropical regions and almost non-existent in polar regions.

In many parts of the ocean, the surface layer is home to large populations of photosynthetic phytoplankton that require the sunlight found there. These organisms also rely on the upwelling of ocean currents to bring a steady supply of nutrients up to the surface. However, if the thermocline gets too steep, the warm surface layer becomes very buoyant, suppressing upwelling and ocean convection. Plankton then die off because they don't get the nutrients they need.

Thermocline Variation This graph shows sample thermoclines for polar, temperate, and tropical regions.

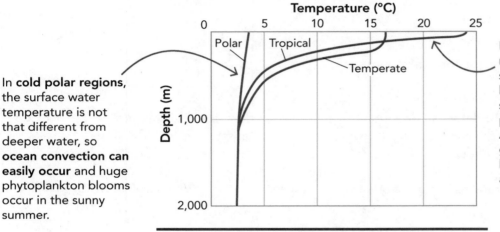

Ocean Thermoclines by Latitude

In **cold polar regions**, the surface water temperature is not that different from deeper water, so **ocean convection can easily occur** and huge phytoplankton blooms occur in the sunny summer.

In **warm tropical regions**, there is no shortage of sunlight, but the surface layer is so **warm that it often prevents upwelling**. As a result, the tropics generally have the lowest phytoplankton activity.

⑲ SEP Construct an Explanation As global atmospheric temperatures continue to rise, scientists are concerned that populations of marine animals that rely on phytoplankton for food might decrease. Construct an explanation for this idea based on what you know about upwelling and the thermocline. ✏

....

....

....

....

....

Ocean Deoxygenation

Another problem associated with global warming is ocean deoxygenation.
Ocean deoxygenation is the expansion of low-oxygen zones in the ocean
as a consequence of rising temperatures. Ocean water loses oxygen when it
gets warmer for two main reasons: decreased O_2 solubility and the decline
of oxygen-producing phytoplankton populations.

Deoxygenation and Hypoxia
How do **rising ocean temperatures** affect **oxygen dissolution?**

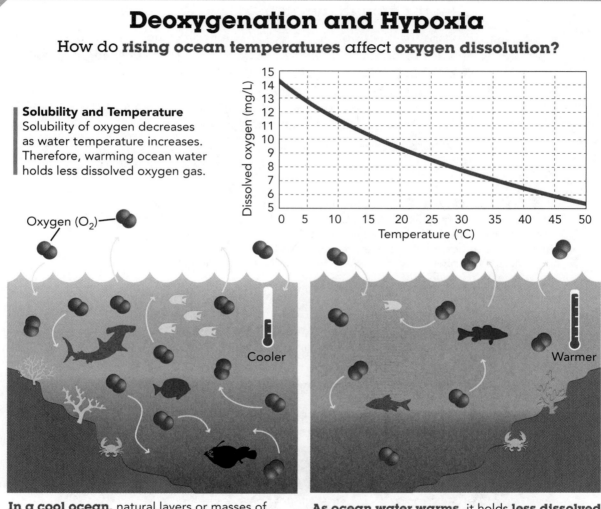

Solubility and Temperature
Solubility of oxygen decreases
as water temperature increases.
Therefore, warming ocean water
holds less dissolved oxygen gas.

Oxygen (O_2)

Cooler

Warmer

In a cool ocean, natural layers or masses of
oxygenated water easily mix. **Mixing transfers
oxygen throughout** the water column all the
way to the ocean floor.

As ocean water warms, it holds **less dissolved
oxygen** gas, and **layers don't mix** as well. This
results in hypoxic, or low-oxygen, layers where
organisms struggle to survive.

(20) **SEP Calculate** Suppose that a beaker of water is 15°C and you raise the
temperature by 5°C. Use the graph above to calculate the percent decrease
in the amount of dissolved O_2 gas. 🖊

El Niño/Southern Oscillation

Ocean currents have a significant effect on regional climates as they redistribute heat around the globe. However, regional climates also change over time as a result of cyclical changes in ocean circulation patterns.

◼ **The cycling of matter and energy between Earth's ocean and atmosphere creates changes in climate patterns around the globe.**

Perhaps the most significant cyclical ocean circulation pattern in terms of energy redistribution is what is known as ENSO. The **El Niño/Southern Oscillation (ENSO)** is a cyclical circulation pattern in the tropical Pacific that results in periodic variation between below-normal and above-normal sea surface temperatures and dry and wet conditions. The ENSO pattern cycles through three phases: Neutral, El Niño, and La Niña. Neutral indicates that conditions are near their long-term average.

"Neutral" ENSO Walker Circulation ENSO cycles are driven by a pattern of atmospheric flow called the Walker Circulation, with warm moist air rising in the western Pacific (bringing rain) and cold dry air falling in the eastern Pacific. Because the atmospheric systems are all coupled, this Neutral ENSO pattern influences atmospheric flow patterns in the Atlantic and Indian Oceans.

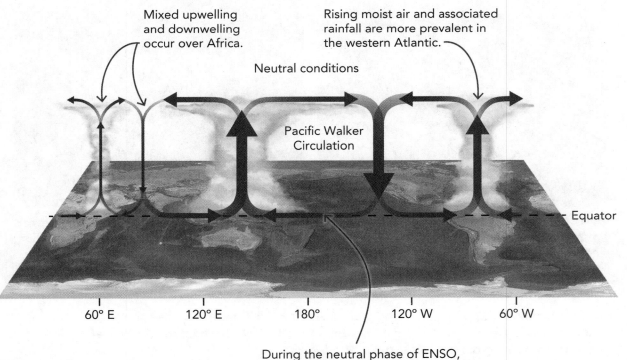

Mixed upwelling and downwelling occur over Africa.

Rising moist air and associated rainfall are more prevalent in the western Atlantic.

Neutral conditions

Pacific Walker Circulation

Equator

60° E   120° E   180°   120° W   60° W

During the neutral phase of ENSO, westward winds above the Pacific Ocean push the ocean currents westward, bringing warm water to the Asian coast.

El Niño is the warm phase of ENSO, as average ocean surface temperatures rise. La Niña is the cool phase, as surface temperatures fall. These two phases shift back and forth irregularly every 2–7 years, triggering predictable disruptions of temperature, air currents, and rainfall that lead to droughts in some places and floods in others. El Niño is usually, but not always, followed by La Niña.

El Niño Walker Circulation During El Niño, there is an increase in rainfall over California and equatorial Africa, but a decrease in rainfall in the Atlantic and western Pacific.

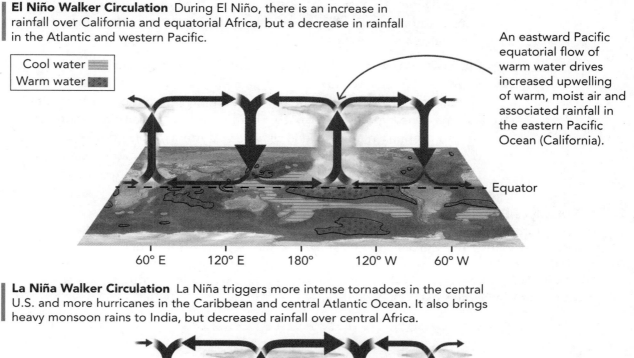

An eastward Pacific equatorial flow of warm water drives increased upwelling of warm, moist air and associated rainfall in the eastern Pacific Ocean (California).

La Niña Walker Circulation La Niña triggers more intense tornadoes in the central U.S. and more hurricanes in the Caribbean and central Atlantic Ocean. It also brings heavy monsoon rains to India, but decreased rainfall over central Africa.

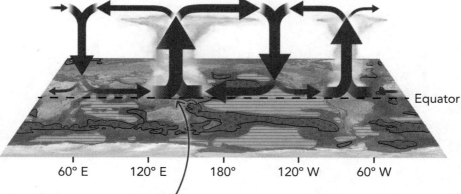

A stronger-than-usual westward equatorial Pacific warm-water current drives very strong upwelling and rains in the western Pacific.

(21) **CCC Patterns** During a La Niña event, rainfall and hurricanes/cyclones generally increase along the east coasts of both North America and Asia, but they all generally decrease during an El Niño event. Use the diagrams on this page to explain why. ✏️

....

....

....

ENSO Variability and Upwelling

ENSO cycle patterns directly impact global temperatures. During El Niño, Pacific Ocean surface temperatures are warmer than usual and the heat borrowed out of the Pacific Ocean generally causes global temperatures to rise. During La Niña, heat goes back into the Pacific Ocean and global temperatures usually fall. These cycles of heating and cooling impact human societies, sometimes in surprising ways.

Flu Epidemics In 1917–1918, the Spanish flu pandemic killed almost 100 million people worldwide. This pandemic, along with the next three big flu epidemics (1957, 1968, 2009), were each preceded the year before by La Niña. One hypothesis proposes that the La Niña ocean circulation patterns caused changes in atmospheric circulation patterns, which caused changes in bird migration patterns. As a result, large human populations were exposed to new strains of avian flu viruses, which caused the epidemics.

22 **SEP Analyze Data** Global mean temperatures vary annually. The average temperature for El Niño years (orange circles) is warmer than for La Niña years (blue circles). The purple squares show the temperature trend for neutral years. Draw a straight line that goes through most of the orange circles (El Niño years). Then draw a second straight line that goes through most of the blue circles (La Niña years). ✏

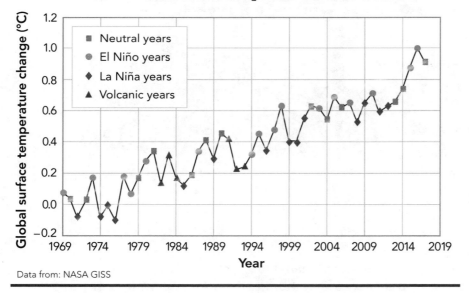

Global Surface Temperature Anomalies

Data from: NASA GISS

23 **SEP Interpret Data** Describe the difference between the lines you drew. ✏

....

....

....

El Niño and the Thermocline During an El Niño phase, the eastward Pacific current of warm water (black arrows) pushes down the thermocline along the South American coast, limiting upwelling and causing a decrease in marine life there.

La Niña and the Thermocline During a La Niña phase, the westward Pacific current causes the thermocline to lift up along the South American coast, bringing nutrient rich waters that feed booming plankton and fish populations.

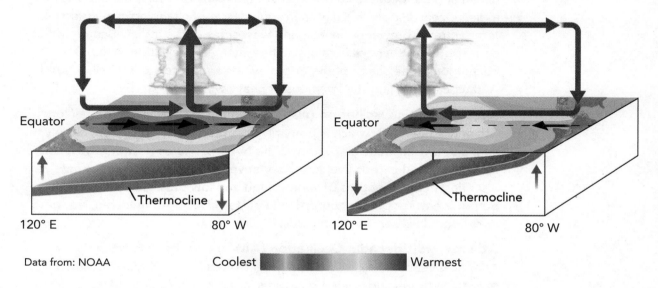

Data from: NOAA   Coolest ▇▇▇▇ Warmest

Economic Effects The ENSO cycle also affects fishing industries. In neutral years, a westward equatorial Pacific current causes upwelling along the coast of South America. This brings nutrients to shallow waters, which supports plankton growth and therefore larger fish and the South American fishing industry.

In addition, a coastal current that travels north along the South American coast veers westward due to the Coriolis effect. This pulls water away from the coast, bringing up more nutrients. This effect is amplified by the stronger currents during a La Niña event, which is usually very good for the fishing industry.

During an El Niño period, warm waters flow east across the Pacific equator and then down the South American coast. The Coriolis effect causes these currents to bend left into the coast and sink, suppressing the upwelling of nutrients. The plankton die and the fishing industry collapses.

(24) SEP Analyze Data Global temperatures actually decreased slightly in the years 2017 and 2018. Some suggest that this means global warming has stopped. Construct another more plausible explanation for the data. ✏️

....

....

....

....

Other Modes of Ocean Variability

The ENSO cycle of El Niño/La Niña is not the only pattern of oscillating ocean and atmosphere currents. There are many others. For example, the Indian Ocean Dipole (IOD) is an irregular cycle of changing sea-surface temperatures between the east and west sides of the Indian Ocean, with corresponding changes in rainfall. The Antarctic Oscillation (AAO) is a fluctuation in the shape of the ring of winds and waters that circle around Antarctica, changing the locations of heavy winds and storms.

North Atlantic Oscillation (NAO) A significant oscillation in the North Atlantic is the NAO, which is primarily an atmospheric oscillation, closely connected with Arctic air patterns. The NAO oscillates between two modes, referred to as the "positive" and "negative" modes. These modes involve a shifting in the strengths of various high and low pressure zones, and determine which parts of Europe and eastern North America receive warm or cold (and wet or dry) air masses.

Atlantic Multidecadal Oscillation (AMO) Another oscillation in the Atlantic Ocean is the AMO. The AMO involves 20- to 40-year oscillations of long-term sea-surface temperatures in the North Atlantic Ocean. These variations affect air temperatures and rainfall patterns over much of the Northern Hemisphere to the extent that there is a significant correlation between the AMO and mean global temperatures over the past century.

North Atlantic Oscillation: Positive Mode
The polar jet stream follows a relatively straight course from North America to Europe. Eastern North America gets warm air, northern Europe gets wet and warm air, and southern Europe gets cool and dry air.

North Atlantic Oscillation: Negative Mode The polar jet stream meanders up over Greenland. Eastern North America is cold and snowy, northern Europe is cold and dry, and southern Europe is warm and wet.

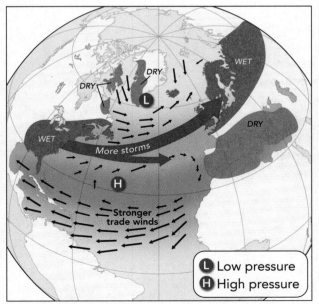

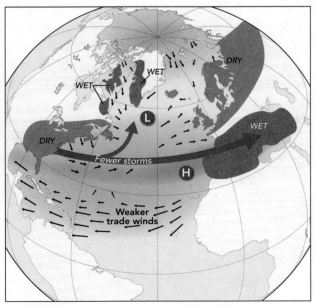

Data from: Yachting World; NAO

(25) **CCC Energy and Matter** The histogram below shows the positive and negative phases of the AMO index. The solid and dashed lines show annual variations in the global mean temperature and its 10-year moving average. The correlation between the AMO index and mean global temperature is strong but not perfect. Draw a box around the parts of the two curves where their trends do not correlate. ✎

Global Average Temperature and the AMO

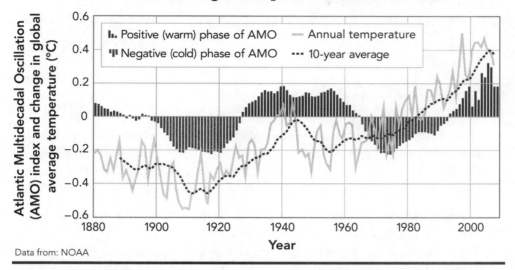

Data from: NOAA

Revisit

INVESTIGATIVE PHENOMENON

GO ONLINE to Elaborate and Evaluate your knowledge of the ocean's influence on Earth's climate by completing the class discussion and data analysis activities.

In the CER worksheet, you drafted a scientific argument to explain what is happening to the world's coral reefs. With a partner, reevaluate the evidence cited in your arguments.

(26) **SEP Engage in Argument** Increasing ocean temperatures cause a decrease in ocean oxygen levels. Explain why this is a problem for coral reefs. ✎

....

....

....

....

Consequences of Ocean Acidification

to Explore and Explain the effects of ocean acidification.

Calcification

Many marine organisms use carbon from dissolved carbon dioxide to build their shells out of calcium carbonate, $CaCO_3$, in a process called **calcification**. Calcification is a form of biomineralization. The calcium enters the ocean as dissolved ions from the weathering of rocks at or below Earth's surface.

Calcium carbonate has two main crystal forms, or polymorphs, used for making shells and skeletons: calcite and aragonite. These crystals have the same chemical composition, but the calcium, carbon, and oxygen atoms are arranged in different structures. Some organisms prefer one form over the other, and some organisms use both forms to make their shells harder.

Calcification in Acidic Seawater
Marine organisms use calcium ions (Ca^{2+}) and carbonate ions (CO_3^{2-}) in seawater to build their shells of calcite or aragonite.

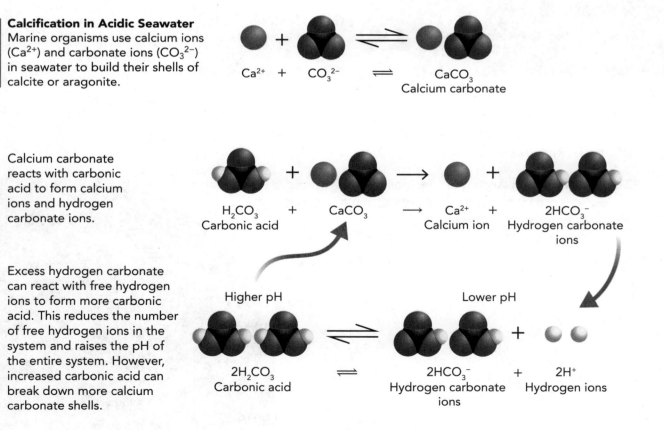

Calcium carbonate reacts with carbonic acid to form calcium ions and hydrogen carbonate ions.

$$Ca^{2+} + CO_3^{2-} \rightleftharpoons CaCO_3$$
Calcium carbonate

$$H_2CO_3 + CaCO_3 \longrightarrow Ca^{2+} + 2HCO_3^-$$
Carbonic acid + Calcium carbonate ⟶ Calcium ion + Hydrogen carbonate ions

Excess hydrogen carbonate can react with free hydrogen ions to form more carbonic acid. This reduces the number of free hydrogen ions in the system and raises the pH of the entire system. However, increased carbonic acid can break down more calcium carbonate shells.

Higher pH   Lower pH

$$2H_2CO_3 \rightleftharpoons 2HCO_3^- + 2H^+$$
Carbonic acid ⇌ Hydrogen carbonate ions + Hydrogen ions

Buffering the Solution Changing the relative concentrations of reactants and products can shift the pH in either direction. This buffers the solution and slows the rate at which the ocean water's acidity changes.

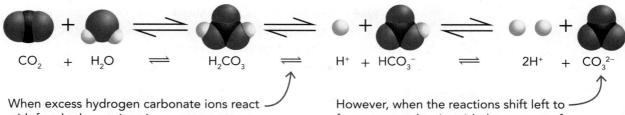

$$CO_2 \ + \ H_2O \ \rightleftharpoons \ H_2CO_3 \ \rightleftharpoons \ H^+ \ + \ HCO_3^- \ \rightleftharpoons \ 2H^+ \ + \ CO_3^{2-}$$

When excess hydrogen carbonate ions react with free hydrogen ions in seawater, more carbonic acid forms, pushing the equation to the left and resisting a drop in pH of the solution.

However, when the reactions shift left to form more carbonic acid, the amount of carbonate ions available for organisms to use to build shells decreases.

Dynamic Equilibrium As the ocean becomes more acidic, the relative concentrations of carbonate ions, hydrogen carbonate ions, and carbon dioxide shift to reach a new equilibrium. As pH drops, carbonate concentrations decrease, and hydrogen carbonate and carbon dioxide concentrations increase.

The vertical axis is a logarithmic plot of the reactant concentrations.

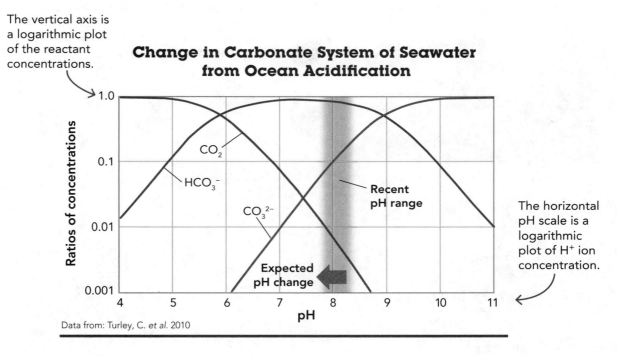

Change in Carbonate System of Seawater from Ocean Acidification

Data from: Turley, C. *et al.* 2010

The horizontal pH scale is a logarithmic plot of H^+ ion concentration.

(27) **SEP Interpret Graphs** Use the vertical logarithmic scale to explain why carbonate ions are mostly converting to hydrogen carbonate ions and not to CO_2 molecules as pH levels fall from the mean ocean surface value of about 8.1. ✏

....

....

....

....

Marine Shell Dissolution

Adding free H^+ ions to the water drives the chemical reactions away from carbonate stability. As the amount of CO_2 in the ocean increases, the amount of CO_3^{2-} decreases, and carbonate ions convert into hydrogen carbonate ions (HCO_3^-), which increases the energy required by organisms to build shells. These changes lower calcification rates and increase dissolution rates.

▶ Changes to carbon dioxide levels and ocean pH disrupt the chemical equilibrium that many ocean organisms depend on to make their shells.

Dissolution of Calcium Carbonate Shells

How are **pH** and **CO₂ concentration** related to **carbonate dissolution?**

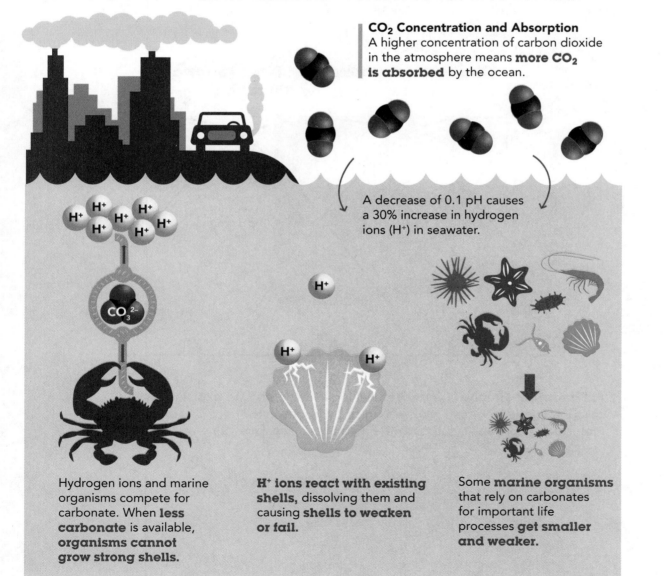

CO₂ Concentration and Absorption
A higher concentration of carbon dioxide in the atmosphere means **more CO₂ is absorbed** by the ocean.

A decrease of 0.1 pH causes a 30% increase in hydrogen ions (H^+) in seawater.

Hydrogen ions and marine organisms compete for carbonate. When **less carbonate** is available, **organisms cannot grow strong shells.**

H⁺ ions react with existing shells, dissolving them and causing **shells to weaken or fail.**

Some **marine organisms** that rely on carbonates for important life processes **get smaller and weaker.**

Calcium Carbonate Dissolution in Acid
Increased ocean acidity increases the dissolution rate of calcium carbonate shells once they are built.

Shells become weaker over time and may fail completely. As shells weaken or fail, populations of carbonate-shelled organisms will likely decline over time.

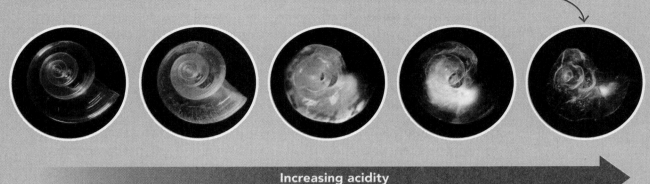

Increasing acidity

Calcite and Aragonite Organisms that use aragonite to build their shells are more at risk than organisms that use only calcite. Aragonite is a harder mineral than calcite, so it adds extra protection from predators, but it is only weakly stable at Earth's surface and is 1.5 times as soluble in seawater than calcite.

Arctic Food Webs Cold, arctic waters absorb atmospheric CO_2 faster than other regions and act as carbon sinks. The Arctic food web is very dependent upon shelled mollusks that have aragonite shells. Damage to the base of the Arctic food web would cause damage all the way up the chain, including damage to fish, seals, and whales.

Larvae Ocean acidification is particularly damaging to marine organisms that have a larval stage, such as plankton, bivalves, and sea urchins. The larvae of marine organisms that grow in high-CO_2 waters tend to be stunted and deformed, making them less able to feed and function properly.

28 **CCC Stability and Change** Suppose there are two closely related species of clam. One makes its shell out of aragonite, the other out of calcite. As the ocean becomes more acidic, predict what will happen to the relative populations of the two species, and what will happen to the population of a predator species that feeds on the aragonite-shelled clams. ✏

....

....

....

....

Disruption of Marine Ecosystems

Increased CO_2 concentrations and ocean acidification are impacting marine organisms and communities in many different ways. Some organisms, such as the jumbo squid, are suffering from reduced metabolic rates. Others, such as the longfin squid, are taking longer to grow and are more frequently small and misshapen. Some species, such as blue mussels, are showing a reduced immune system. Others are showing a decrease in their ability to smell or hear predators.

Some organisms are actually doing better and are thriving in higher-CO_2, lower-pH waters. One study of an ecosystem found that predators such as crabs and lobsters were becoming bigger and stronger, while their prey, such as clams and oysters, were doing worse, disrupting the predator–prey dynamic. In many environments, disruptions and damages to the ecosystem are greater due to the combination of increased temperature, higher acidity, and deoxygenation. These combined effects are much greater than the effects from just one factor.

Jumbo Squid Studies have shown that increased ocean carbon dioxide levels can damage the metabolic rates of marine organisms such as the Humboldt, or jumbo, squid.

Red Tides Blooms of toxic cyanobacteria and algae, commonly called red tides, occur more frequently in warmer and more acidic oceans. When the algae and cyanobacteria die and decay, oxygen is stripped from the water and large "dead zones" form in the ocean. In these hypoxic zones, oxygen levels are so low that fish, turtles, marine mammals, and seabirds cannot survive. Algal blooms often occur near the mouths of large rivers, which carry phosphates and other chemicals from fertilizers that run off farmland into rivers.

Plastics Another ecological hazard comes from human use and disposal of plastics. Plastic floats and degrades slowly and often accumulates within broad ocean gyres, which may hold 100 million tons of plastic. One such gyre had more than 6 times as much plastic in the water as plankton. Synthetic fabrics are one of the largest sources of plastic in the ocean because they release huge numbers of microfibers with each washing. These microfibers pass through filtration plants and into the ocean.

(29) SEP Design Your Solution Propose two different ways that the number of damaging toxic ocean red tides could be reduced. 🖉

....

....

....

....

Toxic Red Tides
Warm water and higher carbon dioxide levels favor photosynthesis, which leads to blooms of toxic cyanobacteria and algae such as this bloom off the coast of South Africa.

Coral Bleaching

Corals are tiny marine animals that enjoy a symbiotic relationship with photosynthetic algae that live in their tissues and supply them with a source of food. If the corals become stressed, the algae will leave, causing the corals to turn white, a phenomenon known as **coral bleaching.** There are many different causes of coral bleaching, including ocean acidification and water pollution. But the greatest cause is warming ocean temperatures.

Corals' Response to Ocean Changes
How do **temperature** and **pH** affect **corals**?

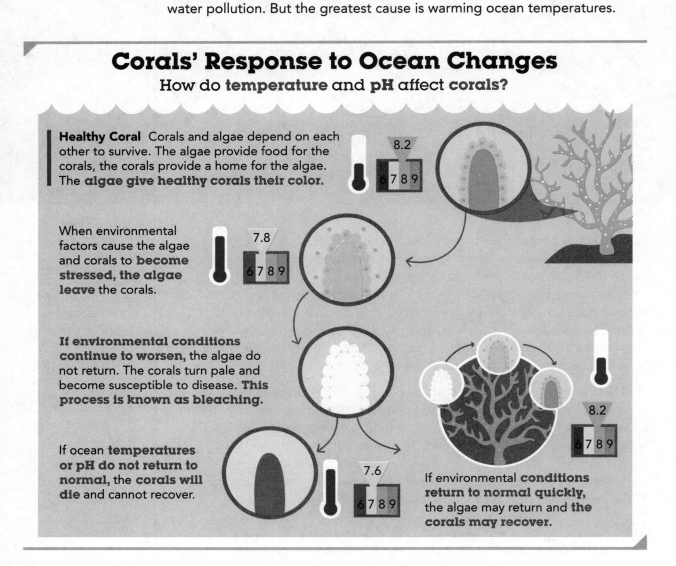

Healthy Coral Corals and algae depend on each other to survive. The algae provide food for the corals, the corals provide a home for the algae. **The algae give healthy corals their color.**

8.2
6 7 8 9

When environmental factors cause the algae and corals to **become stressed, the algae leave** the corals.

7.8
6 7 8 9

If environmental conditions continue to worsen, the algae do not return. The corals turn pale and become susceptible to disease. **This process is known as bleaching.**

If ocean **temperatures or pH do not return to normal, the corals will die** and cannot recover.

7.6
6 7 8 9

If environmental **conditions return to normal quickly,** the algae may return and **the corals may recover.**

8.2
6 7 8 9

30) **CCC Stability and Change** Coral reefs play an important role in many marine ecosystems. Describe what you think would happen to coral reef ecosystems if the corals died.

....

....

....

Analyze Rates of Coral Bleaching Events

Between 2014 and 2017, an ocean heat wave caused 75% of the world's coral reefs to demonstrate bleaching-level heat stress. About 30% of the corals died. Before the 1980s, mass-bleaching events were occurring approximately once every 30 years. As of 2017, these events were happening every 6 years. How many times more frequent are these events occurring now than in the 1980s?

ANALYZE List the knowns and unknowns.

Knowns	Unknown
frequency before 1980s $= \dfrac{1 \text{ event}}{30 \text{ years}}$	multiplicative increase in frequency $= ?$
frequency in 2017 $= \dfrac{1 \text{ event}}{6 \text{ years}}$	

CALCULATE Solve for the unknown.

Express the multiplicative increase in frequency as a ratio.

$$\text{multiplicative increase in frequency} = \frac{\text{new rate}}{\text{old rate}} = \frac{\text{frequency in 2017}}{\text{frequency before 1980s}}$$

Substitute the knowns into the equation and solve.

$$\frac{\text{new rate}}{\text{old rate}} = \frac{\left(\dfrac{1 \text{ event}}{6 \text{ years}}\right)}{\left(\dfrac{1 \text{ event}}{30 \text{ years}}\right)}$$

Rearrange and simplify. Note that the units cancel.

$$= \frac{1 \text{ event}}{6 \text{ years}} \div \frac{1 \text{ event}}{30 \text{ years}} = \frac{1 \text{ event}}{6 \text{ years}} \times \frac{30 \text{ years}}{1 \text{ event}} = 5$$

EVALUATE Does the result make sense?

Mass-bleaching events are happening five times more frequently than before the 1980s. This makes sense because global ocean temperatures have increased significantly since the 1980s.

(31) **SEP Use Math** Scientists project that the frequency of mass-bleaching events will continue to accelerate at a rate of 4% per year. Compared to 2020, how many times more frequent will mass-bleaching events occur in 2050?
(Hint: multiplicative increase $=$ (rate of change)$^{\text{number of years}}$) ✏️

GO ONLINE for more practice problems.

Calcite and Aragonite Stability Depths

Recall that the carbonate compensation depth (CCD) is the depth below which $CaCO_3$ is not stable and will dissolve according to the equation:

$$CaCO_3 + CO_2 + H_2O \rightleftharpoons Ca^{2+} + 2HCO_3^-$$

However, this reaction is different for the two different mineral forms of $CaCO_3$, calcite and aragonite. Because aragonite is more soluble than calcite, its compensation depth is shallower. Solubility also depends on ocean temperature and CO_2 concentration, so the CCDs for calcite and aragonite vary according to geographic location.

Concentrations of CO_2 are often highest in regions of ocean upwelling, causing shallower CCDs in the northern and eastern Pacific Ocean. Concentrations of CO_2 tend to be lower in sinking waters, such as those in the northern Atlantic Ocean. Calcite stability depths are deeper throughout the oceans because of the higher stability of calcite.

32) **SEP Develop Models** At the center of the diagram, draw a seamount with a summit that lies 3,500 m below sea level. Then, use Xs to identify the location(s) on the seamount where calcite sediments would be deposited in each scenario (cooler and warmer ocean). Use Os to identify any location(s) where aragonite sediments may collect.

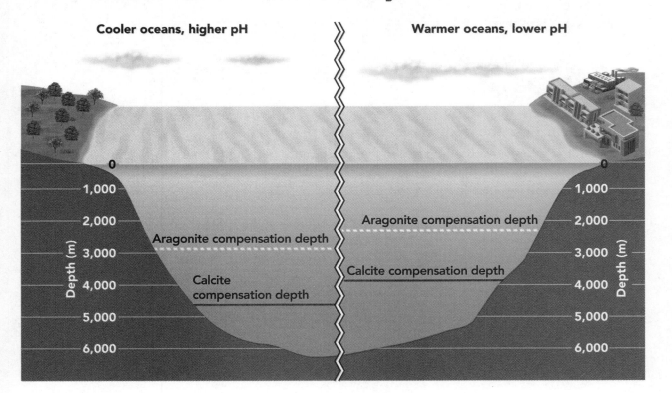

Paleocene-Eocene Thermal Maximum

The fossil record tells us that 55 million years ago, during a time called the Paleocene-Eocene Thermal Maximum (PETM), there was a huge and sudden release of atmospheric carbon, and global temperatures rose 5°C to 8°C. In the ocean, there was a massive die-off of some organisms but an upsurge in others. Fossils show that it took almost 100,000 years for ocean conditions to stabilize. This event gives us some idea of what might occur in the ocean if atmospheric carbon and temperatures continue to rise.

PETM Carbonate Compensation Depths About 55 million years ago, the ocean quickly became very warm and rich in CO_2. The carbonate compensation depth became so shallow that no $CaCO_3$ fossils are found from this time.

These three curves show the weight percentage of $CaCO_3$ in seafloor sediments as a function of time in three different locations at three different depths.

All three curves go to zero at 55 million years ago, but recover at different rates over the next 100,000 years.

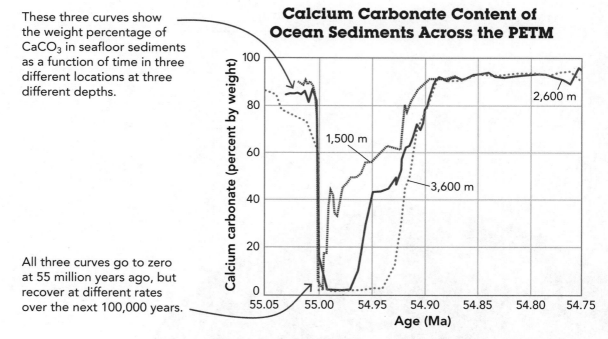

Calcium Carbonate Content of Ocean Sediments Across the PETM

Based on report from Science Magazine, 10 June 2005, Vol 308.

(33) **SEP Use Models** How does the fossil record serve as a model to help us understand what impact we are having on the planet today? ✏️

....

....

....

....

INVESTIGATIVE PHENOMENON

GO ONLINE to Elaborate on and Evaluate your knowledge of the effects of ocean acidification by completing the class discussion and engineering design activities.

In the CER worksheet, you drafted a scientific argument to explain what is happening to the world's coral reefs. With a partner, reevaluate the evidence cited in your arguments.

(34) **SEP Construct an Explanation** Corals are made of calcium carbonate, $CaCO_3$. Carbon dioxide is required to make these coral skeletons. Explain why having too much CO_2 makes it harder for these shells to form.

....

....

....

....

....

....

GO ONLINE to Evaluate what you learned about the role of carbon and human influences in ocean acidification.

In the Performance-Based Assessment, you collected evidence for determining the effects of pH on calcium carbonate shells. Wrap up your analysis by answering the following question.

(35) **SEP Refine Your Plan** How might you modify your investigation procedure if you wanted to test how temperature affects the rate of the chemical reaction between carbonic acid and calcium carbonate shells? Describe alterations to your procedure and list any additional materials or equipment you would need to perform the modified test. 🖉

....

....

....

....

....

....

Revisit

ANCHORING PHENOMENON

(36) **SEP Apply Scientific Reasoning** Based on what you learned in this investigation, select an activity you listed in the Anchoring Phenomenon and describe how you would change it and why. 🖉

....

....

....

 GO ONLINE for a **problem-based learning** activity that you can tackle after completing Storyline 4.

Industrial Applications

How can we sustainably meet the world's energy needs?

Investigation 15
Oxidation-Reduction
Reactions

Investigation 16
Organic Chemistry

Investigation 17
Nuclear Processes

Investigation 18
Green Chemistry

ANCHORING PHENOMENON

Inquiry Launch Over time, many industries, including farms like the one shown in the image, have changed how they acquire and use energy. Which energy sources do you think this farm relied on before installing solar panels? How might the farm acquire energy in the future?

Using nontraditional sources of energy can increase energy efficiency. Propose two sustainable sources of energy, besides solar energy, that could be used on farms in the future. Give a benefit and a cost for each.

....

....

....

....

....

....

GO ONLINE to engage with real-world phenomena. Watch the anchoring phenomenon video and preview the optional **problem-based learning experience**.

GO ONLINE to Engage with real-world phenomena by watching a video and completing a modeling interactive worksheet.

How do batteries store energy?

Oxidation-Reduction Reactions

Batteries are able to store energy because of their chemical properties. The stored chemical energy can then be transformed into electrical energy. Batteries come in various shapes and sizes and make use of different chemical reactions. Once you have viewed the Investigative Phenomenon video and completed the modeling exercise to help explain the phenomenon you observed, answer these reflection questions about batteries and energy.

1 **CCC Energy and Matter** Using what you know about energy and chemical bonds, explain how a battery might store and release energy. ✎

....

....

....

....

2 **SEP Ask Questions** List some questions engineers could ask to help determine what type of battery they should use in a particular application. ✎

....

....

....

....

Oxidation vs. Reduction

GO ONLINE to Explore and Explain the processes of oxidation and reduction.

Gaining and Losing Electrons

Oxidation and Reduction In a chemical reaction, the loss of an electron by a reactant is called **oxidation.** The process in which a reactant gains an electron in a chemical reaction is called **reduction.** Any chemical reaction that involves transferring electrons from one atom to another is called an oxidation-reduction reaction, or a **redox reaction.** In a redox reaction, a reactant that gives up one or more electrons is called a **reducing agent,** and a reactant that gains one or more electrons is called an **oxidizing agent.** Note that the two terms are inverses and that oxidizing and reducing agents always come in pairs. The oxidizing agent is the species that is reduced. The reducing agent is the species that is oxidized.

Electron Transfer When magnesium reacts with sulfur to produce magnesium sulfide, the magnesium atom gives two electrons to the sulfur atom.

Mg is oxidized and is the reducing agent.

$$Mg(s) \ + \ S(s) \ \longrightarrow \ MgS(s)$$

S is reduced and is the oxidizing agent.

Game of Catch The girl throwing the ball represents the reducing agent, since she is losing a ball as it is transferred to the boy. The boy catching the ball represents the oxidizing agent, since he is gaining a ball.

°Mg° + ·S:

Magnesium atom   Sulfur atom

Oxidized: lost a ball
Reducing: giving up a ball

Reduced: gained a ball
Oxidizing: accepting a ball

Redox and Electronegativity Redox reactions are not a new type of reaction. In fact, many of the reaction types you have already learned about are redox reactions. In this Investigation, you will follow the transfer of electrons when discussing the reactions. In ionic compounds, complete electron transfer occurs through ionic bonding. In molecular compounds, however, electrons are shared in the covalent bonds. For a polar covalent bond, you can say the atoms are oxidized or reduced because the bonding electrons are pulled closer to the more electronegative atom. The more electronegative atom undergoes a partial gain of electrons, so it is the oxidizing agent. The less electronegative atom undergoes a partial loss of electrons, so it is the reducing agent.

Identifying Oxidizing and Reducing Agents

How do you identify oxidizing and reducing agents in a chemical reaction?

Ionic Compounds In a reaction that forms an ionic compound, **complete electron transfer occurs.** Electrons are transferred from the metal to the nonmetal. The metal is always the reducing agent, and the nonmetal is always the oxidizing agent.

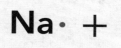

Na· + ·Cl̈: ⟶ Na⁺ + :Cl̈:⁻

Metal
(reducing agent)

Nonmetal
(oxidizing agent)

Molecular Compounds In a reaction that forms a covalent bond, **partial electron transfer occurs.** Identifying the oxidizing and reducing agents for molecular compounds requires comparing electronegativities.

H· + H· + ·Ö: ⟶ H≡Ö:
                                    H

Oxygen is more electronegative than hydrogen, so the electrons in the covalent bonds are pulled more toward the oxygen atom. Oxygen is the oxidizing agent.

Hydrogen is the reducing agent.

③ **SEP Develop a Model** Draw an electron dot structure for hydrogen fluoride formation. In your model, indicate which atom is the reducing agent and which is the oxidizing agent. ✏

Identifying Oxidized and Reduced Reactants

Silver nitrate reacts with copper to form copper nitrate and silver. From the provided chemical equation, determine what is oxidized and what is reduced. Identify the oxidizing agent and the reducing agent.

$$2AgNO_3(aq) + Cu(s) \rightarrow Cu(NO_3)_2(aq) + 2Ag(s)$$

ANALYZE Identify the relevant concepts.

Identify the species (atoms and ions) in the reaction and then trace how the electrons are transferred.

SOLVE Apply the concepts to this situation.

Rewrite the equation in ionic form so it will be easier to analyze the reaction.	$2Ag^+ + 2NO_3^- + Cu \rightarrow Cu^{2+} + 2NO_3^- + 2Ag$
Cross out any spectator ions to simplify the chemical equation.	$2Ag^+ + 2\cancel{NO_3^-} + Cu \rightarrow Cu^{2+} + 2\cancel{NO_3^-} + 2Ag$
The species that loses electrons is oxidized and is the reducing agent.	$Cu \rightarrow Cu^{2+} + 2e^-$ (loss of electrons) Cu is oxidized and is the reducing agent.
The species that gains electrons is reduced and is the oxidizing agent.	$2Ag^+ + 2e^- \rightarrow 2Ag$ (gain of electrons) Ag^+ is reduced and is the oxidizing agent.

④ Determine what is oxidized and what is reduced in each reaction. Identify the oxidizing agent and reducing agent in each case.

a. $2Na(s) + S(s) \rightarrow Na_2S(s)$

....

....

b. $4Al(s) + 3O_2(g) \rightarrow 2Al_2O_3(s)$

....

....

GO ONLINE for more practice problems.

Oxidation Numbers

Assigning Oxidation Numbers The **oxidation number,** or oxidation state, is a positive or negative number assigned to a species to indicate its degree of oxidation or reduction. Positive numbers indicate oxidized species; negative numbers indicate reduced species. Since electrons are not created or destroyed in reactions, which means mass is conserved, any electron lost by one species must be gained by another.

▶ Following from the conservation of mass are a few simple rules that tell how to assign oxidation numbers to the atoms in a chemical reaction.

Rules for Particular Elements In compounds, the elements that are highlighted in this periodic table have specific rules for determining their oxidation numbers.

Hydrogen Rule The oxidation number is +1 in compounds with nonmetals and −1 in compounds with metals.

Fluorine Rule The oxidation number is −1.

Oxygen Rule The oxidation number is −2, except in peroxides, where it is −1, and in compounds with fluorine, where it is +2.

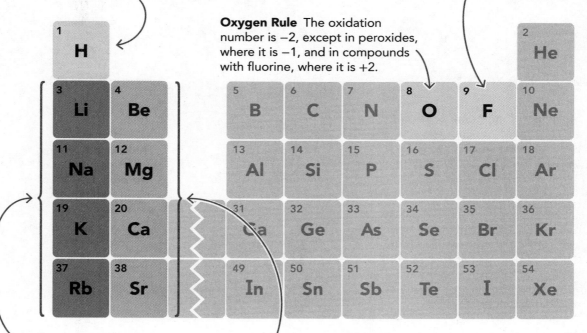

Alkali Metals Rule The oxidation number is +1.

Alkaline Earth Metals Rule The oxidation number is +2.

General Rules After assigning oxidation numbers according to the rules for particular elements in compounds, you use the following general rules, along with the conservation of mass, to assign oxidation numbers to the remaining elements.

General Rules for Other Elements		
Element Rule	**Sum Rule**	**Ion Rule**
In an uncombined element, the oxidation number of every atom is 0.	In any neutral compound, the sum of all the oxidation numbers is 0.	In a polyatomic ion, the sum of all the oxidation numbers equals the charge of the ion.

Oxidation Numbers in Compounds In a compound, you first use the rules for assigning oxidation numbers for all elements that have specific rules. Then you use the concept of conservation of mass to determine the oxidation numbers of the remaining elements.

Ionic Compound Silver nitrate is an ionic compound. Its ions are solvated in aqueous solution. The oxidation numbers of polyatomic ions are the ionic charges.

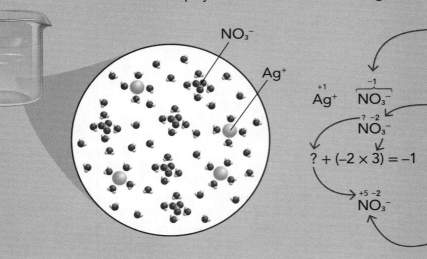

NO_3^-

Ag^+

The oxidation number is equal to the charge of the ion. The entire NO_3^- ion has a charge of 1−.

$\overset{+1}{Ag^+}$ $\overset{-1}{\overbrace{NO_3^-}}$

Oxygen rule The oxidation number of oxygen is −2.

$\overset{?\ -2}{NO_3^-}$

$? + (-2 \times 3) = -1$

Ion rule The sum of both oxidation numbers must equal the ionic charge. Thus, N in a NO_3^- ion has an oxidation number of +5.

$\overset{+5\ -2}{NO_3^-}$

Molecular Compound Ammonia is a molecular compound. The sum of the oxidation numbers has to be zero because the compound is neutral.

$\overset{?\ +1}{NH_3}$

$? + (+1 \times 3) = 0$

$\overset{-3\ +1}{NH_3}$

Hydrogen rule The oxidation number of hydrogen is +1 because it is in a compound with a nonmetal.

Nitrogen's greater electronegativity pulls electrons toward it. The nitrogen atom attracts three electrons from the three hydrogen atoms because of the three polar bonds. Using the sum rule, you can see the nitrogen atom has an oxidation number of −3.

$$H \vdots\vdots \ddot{N} \vdots\vdots H$$
$$H$$

(5) **SEP Construct an Explanation** Look at the models. Then construct an explanation for why the oxidation number for the oxygen atoms is −1 in a hydrogen peroxide molecule instead of −2, as in the water molecule. ✏

....

....

....

....

Assigning Oxidation Numbers in Compounds

What is the oxidation number of each element in the following ions and compounds?

a. SO_2 **b.** CO_3^{2-} **c.** Na_2SO_4 **d.** $(NH_4)_2S$

ANALYZE Identify the relevant concepts.

Use the set of rules you just learned to assign and calculate oxidation numbers.

SOLVE Apply the concepts to this situation.

Oxygen rule: The oxidation number of each oxygen is -2.

Sum rule: The oxidation number of sulfur is $+4$ because the overall charge of the compound is 0; $+4 + (-2 \times 2) = 0$.

a. $\overset{?\ \ -2}{SO_2}$

$\overset{+4\ -2}{SO_2}$

Oxygen rule: The oxidation number of oxygen is -2.

Ion rule: The oxidation number of carbon is $+4$ because the charge of the ion is -2; $+4 + (-2 \times 3) = -2$.

b. $\overset{?\ \ -2}{CO_3^{2-}}$

$\overset{+4\ -2}{CO_3^{2-}}$

Alkali metals rule: The oxidation number of each Na^+ ion is $+1$.

Oxygen rule: The oxidation number of oxygen is -2.

Sum rule: The oxidation number of sulfur must be $+6$ because the overall charge of the compound is 0; $(+1 \times 2) + (+6) + (-2 \times 4) = 0$.

c. $\overset{+1\ \ ?\ -2}{Na_2SO_4}$

$\overset{+1\ \ +6\ -2}{Na_2SO_4}$

Hydrogen rule: The oxidation number of hydrogen is $+1$.

Ion rule: The oxidation number of nitrogen is -3 because the NH_4^+ ion has a charge $+1$; $-3 + (+1 \times 4) = +1$.

Sum rule: The oxidation number of sulfur is -2 because the charge of the compound is 0; $(+1 \times 2) + (-2) = 0$.

d. $\overset{?\ +1\ \ ?}{(NH_4)_2S}$

$\overset{-3\ +1\ \ ?}{(NH_4)_2S}$

$\overset{-3\ +1\ -2}{(NH_4)_2S}$

6 Determine the oxidation number of each element in the following ions and compounds:

a. S_2O_3 **b.** Na_2O **c.** P_2O_5 **d.** NO_3^-

GO ONLINE for more practice problems.

Oxidation Numbers in Reactions

When copper wire is placed in a solution of silver nitrate, a single-replacement reaction occurs, in which the copper replaces the silver. Because they are in element form, the copper in the reactants and the silver in the products both have an oxidation number of 0. The oxidation numbers for silver nitrate and nitrate ions were determined earlier, and now you need to determine the oxidation number of the copper in copper(II) nitrate. You can use the sum rule to determine the oxidation number.

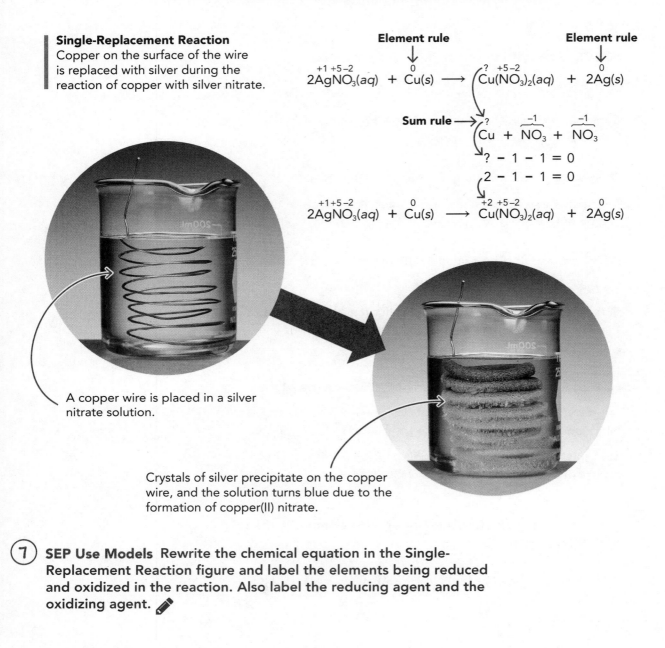

Single-Replacement Reaction
Copper on the surface of the wire is replaced with silver during the reaction of copper with silver nitrate.

Element rule

Element rule

$$\overset{+1\ +5\ -2}{2AgNO_3}(aq)\ +\ \overset{0}{Cu}(s)\ \longrightarrow\ \overset{?\ +5\ -2}{Cu(NO_3)_2}(aq)\ +\ \overset{0}{2Ag}(s)$$

Sum rule →

$$\overset{?}{Cu}\ +\ \overset{-1}{NO_3}\ +\ \overset{-1}{NO_3}$$

$$? - 1 - 1 = 0$$

$$2 - 1 - 1 = 0$$

$$\overset{+1\ +5\ -2}{2AgNO_3}(aq)\ +\ \overset{0}{Cu}(s)\ \longrightarrow\ \overset{+2\ +5\ -2}{Cu(NO_3)_2}(aq)\ +\ \overset{0}{2Ag}(s)$$

A copper wire is placed in a silver nitrate solution.

Crystals of silver precipitate on the copper wire, and the solution turns blue due to the formation of copper(II) nitrate.

(7) **SEP Use Models** Rewrite the chemical equation in the Single-Replacement Reaction figure and label the elements being reduced and oxidized in the reaction. Also label the reducing agent and the oxidizing agent. 🖉

Assigning Oxidation Numbers in Reactions

Use changes in oxidation number to identify which elements are oxidized and which are reduced in the following reactions. Also identify the oxidizing agent and the reducing agent.

a. $Cl_2(g) + 2HBr(aq) \rightarrow 2HCl(aq) + Br_2(l)$ **b.** $C(s) + O_2(g) \rightarrow CO_2(g)$

ANALYZE Identify the relevant concepts.

An increase in oxidation number indicates oxidation. A decrease in oxidation number indicates reduction. The substance that is oxidized in a redox reaction is the reducing agent. The substance that is reduced is the oxidizing agent.

SOLVE Apply the concepts to this situation.

Use the rules to assign oxidation numbers to each element in the equation.

$$\overset{0}{C}l_2(g) + 2\overset{+1\,-1}{HBr}(aq) \rightarrow$$
$$2\overset{+1\,-1}{HCl}(aq) + \overset{0}{Br_2}(l)$$

b. $\overset{0}{C}(s) + \overset{0}{O_2}(g) \rightarrow \overset{+4\,-2}{CO_2}(g)$

Use the changes in oxidation numbers to identify which atoms gain or lose electrons.

$\overset{0}{Cl_2} \rightarrow \overset{-1}{HCl}$ (gain of electrons)

$\overset{-1}{HBr} \rightarrow \overset{0}{Br_2}$ (loss of electrons)

$\overset{0}{C} \rightarrow \overset{+4}{CO_2}$ (loss of electrons)

$\overset{0}{O_2} \rightarrow \overset{-2}{CO_2}$ (gain of electrons)

Identify the oxidizing and reducing agents and the species that are oxidized or reduced.

Cl_2: reduced; oxidizing agent
Br^-: oxidized; reducing agent

C: oxidized; reducing agent
O_2: reduced; oxidizing agent

8 Determine the oxidation numbers for the elements in the following reactions. Then use the changes in oxidation numbers to identify which element is oxidized and which is reduced in each reaction.

a. $2H_2(g) + O_2(g) \rightarrow 2H_2O(l)$

b. $2KNO_3(s) \rightarrow 2KNO_2(s) + O_2(g)$

GO ONLINE for more practice problems.

Redox vs. Non-redox Reactions

All chemical reactions can be assigned to one of two classes: redox reactions and non-redox reactions. Redox reactions are reactions in which electrons are transferred from one reacting species to another. Examples of redox reactions include single-replacement, combustion, and many combination and decomposition reactions. Non-redox reactions are reactions in which no electron transfer occurs. Neutralization and precipitation—two types of double-replacement reactions—are examples of non-redox reactions.

Two Kinds of Reactions Single-replacement reactions are redox reactions because electrons are transferred between reactants. Precipitation reactions are non-redox reactions; none of the species undergoes a change in oxidation number.

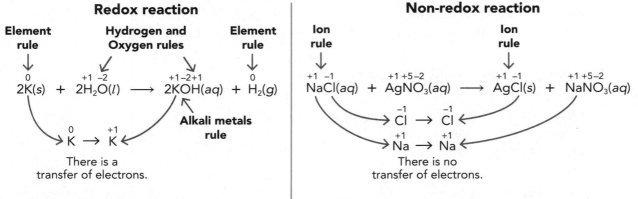

Redox reaction

Element rule / Hydrogen and Oxygen rules / Element rule

$$2K(s) + 2H_2O(l) \longrightarrow 2KOH(aq) + H_2(g)$$

Alkali metals rule

$$K \rightarrow K$$

There is a transfer of electrons.

Non-redox reaction

Ion rule / Ion rule

$$NaCl(aq) + AgNO_3(aq) \longrightarrow AgCl(s) + NaNO_3(aq)$$

$$Cl \rightarrow Cl$$
$$Na \rightarrow Na$$

There is no transfer of electrons.

During this single-replacement reaction, potassium reacts with water to produce hydrogen gas (which ignites) and potassium hydroxide.

When sodium chloride reacts with silver nitrate in a double-replacement reaction, a solid precipitate of silver chloride forms.

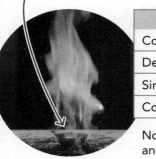

Redox Reactions
Combination
Decomposition
Single-replacement
Combustion

Note: Some combination and decomposition reactions can be non-redox reactions.

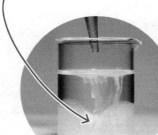

Non-redox Reactions
Double-replacement (neutralization)
Double-replacement (precipitation)

Note: Some other double-replacement reactions can be redox reactions.

(9) CCC Energy and Matter During the reaction of potassium with water, each potassium atom loses an electron. Where do the electrons go? ✏

....

....

Identifying Redox Reactions

Use changes in oxidation number to identify whether each reaction is a redox reaction or a non-redox reaction. If a reaction is a redox reaction, identify the element reduced, the element oxidized, the reducing agent, and the oxidizing agent.

a. $Cl_2(g) + 2NaBr(aq) \rightarrow 2NaCl(aq) + Br_2(aq)$

b. $2NaOH(aq) + H_2SO_4(aq) \rightarrow Na_2SO_4(aq) + 2H_2O(l)$

ANALYZE Identify the relevant concepts.

If changes in oxidation number occur, the element with an oxidation number that increases is oxidized and is the reducing agent. The element with an oxidation number that decreases is reduced and is the oxidizing agent.

SOLVE Apply the concepts to this situation.

Assign oxidation numbers.	**a.** $\overset{0}{Cl_2}(g) + 2\overset{+1\ -1}{NaBr}(aq) \rightarrow$ $2\overset{+1\ -1}{NaCl}(aq) + \overset{0}{Br_2}(aq)$	**b.** $2\overset{+1\ -2+1}{NaOH}(aq) + \overset{+1+6-2}{H_2SO_4}(aq) \rightarrow$ $\overset{+1\ +6-2}{Na_2SO_4}(aq) + 2\overset{+1\ -2}{H_2O}(l)$
Identify any changes in oxidation numbers.	Reduced (oxidizing agent): $\overset{0}{Cl_2} \rightarrow \overset{-1}{HCl}$ Oxidized (reducing agent): $\overset{-1}{HBr} \rightarrow \overset{0}{Br_2}$	None of the atoms or ions change oxidation numbers.
Determine whether it is a redox reaction.	This is a redox reaction.	This is a non-redox reaction.

10 Determine which of the following reactions are redox reactions. If a reaction is a redox reaction, name the element oxidized and the element reduced. Hint: What rule applies to magnesium, an alkaline earth metal?

a. $Mg(s) + Br_2(l) \rightarrow MgBr_2(s)$

b. $H_2CO_3(aq) \rightarrow H_2O(l) + CO_2(g)$

GO ONLINE for more practice problems.

Half-reactions

The reduction and oxidation in redox reactions often do not happen in the same location. A **half-reaction** represents just the oxidation or reduction component of a redox reaction and is determined from the change in oxidation number of the substances.

For example, rust is formed as part of a redox reaction, in which the oxidation and the reduction happen in separate locations. Oxidation happens at a location called the anode. Reduction happens at a location called the cathode. Therefore, oxidation and reduction are two half-reactions, and they can be written with separate chemical equations.

Rust Formation Half-reactions Iron loses electrons (oxidizes) at the anode and oxygen from the air picks up these electrons (reduces) at the cathode. The redox reaction produces hydrated iron(III) oxide.

Sum rule

Element rule | **Oxygen rule**

$$\overset{0}{4Fe} + \overset{0}{3O_2} \rightarrow \overset{+3\ -2}{2Fe_2O_3}$$

$$\overset{0}{Fe} \rightarrow \overset{+3}{Fe_2O_3} \quad \textbf{Oxidized}$$ (loses electrons)

$$\overset{0}{O_2} \rightarrow \overset{-2}{Fe_2O_3} \quad \textbf{Reduced}$$ (gains electrons)

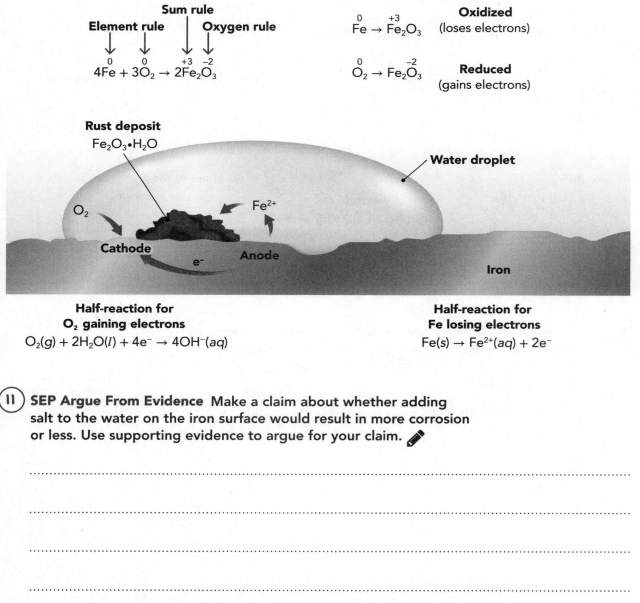

Rust deposit
$Fe_2O_3 \cdot H_2O$

Water droplet

O_2

Fe^{2+}

Cathode

e^-

Anode

Iron

Half-reaction for O_2 gaining electrons

$$O_2(g) + 2H_2O(l) + 4e^- \rightarrow 4OH^-(aq)$$

Half-reaction for Fe losing electrons

$$Fe(s) \rightarrow Fe^{2+}(aq) + 2e^-$$

(11) SEP Argue From Evidence Make a claim about whether adding salt to the water on the iron surface would result in more corrosion or less. Use supporting evidence to argue for your claim. ✏️

....

....

....

....

INVESTIGATIVE PHENOMENON

GO ONLINE to Elaborate on and Evaluate your knowledge of the processes of oxidation and reduction by completing the class discussion and writing activities.

In the modeling worksheet you completed at the beginning of the Investigation, you constructed a model to explain how a lemon battery works. With a partner, reevaluate your models.

12. **SEP Use a Model** Alkaline batteries use a potassium hydroxide electrolyte. Sometimes, the potassium hydroxide can leak from the battery and react with carbon dioxide in the air, producing a crust of potassium carbonate on the battery terminals. Write the chemical equation for the reaction, assign oxidation numbers, and determine whether the reaction is a redox or non-redox reaction. ✏️

Modeling Redox Reactions

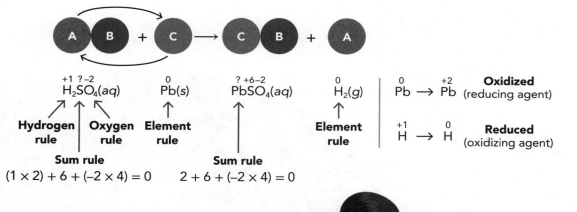

GO ONLINE to Explore and Explain how to model redox reactions.

Single-Replacement Reactions

Single-replacement reactions are examples of redox reactions. In a single-replacement reaction, one atom replaces another in the reactants. When identifying redox reactions, you look for changes in the oxidation numbers of atoms in the reaction. In the example here, the oxidation numbers of lead and hydrogen both change when lead reacts with sulfuric acid.

A particularly important type of single-replacement reaction occurs when one metal replaces another, as in the reaction of copper with silver nitrate that you studied previously. You can write chemical equations for many single-replacement reactions, but not all of them will occur as written. To understand why, you need to consider the activity series of metals. The series ranks metals in order of reactivity, or tendency to give up electrons.

Single-Replacement Reaction The single-replacement reaction of lead with sulfuric acid is a redox reaction. One element is swapped for another, with the hydrogen ions taking the lead's electrons.

Storage batteries are used in automobiles and other applications where high current is needed. Although the actual reaction is slightly more complicated than what is shown, lead-acid batteries work by transferring electrons from lead to hydrogen ions in sulfuric acid.

Using the Activity Series of Metals

How can you **make predictions for redox reactions?**

Comparing Metals Any metal that is **above another metal** in the activity series table is **more reactive** and **more readily oxidized.** In a single-replacement reaction, a more-reactive metal will replace a less-reactive metal.

Compared to most other metals, lithium easily loses an electron and becomes oxidized. That is one reason lithium is the most common choice for batteries that power electronic devices.

Activity Series of Metals

Name	Symbol	
Lithium	Li	
Potassium	K	
Calcium	Ca	
Sodium	Na	
Magnesium	Mg	
Aluminum	Al	
Zinc	Zn	
Iron	Fe	
Lead	Pb	
Copper	Cu	
Mercury	Hg	
Silver	Ag	

Decreasing reactivity →
Increasing ease of oxidation →

$$Zn \longrightarrow Zn^{2+} + 2e^-$$
$$Fe \longrightarrow Fe^{2+} + 2e^-$$

Blocks of zinc are used as sacrificial anodes on ship hulls (made of steel, an alloy of iron). The zinc blocks corrode instead of the hull due to zinc's relative ease of oxidation compared to iron.

Predicting Reactions In a single-replacement reaction, **the more-reactive metal replaces the less-reactive metal.** Examine the equations and the positions of the metals in the table.

Zinc is more reactive than lead. $\longrightarrow$ **Zn**(s) + **Pb(NO$_3$)$_2$**(aq) $\longrightarrow$ **Zn(NO$_3$)$_2$**(aq) + **Pb**(s)

Copper is less reactive than iron. $\longrightarrow$ **Cu**(s) + **FeSO$_4$**(aq) $\longrightarrow$ no reaction

(13) **SEP Design a Solution** Silver can react with hydrogen sulfide in the air to produce a silver sulfide tarnish on the surface. Write the chemical equation for the single-replacement reaction and design a solution that might help prevent the silver from tarnishing. ✏️

....

....

....

Combination and Decomposition Redox Reactions

A combination reaction is a chemical process in which two or more substances react to form a single new substance. A decomposition reaction is a chemical process in which a single compound breaks down into two or more products. In both types of reactions, one side of the chemical equation often has uncombined elements, and the other side has a compound. Since atoms in uncombined elements have oxidation number 0, and atoms in compounds have nonzero oxidation numbers, it is clear that those particular kinds of combination and decomposition reactions involve changes in oxidation number. Some other combination and decomposition reactions are non-redox reactions.

▶ Following the movement of electrons in a reaction allows you to model it as a redox or non-redox reaction.

Combination Reaction Sulfur combines with oxygen to produce sulfur dioxide (SO_2). The oxygen rule assigns an oxidation number of -2 to the oxygen in SO_2. The sum rule can be used to determine that sulfur in SO_2 has an oxidation number of $+4$. Sulfur is heavily oxidized in this reaction.

Decomposition Reaction Water decomposes into hydrogen gas and oxygen gas. The hydrogen, oxygen, and element rules are used to assign oxidation numbers. Oxygen is oxidized in this reaction.

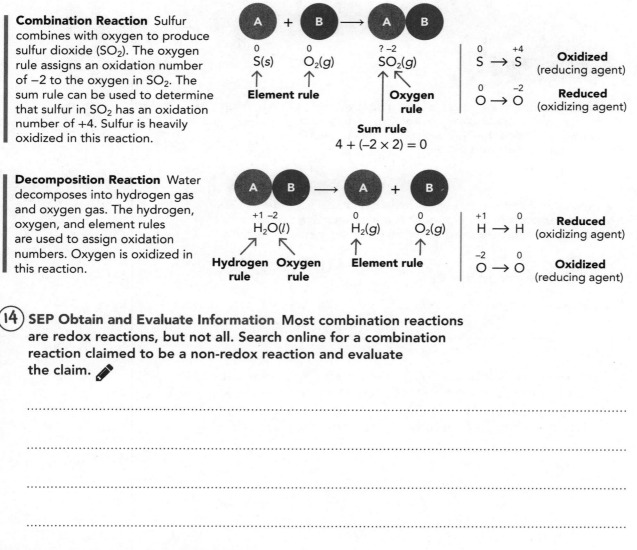

(14) SEP Obtain and Evaluate Information Most combination reactions are redox reactions, but not all. Search online for a combination reaction claimed to be a non-redox reaction and evaluate the claim. ✏️

....

....

....

....

Combustion Reactions

Why is oxidation the loss of an electron and reduction the gain of an electron? Gaining something in a reduction doesn't seem to make sense. The word *oxidized* comes from early chemists' investigations of combustion reactions. Since all combustion reactions involve a substance reacting with oxygen to produce an oxygen-containing compound, they are all redox reactions. *Oxidized* originally meant gaining an oxygen atom, and *reduced* meant losing an oxygen atom. It wasn't until the early 1900s, after the discovery of the electron, that chemists realized that the more fundamental process was the transfer of electrons. However, the names were never changed to reflect the new understanding!

Combustion of Carbon The combustion of carbon results in carbon dioxide. The carbon atoms become heavily oxidized, meaning a large number of electrons are transferred in this reaction, along with a large amount of energy.

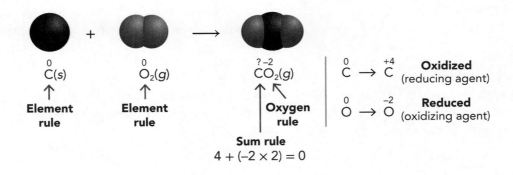

15) **SEP Construct an Explanation** Elemental oxygen (O_2) is very good at oxidizing other elements. However, fluorine (F_2) is the strongest oxidizer. Construct an explanation for why elemental oxygen and fluorine are such good electron stealers. 🖉

....

....

....

Iron is produced by reacting iron(III) oxide and carbon monoxide in a blast furnace.

Balancing by the Oxidation-Number-Change Method

You can use oxidation numbers to keep track of electron transfer. Due to the conservation of mass, the total number of electrons gained in reduction must equal the total number of electrons lost in oxidation. Therefore, the oxidation numbers of atoms and ions in reactions can be used to balance chemical equations for redox reactions. In the **oxidation-number-change method,** you balance a redox chemical equation by comparing the increase and the decrease in oxidation numbers.

Oxidation-Number-Change Method Balance the skeleton equation by determining the changes in oxidation numbers and then balancing the oxidation and reduction. Study the steps for the following example.

$$Fe_2O_3(s) + CO(g) \longrightarrow Fe(s) + CO_2(g)$$

Identify the oxidized and reduced elements.

Step 1: Assign oxidation numbers using the rules set out previously.

$$\begin{array}{ccc} \textbf{Oxygen} & \textbf{Element} & \textbf{Oxygen} \\ \textbf{rule} & \textbf{rule} & \textbf{rule} \\ \downarrow & \downarrow & \downarrow \end{array}$$

$$\overset{?\ -2}{Fe_2O_3} + \overset{+2\ -2}{CO} \longrightarrow \overset{0}{Fe} + \overset{?\ -2}{CO_2}$$

— **Sum rule** —

$$(3 \times 2) - 6 = 0 \qquad\qquad 4 - 4 = 0$$

Step 2: Identify which element is oxidized and which element is reduced.

$$\overset{+3}{Fe} \longrightarrow \overset{0}{Fe} \qquad\qquad \overset{+2}{C} \longrightarrow \overset{+4}{C}$$

Reduced **Oxidized**
(gains electrons) (loses electrons)

In changing from +3 to 0, iron becomes less positive, which means means it gains electrons.

Balance oxidation and reduction.

Step 3: Draw a bracket connecting the oxidized element on both sides of the equation and another bracket for the reduced element.

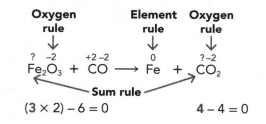

+2 oxidation

$$\overset{+3\ -2}{Fe_2O_3} + \overset{+2-2}{CO} \longrightarrow \overset{0}{Fe} + \overset{+4-2}{CO_2}$$

−3 reduction

Step 4: Choose coefficients that will make the increase in oxidation number equal to the decrease in oxidation number.

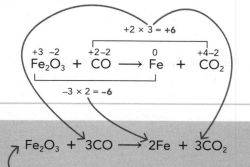

$$+2 \times 3 = \textbf{+6}$$

$$\overset{+3\ -2}{Fe_2O_3} + \overset{+2-2}{CO} \longrightarrow \overset{0}{Fe} + \overset{+4-2}{CO_2}$$

$$-3 \times 2 = -6$$

Write the balanced equation.

Step 5: Use the coefficients to balance the chemical equation. If you need to, finish balancing by inspection.

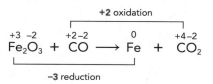

$$Fe_2O_3 + 3CO \longrightarrow 2Fe + 3CO_2$$

This Fe does not need a coefficient since it has a 2 in the subscript.

Balancing Redox Equations by Change in Oxidation Number

Balance this redox equation by using the oxidation-number-change method.

$$K_2Cr_2O_7(aq) + H_2O(l) + S(s) \rightarrow KOH(aq) + Cr_2O_3(s) + SO_2(g)$$

ANALYZE Identify the relevant concepts.

You can balance redox equations by determining changes in oxidation numbers and applying the five steps.

SOLVE Apply the concepts to the problem.

Step 1 Assign oxidation numbers.

$$\overset{+1\ +6\ -2}{K_2Cr_2O_7(aq)} + \overset{+1\ -2}{H_2O(l)} + \overset{0}{S(s)} \rightarrow \overset{+1-2+1}{KOH(aq)} + \overset{+3\ -2}{Cr_2O_3(s)} + \overset{+4-2}{SO_2(g)}$$

Step 2 Identify the elements that are oxidized and reduced.

Reduced: $\overset{+6}{K_2Cr_2O_7} \rightarrow \overset{+3}{Cr_2O_3}$

Oxidized: $\overset{0}{S} \rightarrow \overset{+4}{SO_2}$

Step 3 Use brackets to show the signs and magnitudes of the changes.

$$\overset{+6}{K_2Cr_2O_7(aq)} + H_2O(l) + \overset{0}{S(s)} \rightarrow KOH(aq) + \overset{+3}{Cr_2O_3(s)} + \overset{+4}{SO_2(g)}$$

with -3 shown over the reduction and $+4$ shown under the oxidation.

Step 4 Balance the increase and the decrease in oxidation numbers.

$$\overset{+6}{2K_2Cr_2O_7(aq)} + H_2O(l) + \overset{0}{3S(s)} \rightarrow KOH(aq) + \overset{+3}{2Cr_2O_3(s)} + \overset{+4}{3SO_2(g)}$$

with $(4)(-3) = -12$ shown over and $(3)(+4) = +12$ shown under.

Step 5 Check the equation and balance by inspection, if necessary.

$$2K_2Cr_2O_7(aq) + 2H_2O(l) + 3S(s) \rightarrow 4KOH(aq) + 2Cr_2O_3(s) + 3SO_2(g)$$

16 Balance each redox equation using the oxidation-number-change method. ✏️

a. $KClO_3(s) \rightarrow KCl(s) + O_2(g)$

b. $HNO_2(aq) + HI(aq) \rightarrow NO(g) + H_2O(l) + I_2(s)$

GO ONLINE for more practice problems.

Balancing by the Half-reaction Method

Another method for balancing redox equations is by means of half-reactions. The equation for a half-reaction shows just the oxidation or just the reduction that takes place in a redox reaction. In the **half-reaction method,** you write and balance the half-reaction equations separately before combining them into a balanced redox equation. You will learn in the next Experience that batteries are often described in terms of half-reactions, so the half-reaction method is helpful when examining redox reactions in batteries. The procedure is different, but the outcome is the same as with the oxidation-number-change method.

The half-reaction method is very useful in balancing equations for redox reactions that take place in acidic or basic solutions. If the reaction takes place in acidic solution, assume H_2O and H^+ are present, and use them to balance hydrogen and oxygen atoms as needed. If the reaction takes place in basic solution, assume H_2O and OH^- are present, and use them to balance hydrogen and oxygen atoms as needed.

Half-reaction Method Balance the skeleton equation by writing the half-reactions, determining oxidation number changes, balancing the mass and charge, and then recombining the half-reactions. Study the steps for the following example.

Sulfur dioxide (SO_2) is used to preserve dried fruit.

$$S(s) + HNO_3(aq) \longrightarrow SO_2(g) + NO(g) + H_2O(l)$$

Identify and write the half-reactions.

Step 1: Write the skeleton equation in ionic form and assign oxidation numbers.

$$
\overset{\overset{\textstyle \text{Element}}{\textstyle \text{rule}}}{\underset{0}{S}} \; + \; \overset{\overset{\textstyle \text{Ion}}{\textstyle \text{rule}}}{\underset{+1}{H^+}} \; + \; \overset{\overset{\textstyle \text{Oxygen}}{\textstyle \text{rule}}}{\underset{?\,-2}{NO_3^-}} \; \longrightarrow \; \overset{?\,-2}{SO_2} \; + \; \overset{?\,-2}{NO} \; + \; \overset{+1\,-2}{H_2O}
$$

Ion rule: $5 + (-6) = -1$ Sum rule: $4 + (-4) = 0$ Sum rule: $2 + (-2) = 0$

(Hydrogen and oxygen rules apply to SO_2, NO, and H_2O.)

Step 2: Write separate half-reactions for the oxidation and reduction processes. Identify which elements are oxidized and reduced.

$$\overset{0}{S} \rightarrow \overset{+4}{SO_2} \quad \textbf{Oxidized} \; \text{(loses electrons)}$$

Sulfur is oxidized; its oxidation number increases from 0 to +4.

$$\overset{+5}{NO_3^-} \rightarrow \overset{+2}{NO} \quad \textbf{Reduced} \; \text{(gains electrons)}$$

Nitrogen is reduced; its oxidation number decreases from +5 to +2.

Balance mass and charge.

Step 3: Use H_2O and H^+ or OH^- (depending on what is present in solution) to balance the half-reactions in terms of atoms.

In aqueous solutions, H_2O is present and can be used.

$$S \longrightarrow SO_2 \qquad\qquad 2H_2O + S \longrightarrow SO_2 + 4H^+$$

$$NO_3^- \longrightarrow NO \qquad\qquad 4H^+ + NO_3^- \longrightarrow NO + 2H_2O$$

If a reactant is an acid, H^+ can be used.

Step 4: Add electrons to balance the charge of each half-reaction.

$$2H_2O + S \longrightarrow SO_2 + 4H^+ + 4e^-$$

Not balanced

$$3e^- + 4H^+ + NO_3^- \longrightarrow NO + 2H_2O$$

Step 5: Multiply each equation by an appropriate integer to get the electrons balanced.

$$6H_2O + 3S \longrightarrow 3SO_2 + 12H^+ + 12e^-$$

Balanced

$$12e^- + 16H^+ + 4NO_3^- \longrightarrow 4NO + 8H_2O$$

Multiplying the first equation by 3, and the second equation by 4, balances the electrons.

Add the half-reactions.

Step 6: Add the two half-reactions and subtract the terms that appear on each side.

$$\cancel{6H_2O} + 3S + \cancel{12e^-} + \overset{4}{\cancel{16H^+}} + 4NO_3^- \longrightarrow 3SO_2 + \cancel{12H^+} + \cancel{12e^-} + 4NO + \overset{2}{\cancel{8H_2O}}$$

Notice that the electrons cancel. If they don't, then something is wrong!

$$3S + 4H^+ + 4NO_3^- \longrightarrow 3SO_2 + 4NO + 2H_2O$$

Write the balanced equation.

Step 7: Add back in any spectator ions and take the equation out of ionic form. If you need to, finish balancing by inspection.

$$3S + 4HNO_3 \longrightarrow 3SO_2 + 4NO + 2H_2O$$

There are no spectator ions in this example.

---

(17) **CCC Energy and Matter** Explain, in your own words, why you must add electrons to balance the charge if the charge is not already balanced. ✏️

....

....

....

INVESTIGATIVE PHENOMENON

GO ONLINE to Elaborate on and Evaluate your knowledge of how to model redox reactions by completing the peer review and data analysis activities.

In the modeling worksheet you completed at the beginning of the Investigation, you constructed a model to explain how a lemon battery works. With a partner, reevaluate your models.

18 **CCC Systems and System Models** In an alkaline battery, zinc is oxidized, and manganese dioxide is reduced. The overall reaction happening within the battery is the following:

$$Zn(s) + 2MnO_2(s) \rightleftharpoons ZnO(s) + Mn_2O_3(s)$$

Assign oxidation numbers and explain how electrons are transferred from one part of the battery to another.

....

....

19 **SEP Construct an Explanation** In terms of the relative activities of the two metals, explain why the reaction in the previous question occurs. Then use the assigned oxidation numbers to explain why the zinc part is described as negative. ✏️

....

....

....

....

Electrochemical Cells

 **GO ONLINE** to Explore and Explain how electrochemical cells function.

Energy Conversion

If you hold up an apple and then let go, it will fall. Its potential energy will be converted into kinetic energy as it speeds up. The same is true for an electric charge. If you hold an electron near a positively charged plate and then let it go, it will move toward the plate. Moving electric charges are what power electrical devices. Since electrons move in redox reactions, you can use such reactions to convert chemical energy into electrical energy. Redox reactions involve the movement of large numbers of electrons, so you can think of electrical potential energy in terms of the energy per charge, or the electric potential. The **electric potential** is the electric potential energy divided by the charge. Electric potential has units of volts, or joules/coulomb.

Potential Energy Like the gravitational potential energy of an apple in a tree, the electrical potential energy of a charged object depends on its position in the field.

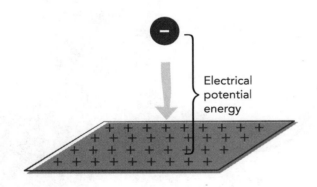

Electrical potential energy

Gravitational potential energy

(20) **SEP Analyze Data** The table shows the electrical potential energy in units of eV (electron volts) and the electric potential in units of V (volts) for three different charges. Does the electric potential depend on the charge? Explain.

Charge (e⁻)	Energy (eV)	Potential (V)
1	10	10
2	20	10
3	30	10

Voltaic Cells

An **electrochemical process** is any conversion between chemical potential energy and electrical energy, a type of kinetic energy. Atoms have electrons with potential energy.

▶ **When electrons are transferred from one atom to another in a redox reaction, the potential energy is converted into electrical energy.**

The energy conversion can go in either direction. Any device that converts chemical energy into electrical energy or electrical energy into chemical energy is called an **electrochemical cell.** Redox reactions occur in all electrochemical cells.

What Is a Voltaic Cell? A **voltaic cell** is an electrochemical cell used to convert chemical energy into electrical energy. A voltaic cell consists of two half-cells. A **half-cell** is one part of a voltaic cell in which either oxidation or reduction takes place.

Parts of a Voltaic Cell The diagram shows the makeup of a voltaic cell. Oxidation happens in one half-cell, while reduction happens in the other half-cell. The two half-cells are connected by a bridge that allows the movement of ions between the two half-cells.

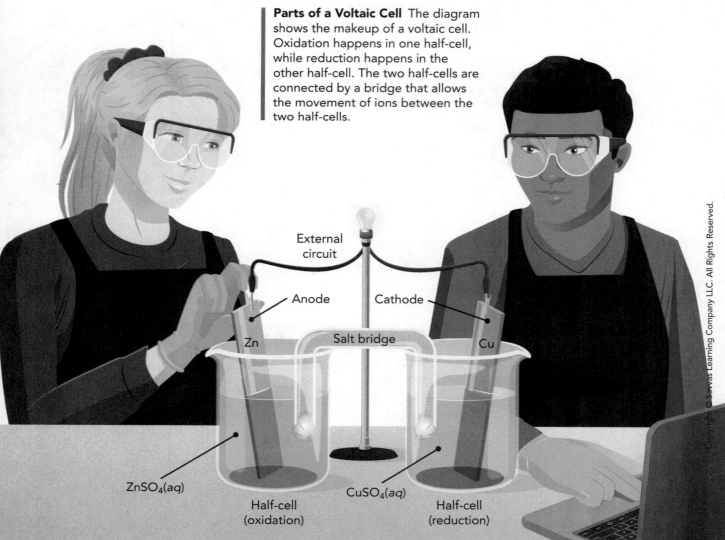

External circuit

Anode

Cathode

Zn

Salt bridge

Cu

$ZnSO_4(aq)$

$CuSO_4(aq)$

Half-cell (oxidation)

Half-cell (reduction)

How Does a Voltaic Cell Work? The zinc and copper strips in the voltaic cell serve as electrodes. An **electrode** is a conductor in a circuit that carries electrons. The electrode at which oxidation occurs is called the **anode.** The electrode at which reduction occurs is called the **cathode.**

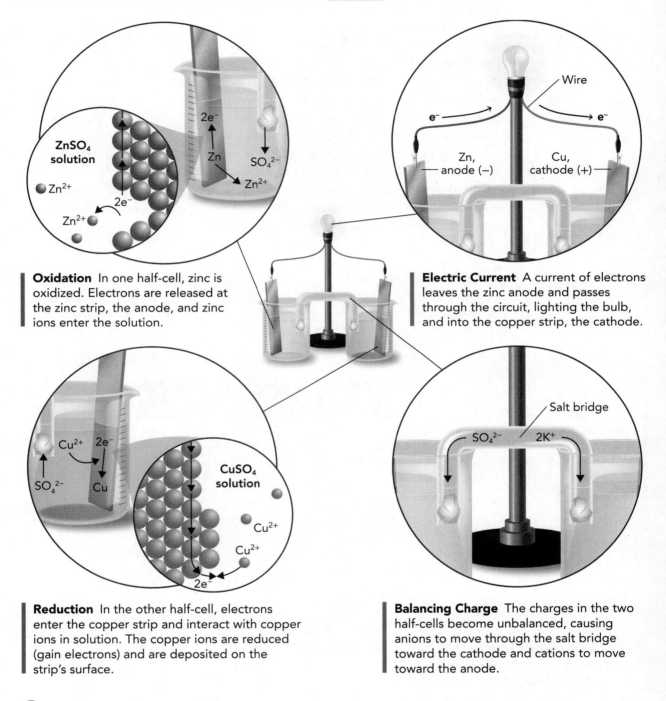

Oxidation In one half-cell, zinc is oxidized. Electrons are released at the zinc strip, the anode, and zinc ions enter the solution.

Reduction In the other half-cell, electrons enter the copper strip and interact with copper ions in solution. The copper ions are reduced (gain electrons) and are deposited on the strip's surface.

Electric Current A current of electrons leaves the zinc anode and passes through the circuit, lighting the bulb, and into the copper strip, the cathode.

Balancing Charge The charges in the two half-cells become unbalanced, causing anions to move through the salt bridge toward the cathode and cations to move toward the anode.

21) **SEP Develop a Model** Sketch a voltaic cell with magnesium and copper electrodes and a sodium sulfate salt bridge. On your sketch, label the half-cell where oxidation takes place and the half-cell where reduction takes place. ✏️

Standard Reduction Potentials

The electric potential of a voltaic cell is a measure of the cell's ability to produce an electric current. The potential results from a competition for electrons between the two half-cells. The half-cell that has the greater tendency to acquire electrons is where reduction occurs. The **reduction potential** is a measure of a half-reaction's tendency to occur as a reduction, or a gain of electrons. The **oxidation potential** is a measure of a half-reaction's tendency to occur as an oxidation, or a loss of electrons. For a given half-reaction, the reduction and oxidation potentials are the same but opposite in sign. Since absolute potentials cannot be measured, scientists use the **standard reduction potential,** which is the reduction potential of a half-cell measured with respect to a standard hydrogen electrode. When comparing the standard reduction potentials for two half-reactions in a voltaic cell, the half-reaction with the more positive value will occur as a reduction, and the other will occur as an oxidation.

$Cu^{2+} + 2e^- \longrightarrow Cu$

Potential energy is lowered when electrons recombine with the copper ion. This process has a reduction potential of +0.34.

$Zn \longrightarrow Zn^{2+} + 2e^-$

Removing electrons from zinc is oxidation, which is the reverse of reduction. The oxidation potential of this process is +0.76, the opposite of the reduction potential.

Standard Reduction Potentials When analyzing voltaic cells, you can refer to tables of standard reduction potentials for various half-reactions.

Reduction Half-reaction	Standard Reduction Potential (V)
$Li^+ + e^- \rightarrow Li$	−3.05
$Zn^{2+} + 2e^- \rightarrow Zn$	−0.76
$Pb^{2+} + 2e^- \rightarrow Pb$	−0.13
$2H^+ + 2e^- \rightarrow H_2$	0.00
$Cu^{2+} + 2e^- \rightarrow Cu$	+0.34
$Ag^+ + e^- \rightarrow Ag$	+0.80
$F_2 + 2e^- \rightarrow 2F^-$	+2.87

(22) **SEP Develop a Model** Use the zinc oxidation half-reaction shown to sketch a Bohr model of the half-reaction. Show the loss of valence electrons.✎

Standard Cell Potential

The electric potential of a voltaic cell can be estimated from the half-reaction standard reduction potentials. The **standard cell potential** (E°_{cell}) is the measured cell potential when the ion concentrations in the half-cells are $1M$ and at a temperature of 25°C and a pressure of 100 kPa. You can estimate the standard cell potential by using the standard reduction potentials for the reduction (E°_{red}) and oxidation (E°_{oxid}) half-reactions in the following mathematical equation:

$$E^\circ_{cell} = E^\circ_{red} - E^\circ_{oxid}$$

Calculating Cell Potential To calculate the cell potential, plug the reduction potentials from the table into the equation. Study the example for a zinc-copper cell.

To write the chemical equation for the reaction that occurs in a voltaic cell, called the cell reaction, combine the two half-reactions.

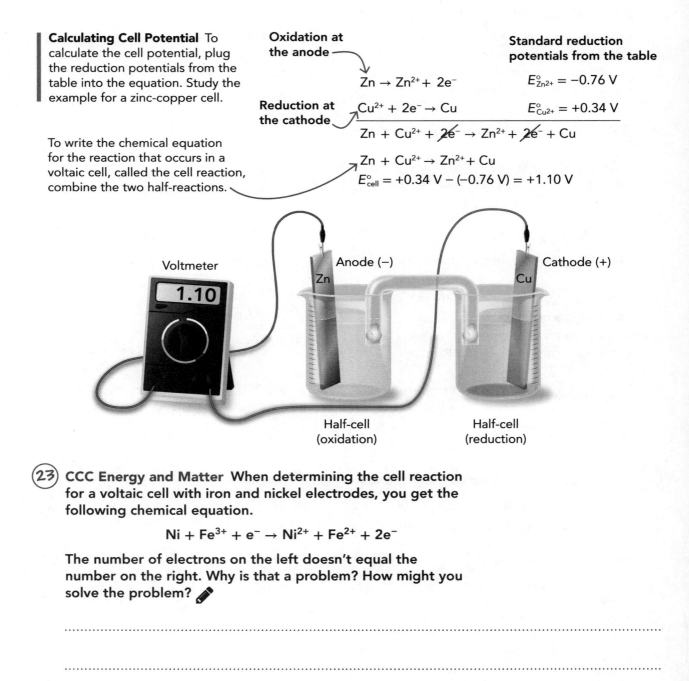

Oxidation at the anode

$$Zn \rightarrow Zn^{2+} + 2e^-$$

Reduction at the cathode

$$Cu^{2+} + 2e^- \rightarrow Cu$$

Standard reduction potentials from the table

$$E^\circ_{Zn^{2+}} = -0.76 \text{ V}$$

$$E^\circ_{Cu^{2+}} = +0.34 \text{ V}$$

$$Zn + Cu^{2+} + 2e^- \rightarrow Zn^{2+} + 2e^- + Cu$$

$$Zn + Cu^{2+} \rightarrow Zn^{2+} + Cu$$

$$E^\circ_{cell} = +0.34 \text{ V} - (-0.76 \text{ V}) = +1.10 \text{ V}$$

Voltmeter

1.10

Anode (−)

Zn

Cathode (+)

Cu

Half-cell (oxidation)

Half-cell (reduction)

(23) **CCC Energy and Matter** When determining the cell reaction for a voltaic cell with iron and nickel electrodes, you get the following chemical equation.

$$Ni + Fe^{3+} + e^- \rightarrow Ni^{2+} + Fe^{2+} + 2e^-$$

The number of electrons on the left doesn't equal the number on the right. Why is that a problem? How might you solve the problem?

....

....

....

Writing the Cell Reaction

Determine the cell reaction for a voltaic cell composed of the following half-cells:

$$Fe^{3+}(aq) + e^- \rightarrow Fe^{2+}(aq) \qquad E^\circ_{Fe^{3+}} = +0.77 \text{ V}$$

$$Ni^{2+}(aq) + 2e^- \rightarrow Ni(s) \qquad E^\circ_{Ni^{2+}} = -0.25 \text{ V}$$

ANALYZE Identify the relevant concepts.

The half-cell with the more positive reduction potential is the one in which reduction occurs (the cathode). The oxidation reaction occurs at the anode. Add the half-reactions, making certain that the number of electrons lost equals the number of electrons gained.

SOLVE Apply the concepts to this problem.

Identify the cathode by determining which half-cell has the more positive reduction potential.

$E^\circ_{Fe^{3+}} = +0.77 \text{ V} > E^\circ_{Ni^{2+}} = -0.25 \text{ V}$
The iron half-cell is the cathode.

Write the half-cell reactions in the direction in which they actually occur.

Oxidation (at anode): $Ni(s) \rightarrow Ni^{2+}(aq) + 2e^-$
Reduction (at cathode): $Fe^{3+}(aq) + e^- \rightarrow Fe^{2+}(aq)$

If necessary, multiply the half-reactions by the appropriate integer(s) to get equal numbers of electrons on both sides of the equation.

$$Ni(s) \rightarrow Ni^{2+}(aq) + 2e^-$$
$$2Fe^{3+}(aq) + 2e^- \rightarrow 2Fe^{2+}(aq)$$

Add the half-reactions.

$$Ni(s) \rightarrow Ni^{2+}(aq) + 2e^-$$
$$2Fe^{3+}(aq) + 2e^- \rightarrow 2Fe^{2+}(aq)$$
$$\overline{Ni(s) + 2Fe^{3+}(aq) \rightarrow Ni^{2+}(aq) + 2Fe^{2+}(aq)}$$

(24) A voltaic cell is constructed using the following half-reactions:

$$Cu^{2+}(aq) + 2e^- \rightarrow Cu(s) \qquad E^\circ_{Cu^{2+}} = +0.34 \text{ V}$$

$$Al^{3+}(aq) + 3e^- \rightarrow Al(s) \qquad E^\circ_{Al^{3+}} = -1.66 \text{ V}$$

Write the cell reaction. ✏

GO ONLINE for more practice problems.

Calculating the Cell Potential

Calculate the standard cell potential for the voltaic cell described in the previous Sample Problem. The half-reactions are as follows:

$$Fe^{3+}(aq) + e^- \rightarrow Fe^{2+}(aq) \quad E^\circ_{Fe^{3+}} = +0.77 \text{ V}$$

$$Ni^{2+}(aq) + 2e^- \rightarrow Ni(s) \quad E^\circ_{Ni^{2+}} = -0.25 \text{ V}$$

ANALYZE List the knowns and the unknown.

Knowns	Unknown
$E^\circ_{Fe^{3+}} = +0.77$ V	$E^\circ_{cell} = ?$
$E^\circ_{Ni^{2+}} = -0.25$ V	
Anode: Ni^{2+} half-cell	
Cathode: Fe^{3+} half-cell	

CALCULATE Solve for the unknown.

First, write the equation for the standard cell potential.

$$E^\circ_{cell} = E^\circ_{red} - E^\circ_{oxid}$$
$$= E^\circ_{Fe^{3+}} - E^\circ_{Ni^{2+}}$$

Substitute the values for the standard reduction potentials and solve the equation.

$$E^\circ_{cell} = +0.77 \text{ V} - (-0.25 \text{ V}) = +1.02 \text{ V}$$

EVALUATE Does the result make sense?

Yes, the reduction potential of the reduction is positive, and the reduction potential of the oxidation is negative. Therefore, the calculated E°_{cell} must be positive, and it is.

(25) Calculate the standard cell potential of a voltaic cell constructed using the half-reactions described in Activity 24. ✏️

GO ONLINE for more practice problems.

Types of Electrochemical Cells

Electrochemical cells are classified into two categories: voltaic and electrolytic. An **electrolytic cell** is an electrochemical cell that causes a chemical change through the application of electrical energy. The sign of the cell potential indicates whether or not the reaction is thermodynamically favorable, meaning whether or not it occurs spontaneously, and therefore whether the cell is a voltaic cell or an electrolytic cell. A voltaic cell's cell potential is positive; the reaction is thermodynamically favorable. An electrolytic cell's cell potential is negative; the reaction is thermodynamically unfavorable and must be driven by an outside power source.

Energy Conversions A voltaic cell converts chemical energy into electrical energy, and an electrolytic cell converts electrical energy into chemical energy.

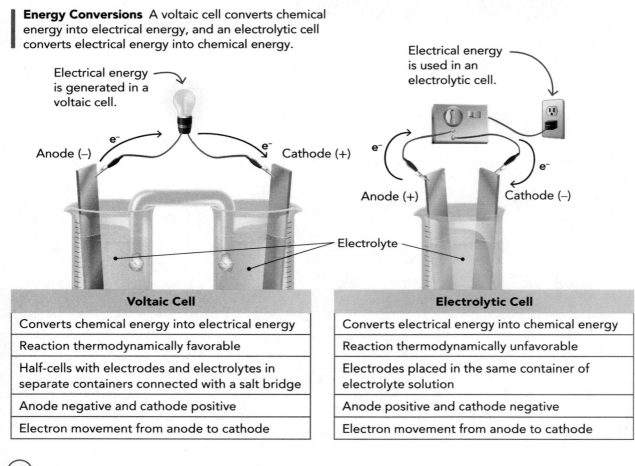

Voltaic Cell
Converts chemical energy into electrical energy
Reaction thermodynamically favorable
Half-cells with electrodes and electrolytes in separate containers connected with a salt bridge
Anode negative and cathode positive
Electron movement from anode to cathode

Electrolytic Cell
Converts electrical energy into chemical energy
Reaction thermodynamically unfavorable
Electrodes placed in the same container of electrolyte solution
Anode positive and cathode negative
Electron movement from anode to cathode

(26) **SEP Argue From Evidence** Suppose a friend claims that energy from batteries is released spontaneously, so energy must not be conserved. Use evidence to argue against your friend's claim. ✏

....

....

....

....

Electrolysis of Water A power supply is attached between the two electrodes. Water is oxidized at the anode, producing oxygen gas, and is reduced at the cathode, producing hydrogen gas.

The hydrogen and oxygen gases bubble up into the tops of the upside-down tubes, one gas on each side.

Power supply

e^-

e^-

A low concentration of KNO_3 is added to the water to facilitate charge transfer.

Electrolyte solution

Electrolytic Cells

An electrolytic cell uses electrical energy to drive a thermodynamically unfavorable reaction. For example, the decomposition of a compound such as water does not happen without a significant input of energy. However, a process called electrolysis can be used to split the water molecules into their component elements—hydrogen and oxygen gas. **Electrolysis** is a process by which electrical energy is used to bring about a chemical change. Electrolysis of other solutions or of melted ionic compounds can also result in the decomposition of the compounds into their component elements.

An electrolytic cell is composed of an electrolyte and two electrodes in a single container. The electrolyte conducts electric current, allowing for charge transfer from the cathode to the anode. An electric potential between the two electrodes drives the charge transfer, so that, as in a voltaic cell, electrons flow from the anode to the cathode through an external circuit. For the electrolysis of water, an electrolyte such as potassium nitrate (KNO_3) must be added to the water in low concentration to facilitate the charge transfer, but the electrolyte does not participate in the reaction.

(27) **SEP Analyze Data** The net reaction for the electrolysis of water can be written as follows: $2H_2O(l) \rightarrow 2H_2(g) + O_2(g)$. From the reaction and the relative volumes of gases in the Electrolysis of Water figure, how can you tell which side is the anode and which side is the cathode? ✏️

....

....

....

....

Applications

Batteries Another name for a battery is a voltaic cell. Batteries come in many different shapes and sizes, as well as different chemical compositions. For example, all alkaline batteries have zinc and manganese(IV) oxide electrodes. Lead-acid batteries have lead and lead(IV) oxide electrodes and a sulfuric acid electrolyte. Aluminum-air (Al-air) batteries generate electricity from the reaction of oxygen in the air with an aluminum electrode.

Choosing Batteries

What makes **different types of batteries** suitable for different applications?

Battery Type Batteries come in all shapes and sizes. Lead-acid batteries can supply large amounts of energy in **applications where weight doesn't matter.** Lithium-ion batteries can pack **a great deal of energy into a small package.** Alkaline batteries have a **long storage life.**

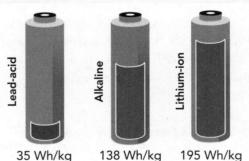

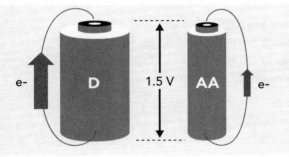

Battery Size All alkaline batteries work using the same chemistry. They have Zn anodes and MnO_2 cathodes. They have the same cell potential, or energy per charge. **Larger batteries have access to more charges so they can produce more current and hence supply more power.**

Energy Density The **energy storage (watt hours) per kilogram** is important in many applications. Electric cars, cell phones, and cordless tools such as drills use lithium-ion batteries because of their high energy density. They store a large amount of energy but weigh very little.

Lead-acid 35 Wh/kg   Alkaline 138 Wh/kg   Lithium-ion 195 Wh/kg

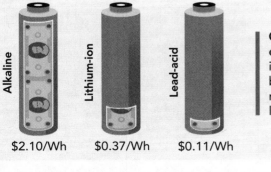

Alkaline $2.10/Wh   Lithium-ion $0.37/Wh   Lead-acid $0.11/Wh

Cost Price per unit of energy stored is always a concern, but it may be offset by other factors. For instance, lead-acid batteries store energy at low cost, but they are very heavy. Lithium-ion batteries may cost more per unit of energy stored, but the cost may be less important than their much lighter weight.

Fuel Cells A **fuel cell** is type of voltaic cell in which a fuel undergoes oxidation and from which electrical energy can be continuously obtained. The difference between a battery and a fuel cell is that a fuel cell does not have to be recharged. In a hydrogen-oxygen fuel cell, the only products are electricity and water.

Fuel Cell Anatomy Oxygen from the air flows into the cathode. Hydrogen flows into the anode. A thin layer separating the cathode and the anode allows hydrogen ions to pass but not electrons. The electrons instead flow through an external circuit, powering a device.

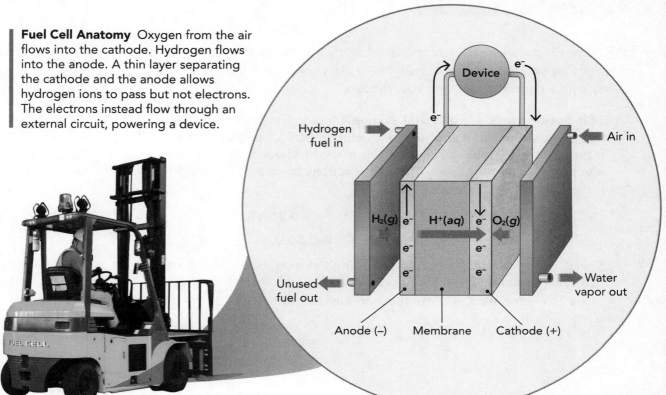

Forklifts powered by fuel cells release no harmful emissions, and they can refuel quickly. As of 2020, more than 20,000 of them were operating in the United States.

Electroplating The deposition of a thin layer of metal on an object in an electrolytic cell is **electroplating.** Electroplating is typically done either to protect a surface or to make it more appealing.

Copper Plating The lower half of this nickel was plated with copper by immersing it in a solution of a copper salt and passing a current through it. The nickel was the cathode, and a piece of copper was the anode.

(28) SEP Construct an Explanation The energy density of jet airplane fuel is about 12,500 Wh/kg. Explain why cars with lithium-ion batteries are becoming more common, but as of 2020 there were no airplanes with lithium-ion batteries. ✏️

....

....

GO ONLINE to Elaborate on and Evaluate your knowledge of how electrochemical cells function by completing the class discussion and writing activities.

In the modeling worksheet you completed at the beginning of the Investigation, you constructed a model to explain how a lemon battery works. With a partner, reevaluate your models.

(29) **SEP Develop and Use a Model** A simple lemon battery consists of a zinc-coated nail and another conducting metal (usually copper) inserted into a lemon. When a wire is placed between the two electrodes, a current flows. The half-reactions for the lemon battery are as follows:

$$Zn \rightarrow Zn^{2+} + 2e^- \quad E^\circ_{Zn^{2+}} = -0.76 \text{ V}$$

$$2H^+ + 2e^- \rightarrow H_2 \quad E^\circ_{H^+} = 0.00 \text{ V}$$

Sketch a diagram of the battery, showing the oxidation and reduction half-reactions and where they occur. Write the cell reaction and assign oxidation numbers. Calculate the standard cell potential.

GO ONLINE to Evaluate what you learned about oxidation-reduction reactions by using the available assessment resources.

In the Performance Based-Assessment, you designed, constructed, and refined two batteries and compared them to the batteries your classmates constructed. Wrap up your analysis by answering the following questions.

30 **SEP Design a Solution** Your class built electrochemical cells using pairs of the metals Ag, Cu, Fe, Mg, and Pb. You observed which pair of metals produced a cell with the greatest voltage. If you wanted to produce a still greater voltage, would using aluminum instead of one of the other metals be suitable?

....

....

....

....

31 **CCC Matter and Energy** Describe the flow of electrons in the electrochemical cell that produced the greatest voltage.

....

....

....

32 **Revisit the Anchoring Phenomenon** Recall the photograph of the farm with solar panels that introduced Storyline 5. In thinking about the energy conversions involved, how is a solar panel similar to a battery? How is it different?

....

....

....

....

GO ONLINE to Engage with real-world phenomena by watching a video and to complete a CER interactive worksheet.

How is energy stored in food?

Organic Chemistry

We get the energy our bodies need from the foods that we eat. You've probably heard of carbohydrates, proteins, and fats. These essential nutrients are different types of organic compounds that our bodies use to support life. Similarly, the fuels we burn to light our homes and power our cars are also organic compounds. Once you have viewed the Investigative Phenomenon video and worked on a first draft of a modeling exercise to explain how energy is stored in food, discuss with a partner the following questions.

1. **CCC Energy and Matter** How do our bodies get energy from the foods that we eat? Sketch the flow of energy and matter into, out of, and within the body.

2. **SEP Obtain and Evaluate Information** Carbohydrates, proteins, and fats have different average energy densities, measured as Calories (1000 calories) per gram. Go online and find the energy density of these nutrients. Describe how the differences in energy density could affect diet.

....

....

....

....

Hydrocarbons

 GO ONLINE to Explore and Explain the structures and properties of hydrocarbons and the energy stored within hydrocarbons.

Carbon Bonding

A chemical compound that contains carbon is generally classified as an **organic compound.** Only a few types of carbon compounds, such as carbonates, oxides, alloys, and cyanide salts, are not organic. A carbon atom has four valence electrons, so it can form up to four stable covalent bonds. Carbon is unique in that it can form covalent bonds with other carbon atoms, hydrogen atoms, and many other types of atoms. Specifically, carbon can form long chains with other carbon atoms, resulting in millions of possible organic compounds. These long carbon chains and complex structures are the components of the living organisms all around us.

Electron Dot Structures Carbon has four valence electrons, and hydrogen has one. In methane, one carbon atom forms four single covalent bonds, each of them with one hydrogen atom.

$$\cdot \overset{\cdot}{C} \cdot \ + \ 4H \cdot \ \longrightarrow \ H \!:\! \overset{..}{\underset{H}{\overset{H}{C}}} \!:\! H$$

Structural Formulas We draw a single line in place of the two electron "dots" to show a single covalent bond. This is called a structural formula. Methane is commonly used as a fuel in combustion reactions with oxygen.

Two lines represent a double bond.

H—C single bond shown as one line

Lone pair

Methane trapped underground near Hawaii's Kilauea volcano ignites near lava flows and is detectable by its blue flame color.

Representing Hydrocarbons

A **hydrocarbon** is an organic compound that contains only hydrogen and carbon. Three of the simplest hydrocarbons are methane, ethane, and propane. Methane is a major component of natural gas, which is used to heat homes and cook food. Methane has only one carbon, so there are no carbon bonds. Ethane and propane have two and three carbon atoms, respectively, and each carbon atom shares a pair of electrons with at least one other carbon atom.

In organic chemistry, the structure of molecules is very important, so organic compounds are often represented using structural formulas. A **structural formula** is a graphic representation of a molecule's shape, with lines used to show chemical bonding. Three-dimensional structures can be represented with either ball-and-stick models or space-filling models.

Representing Structure Hydrocarbon structures are represented in two dimensions with structural formulas and in three dimensions with ball-and-stick and space-filling models.

An indoor gas range burns **methane** piped into the house.

Examples of Hydrocarbons			
Name	**Structural formula**	**Ball-and-stick model**	**Space-filling model**
Methane	H–C–H with H above and H below (H on top, H–C–H, H on bottom)		
Ethane	H–C–C–H with H atoms above and below each C		
Propane	H–C–C–C–H with H atoms above and below each C		

Many outdoor grills burn **propane** stored in tanks.

(3) **CCC Patterns** If there were another row in the table after propane, it would be for butane. Recognize the pattern in the table and sketch the structural formula for butane. ✏️

Hydrocarbon Structures

The structure of a hydrocarbon determines its properties. Structure is defined by the types of bonds that form between the carbon atoms, the number of carbon atoms, and the overall shape of the molecule. The naming system for hydrocarbons identifies this structure.

Types of Hydrocarbons

How do you **distinguish and name** the various types of **hydrocarbons?**

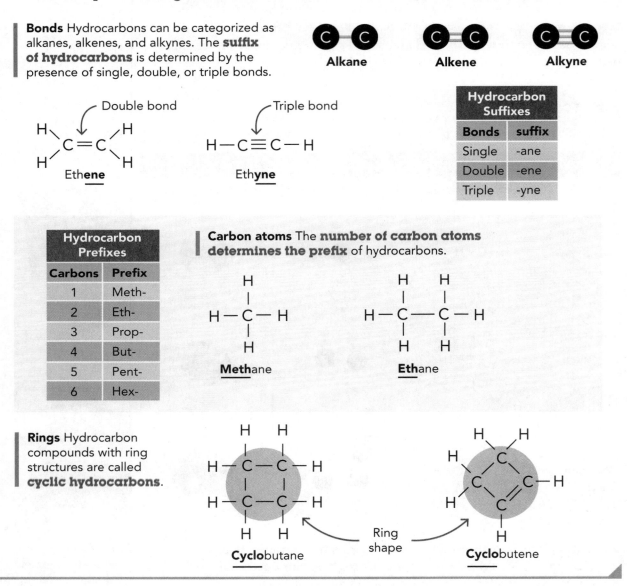

Bonds Hydrocarbons can be categorized as alkanes, alkenes, and alkynes. The **suffix of hydrocarbons** is determined by the presence of single, double, or triple bonds.

Alkane   Alkene   Alkyne

Double bond

Eth**ene**

Triple bond

Eth**yne**

Hydrocarbon Suffixes	
Bonds	suffix
Single	-ane
Double	-ene
Triple	-yne

Hydrocarbon Prefixes	
Carbons	Prefix
1	Meth-
2	Eth-
3	Prop-
4	But-
5	Pent-
6	Hex-

Carbon atoms The **number of carbon atoms determines the prefix** of hydrocarbons.

Methane

Ethane

Rings Hydrocarbon compounds with ring structures are called **cyclic hydrocarbons**.

Cyclobutane

Ring shape

Cyclobutene

(4) **SEP Develop a Model** Sketch the structural formula for cyclopropene. Then research cyclopropene online to check your model. ✏️

Alkanes

An **alkane** is a hydrocarbon with only single covalent bonds. The carbon atoms in an alkane can be arranged in either a straight chain, in a chain that has branches, or in a ring. A **straight-chain alkane** can have any number of carbon atoms, one after another. A group of compounds forms a homologous series if there is a constant unit of change from one compound in the series to the next.

A **branched-chain alkane** contains at least one carbon atom bonded to three other carbon atoms. The result is a molecule that has a main chain of carbon atoms and one or more side chains. An atom or group of atoms that takes the place of a hydrogen atom on a parent hydrocarbon molecule is called a **substituent.**

Straight-Chain Alkanes
Adding a CH_2^{2-} unit into the straight-chain ethane molecule results in a propane molecule. Ethane and propane are part of a homologous series.

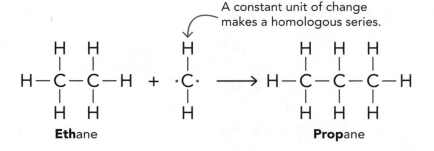

A constant unit of change makes a homologous series.

Ethane   **Prop**ane

Branched-Chain Alkanes
When carbon atoms replace a hydrogen in a parent alkane, a branch is formed.

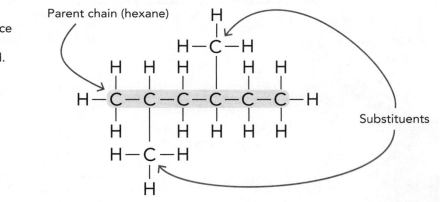

Parent chain (hexane)

Substituents

(5) **SEP Interpret Data** From the data shown in the graph, determine how the size of a straight-chain alkane affects the boiling point. Plot a prediction for the boiling point of hexane (6 carbon atoms) on the graph. ✎

....

....

....

....

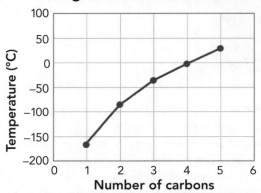

Boiling Points of Straight-Chain Alkanes

Drawing Alkane Structures

To draw the structural formula for a straight-chain alkane, write the carbons and then complete the formula with hydrogens and lines representing covalent bonds.

Step 1: Sketch the carbons. Write enough carbons to get the proper chain length.

Step 2: Add the hydrogens with lines representing the bonds.

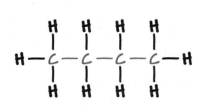

As hydrocarbon molecules get more complicated, it gets difficult to continually draw carbon and hydrogen atoms. A **condensed structural formula** leaves out some bonds and/or atoms, resulting in a simpler representation.

> **Multiple Representations** Molecules can be represented in multiple ways.

Formulas for Butane	
Formula	**Description**
C_4H_{10}	Molecular formula
H—C—C—C—C—H (complete structural)	Complete structural formula
$CH_3—CH_2—CH_2—CH_3$	Condensed structural formula (C—H bonds are understood.)
$CH_3CH_2CH_2CH_3$	Condensed structural formula (C—H and C—C bonds are understood.)
$CH_3(CH_2)_2CH_3$	Condensed structural formula (All bonds are understood.)
C—C—C—C	Carbon skeleton (Hydrogens and C—H bonds understood.)
∧∨	Line-angle formula (Carbon and hydrogen atoms are understood, carbon atoms are located at each intersection and the ends of lines.)

Butane torch

(6) **SEP Use a Model** Sketch the electron dot structure of butane. Use your model to explain why three hydrogens are bonded to the carbons on the ends and only two hydrogens are bonded to each middle carbon. ✏️

Drawing Structural Formulas of Alkanes

Draw the complete structural formula for the straight-chain alkane that has five carbon atoms. Then, write the condensed structural formula and draw the line-angle formula.

ANALYZE Identify the relevant concepts.

To draw the structural formula, write the carbon atoms in a straight line and add the appropriate number of hydrogen atoms. To write the condensed formula, list each carbon atom and the number of hydrogen atoms bonded to it. To draw the line-angle formula, draw only the bonds representing the carbon skeleton.

SOLVE Apply the concepts to the problem.

Sketch the carbons.	C—C—C—C—C

Add the hydrogens.

$$\begin{array}{ccccc} H & H & H & H & H \\ | & | & | & | & | \\ H-C-C-C-C-C-H \\ | & | & | & | & | \\ H & H & H & H & H \end{array}$$

Count the hydrogen atoms bonded to each carbon atom.

The carbon atoms at the ends of the chain bond with 3 hydrogen atoms. The interior carbons bond with 2 hydrogens.

Write the condensed formula.

$CH_3CH_2CH_2CH_2CH_3$ or $CH_3(CH_2)_3CH_3$

Examine the carbon skeleton.

The carbon skeleton consists of 5 carbon atoms and 4 C—C bonds.

Draw the line-angle formula.

(7) **SEP Develop Models** Draw the complete structural formula and the line-angle formula for hexane, the straight-chain alkane that has six carbon atoms. Then, write the condensed structural formula. ✏

GO ONLINE for more practice problems.

Comparing Single and Double Bonds Objects with two attachments do not rotate as freely as objects with only one attachment.

With only one rope attached, a tire swing can easily spin around.

When both arms are holding on to the bars, it is very difficult to rotate.

Alkenes and Alkynes

An **alkene** is a hydrocarbon that contains one or more carbon-carbon double covalent bonds. A hydrocarbon that contains one or more carbon-carbon triple covalent bonds is called an **alkyne.** For both alkenes and alkynes, only one double or triple bond is necessary. Other bonds may be single or double C—C or C—H bonds. The presence of either a double or triple bond in a hydrocarbon affects its structure. Specifically, double and triple bonds restrict rotations.

Molecular Models These models show the structural difference between ethane, ethene, and ethyne.

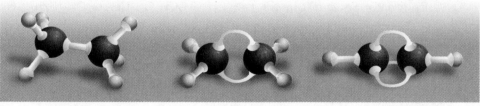

| Ethane | Ethene | Ethyne |

8) **SEP Construct an Explanation** Electrons in the C—H bond are closer to the carbon due to greater electronegativity. This leaves a partial positive charge on the hydrogen. Knowing this, construct an explanation for why the hydrogens in ethane on one side are rotated with respect to those on the other side. Why is there no rotation for ethene? ✏

....

....

....

Saturation

An organic compound that contains the maximum number of hydrogen atoms per carbon atom is called a **saturated compound.** The presence of a double or triple bond results in an **unsaturated compound.** Fewer carbon valence electrons are available for hydrogen atoms, thus reducing the number of hydrogen atoms in the compound. The ratio of hydrogen atoms to carbon atoms (H/C) is called the **degree of saturation.** For hydrocarbons, the degree of saturation is also equal to the average oxidation number of the carbon atoms in the compound.

| **Saturation** Propane, propene, and propyne all have the same number of carbon atoms, but they have different degrees of saturation.

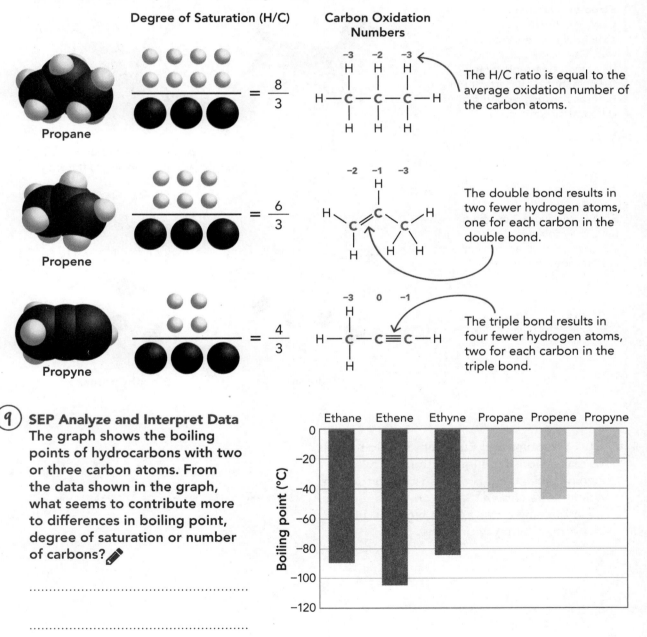

Degree of Saturation (H/C)   Carbon Oxidation Numbers

Propane $= \frac{8}{3}$

The H/C ratio is equal to the average oxidation number of the carbon atoms.

Propene $= \frac{6}{3}$

The double bond results in two fewer hydrogen atoms, one for each carbon in the double bond.

Propyne $= \frac{4}{3}$

The triple bond results in four fewer hydrogen atoms, two for each carbon in the triple bond.

(9) SEP Analyze and Interpret Data The graph shows the boiling points of hydrocarbons with two or three carbon atoms. From the data shown in the graph, what seems to contribute more to differences in boiling point, degree of saturation or number of carbons? ✏️

....

....

Isomers

Structural Isomers Compounds that have the same molecular formula but different molecular structures are called **isomers.** Because the structures of isomers are different, they are different substances. **Structural isomers,** also called constitutional isomers, are compounds that have the same molecular formula, but the atoms are joined together in different orders. Structural isomers differ in physical properties such as boiling point and chemical reactivities. For example, the more highly branched the hydrocarbon structure, the lower the boiling point compared to less-branched isomers.

Structural Isomers
Compounds that are structural isomers are made up of the same parts and have the same molecular formula, but their parts are in different orders, resulting in different structures.

Both dogs have the same parts, but this dog will function very differently!

Both butane and 2-methylpropane have the molecular formula C_4H_{10}, but the atoms in each compound are arranged differently.

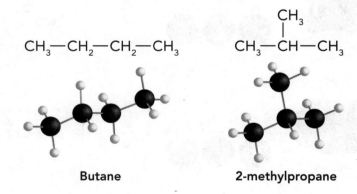

Butane   **2-methylpropane**

(10) **CCC Structure and Function** Simple models of dispersion-force interactions between straight-chain and branched-chain structural isomers are shown. Based on these models, describe why butane has a higher boiling point than 2-methylpropane. ✏️

....

....

Stereoisomer Molecules in which the atoms are joined in the same order, but the positions of the atoms in space are different, are called **stereoisomers.** Compounds that are stereoisomers also have different properties from each other. There are two types of stereoisomers: geometric and optical. **Geometric isomers,** also called *cis-trans* isomers, have atoms joined in the same order, but the spatial orientations of the groups differ.

Pairs of isomers that are mirror images and not superimposable are called **optical isomers,** or enantiomers.

◼ **Structure determines properties, even when molecules are made of the same atoms.**

Geometric Isomers The atoms are joined in the same order, but the spatial orientation of the groups differs. The double bonds don't allow rotation, so these are very different structures with different properties.

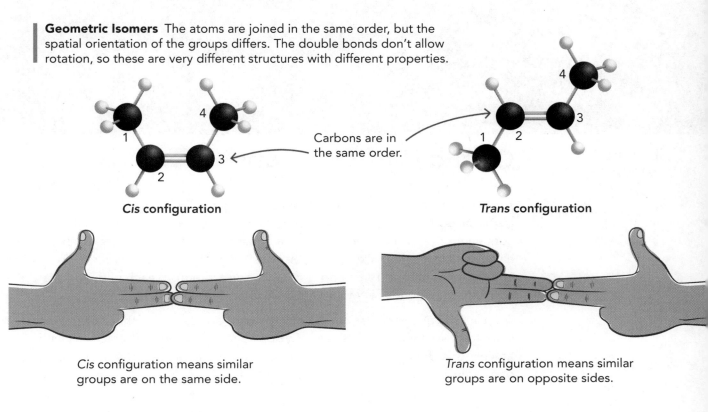

Cis configuration

Trans configuration

Carbons are in the same order.

Cis configuration means similar groups are on the same side.

Trans configuration means similar groups are on opposite sides.

Optical Isomers A carbon atom with four different attachments is called an asymmetric carbon. A pair of asymmetric carbons that are mirror images but not superimposable are optical isomers.

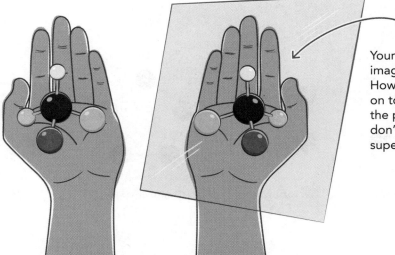

Your right hand is a mirror image of your left hand. However, if you put them on top of each other with the palms up, your thumbs don't align. This is what "not superimposable" means.

Linking Together
When skydivers link arms, they form a ring. Three or more carbon atoms can also link to form a ring.

Cyclic Hydrocarbons

A compound that contains a hydrocarbon ring is called a **cyclic hydrocarbon.** Many molecules in nature contain cyclic hydrocarbons. Rings containing five and six carbons are the most abundant. Cyclic versions of alkanes, alkenes, and alkynes can be constructed by taking their straight-chain configurations, removing one hydrogen atom from each end, and then connecting the ends together with a C—C covalent bond.

A cyclic hydrocarbon that contains only single bonds, and is therefore saturated, is called a cycloalkane. Cycloalkenes are cyclic hydrocarbons with at least one double bond. Cycloalkynes are cyclic hydrocarbons with at least one triple bond.

Cycloalkanes These models show the first four members of the homologous series of cycloalkanes. Boiling points are given under each compound.

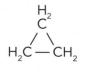

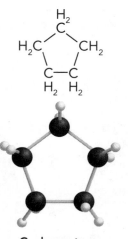

Cyclopropane
(−32.8°C)

Cyclobutane
(12.6°C)

Cyclopentane
(49.3°C)

Cyclohexane
(80.7°C)

11) **SEP Analyze Data** Graph the boiling point as a function of the number of carbons for the cycloalkanes shown. Predict the boiling point for cycloheptane (7 carbons). ✎

....

....

Aromatic Compounds

An **aromatic compound**, or arene, is an organic compound that contains a benzene ring or other ring in which the bonding is like that of benzene. The benzene molecule is a six-membered carbon ring with one hydrogen atom attached to each carbon. This arrangement leaves one electron from each carbon free to participate in a double bond. The free electron can alternate back and forth from one side of the carbon to the other, swapping where the double and single bonds are found in the ring.

Structure of Benzene Because the double bond can form on either side, two different structures with alternating bonds can be written. The structures shown are the extremes for electron sharing in the ring. In reality, all the bonds in the ring are hybrids of single and double bonds.

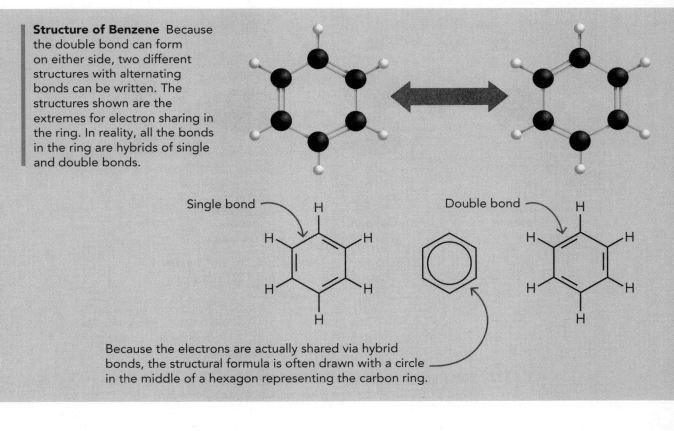

Single bond

Double bond

Because the electrons are actually shared via hybrid bonds, the structural formula is often drawn with a circle in the middle of a hexagon representing the carbon ring.

Cinnemaldehyde An example of an aromatic compound is cinnemaldehyde, which gives cinnamon its distinct scent. These compounds were originally called aromatic because many have distinct, pleasant odors.

Energy From Hydrocarbons

The combustion of hydrocarbons produces much of the world's energy. Natural gas, used to heat many homes, is composed of about 80 percent methane, 10 percent ethane, 4 percent propane, and 2 percent butane. Methane in particular burns hot with a clean flame, making it excellent for home use. Recall that there are two ways of understanding energy released from combustion reactions: net energy obtained from the breaking and reforming of bonds, and transfer of electrons in redox reactions.

Combustion of Methane The energy released during the combustion of a hydrocarbon can be estimated from the bond energies. The amount of energy released is also dependent on the change in oxidation number of the carbon atoms.

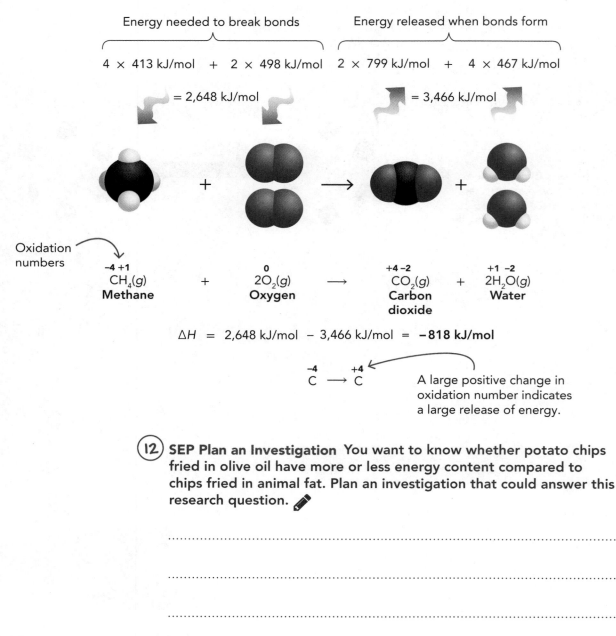

Energy needed to break bonds

4×413 kJ/mol $+ 2 \times 498$ kJ/mol

= 2,648 kJ/mol

Energy released when bonds form

2×799 kJ/mol $+ 4 \times 467$ kJ/mol

= 3,466 kJ/mol

Oxidation numbers

–4 +1
$CH_4(g)$
Methane

$+$

0
$2O_2(g)$
Oxygen

$\longrightarrow$

+4 –2
$CO_2(g)$
Carbon dioxide

$+$

+1 –2
$2H_2O(g)$
Water

$\Delta H = 2{,}648$ kJ/mol $- 3{,}466$ kJ/mol $= \mathbf{-818}$ **kJ/mol**

–4   **+4**
C $\longrightarrow$ C

A large positive change in oxidation number indicates a large release of energy.

(12) **SEP Plan an Investigation** You want to know whether potato chips fried in olive oil have more or less energy content compared to chips fried in animal fat. Plan an investigation that could answer this research question. ✏

....

....

....

Energy and Saturation

In every combustion reaction of a hydrocarbon, all of the carbon atoms are used in the production of carbon dioxide. Since the carbon atom in a carbon dioxide molecule always has the same oxidation number (+4), the total change in oxidation number will be determined by the average oxidation number of the carbons in the original hydrocarbon. The energy density of a hydrocarbon is therefore dependent on its saturation.

Combustion of Propane The combustion of one mole of propane produces more energy than the combustion of one mole of methane. However, propane has significantly more mass per mole.

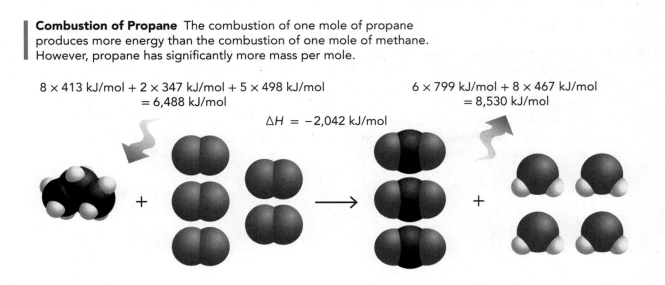

8×413 kJ/mol $+ 2 \times 347$ kJ/mol $+ 5 \times 498$ kJ/mol
$= 6{,}488$ kJ/mol

6×799 kJ/mol $+ 8 \times 467$ kJ/mol
$= 8{,}530$ kJ/mol

$\Delta H = -2{,}042$ kJ/mol

Energy Density When comparing the energy content of various fuels, we compare the energy density, or how much energy is released per unit of mass. In this example, it is the mass in one mole of the fuel.

Methane: $\left(\dfrac{-818 \text{ kJ}}{1 \text{ mol}}\right)\left(\dfrac{1 \text{ mol}}{16.0 \text{ g}}\right) = -51.1 \ kJ/g$ H/C = 4

Methane has greater saturation, greater oxidation number change, and therefore greater energy density.

Propane: $\left(\dfrac{-2{,}042 \text{ kJ}}{1 \text{ mol}}\right)\left(\dfrac{1 \text{ mol}}{44.1 \text{ g}}\right) = -46.3 \ kJ/g$ H/C = 2.7

(13) **SEP Interpret Data** The table shows the approximate H/C ratio, energy density, and carbon dioxide released per unit of energy for several common fuels. How does the degree of saturation affect the energy density and carbon dioxide production? ✏

Energy Density in Common Fuels			
Name	H/C Ratio	Energy Density (kJ/g)	CO_2 released (mol/10^3 kJ)
Natural gas	4:1	51.6	1.2
Petroleum	2:1	43.6	1.6
Coal	1:1	39.3	2.0

....

....

INVESTIGATIVE PHENOMENON

GO ONLINE to Elaborate on and Evaluate your knowledge of the structure and properties of hydrocarbons by completing the class discussion and data analysis activities.

In the CER worksheet, you drafted an explanation of why the combustion energy differs for two substances. With a partner, reevaluate the evidence cited in your arguments.

14 **SEP Construct an Explanation** Fats are more complex than simple hydrocarbons. However, different types of fats in food can also be distinguished by whether or not they are saturated or unsaturated. For example, butter and beef fat are primarily considered saturated, while olive oil is considered unsaturated. Construct an explanation for why unsaturated fats have a slightly lower energy density, or calories per gram, than saturated fats.

....

....

....

....

....

....

Functional Groups and Polymers

 GO ONLINE to Explore and Explain identifying compounds using functional groups and synthesizing polymers.

Types of Organic Compounds

Hydrocarbons contain only hydrogen and carbon atoms. However, most organic chemistry involves substituents, which are groups attached to hydrocarbon chains or rings. The substituents of organic molecules are often composed of nitrogen, oxygen, sulfur, and phosphorous. A **functional group** is a specific arrangement of atoms in an organic compound that is capable of characteristic chemical reactions. We will look at six different functional groups that create eight different organic compound types. In the structural diagrams of functional groups, the letter R represents any hydrocarbon chains or rings attached to functional groups.

Organic Compounds Many items contain hydrocarbon derivatives. The hydrocarbon skeletons (R) in these products are chemically similar. Functional groups give each product unique properties and uses.

Functional groups replace the hydrogens in a hydrocarbon. In an amine, H is replaced with NH_2.

Organic Compounds Classified by Functional Group		
Compound Type	**General Structure**	**Functional Group**
Halocarbon	R—X (X = F, Cl, Br, or I)	Halogen
Alcohol	R—OH	Hydroxy
Ether	R—O—R	Ether
Amine	R—NH_2	Amino
Aldehyde	$R-\overset{\overset{\displaystyle O}{\|\|}}{C}-H$	Carbonyl
Ketone	$R-\overset{\overset{\displaystyle O}{\|\|}}{C}-R$	Carbonyl
Carboxylic acid	$R-\overset{\overset{\displaystyle O}{\|\|}}{C}-OH$	Carboxyl
Ester	$R-\overset{\overset{\displaystyle O}{\|\|}}{C}-O-R$	Carbonyl

Halocarbons

A **halocarbon** is an organic compound that contains at least one covalently bonded halogen atom, such as fluorine, chlorine, bromine, or iodine. A halocarbon in which the halogen atom is attached to a hydrocarbon chain is called an **alkyl halide.** A halocarbon in which the halogen atom is attached to an aromatic hydrocarbon is called an **aryl halide.** The **halogen group** consists of the halogen atom or atoms attached to the hydrocarbon. The halogen atoms are more electronegative than the carbon atoms, so most halocarbons are polar. As a result, halocarbons are attracted to each other via weak dispersion forces. As the degree of halogenation increases, the boiling point also increases.

◼ The chemical properties of compounds change based on the number and type of functional groups.

Alkyl and Aryl Halides
Chloromethane, chloroethene, and chlorobenzene each contain one halogen atom.

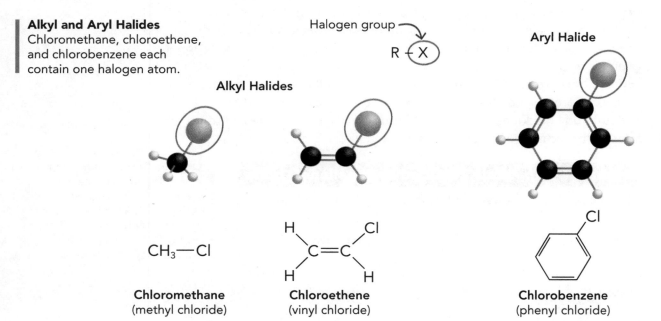

Halogen group

R─X

Alkyl Halides

CH_3—Cl

Chloromethane
(methyl chloride)

Chloroethene
(vinyl chloride)

Aryl Halide

Chlorobenzene
(phenyl chloride)

⑮ **SEP Develop a Model** The table shows methane, three of the four chloromethanes, and their boiling points. Write the molecular formula and sketch the structural formula for tetrachloromethane. Analyze and interpret the data in the table to estimate the boiling point of tetrachloromethane. ✏

Comparing Methane and Chloromethanes

Molecular Formula	Name	Molar Mass (g)	Boiling Point (°C)
CH_4	Methane	16.0	−161
CH_3Cl	Chloromethane (methyl chloride)	50.5	−24
CH_2Cl_2	Dichloromethane (methylene chloride)	85.0	40
$CHCl_3$	Trichloromethane (chloroform)	119.5	61

Alcohols

An **alcohol** is an organic compound with an —OH group. The —OH functional group in alcohols is called a **hydroxy group.** Similar to a water molecule, the oxygen atom in the hydroxy group has lone pairs of electrons causing the alcohol to be polar and have a bent structure. Also like water, alcohols are capable of hydrogen bonding due to the hydroxy group, resulting in relatively high boiling points.

Hydroxy Functional Group The hydroxy functional group looks like and has properties similar to a water molecule. Alcohols are typically soluble in water.

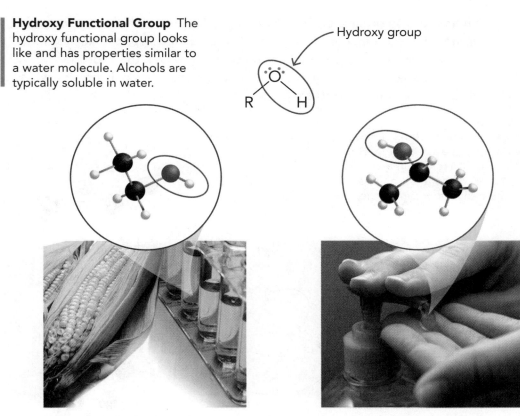

Hydroxy group

Ethyl alcohol, or ethanol, can be made from corn and used as a fuel source for cars and trucks.

Isopropyl alcohol, or rubbing alcohol, is used as an antiseptic and in hand sanitizers.

(16) **SEP Construct an Explanation** Because the oxygen in the hydroxy group has two lone pairs of electrons, hydrogen bonds can form between the oxygen of one alcohol and the hydrogen of another. Knowing this, construct an explanation for why alcohols have relatively high boiling points and are typically liquids at STP. 🖉

....

....

....

....

Ethers and Amines

An **ether** is an organic compound in which oxygen is bonded to two carbon groups. Ethers are similar to alcohols, but another carbon atom, chain, or cyclic hydrocarbon takes the place of the hydrogen in the hydroxy group. The O functional group is called an **ether group.** The two lone electron pairs on oxygen result in a bent shape like water and alcohols. However, because there are no hydrogen atoms in the group, ethers do not form hydrogen bonds.

An **amine** is an organic compound in which NH_2 is bonded to a carbon group. The NH_2 functional group is called an **amino group.** Like alcohols, some smaller amines form hydrogen bonds. However, the hydrogen bonds in amines are not as strong since the nitrogen atom has only one lone electron pair compared to oxygen's two.

Symmetry in Ethers For methoxyethane, the R groups on either side of the ether group are different. This results in a nonsymmetric ether. When the R groups are the same, the molecule is symmetric.

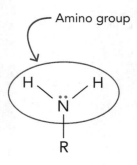

Ether

Methoxyethane ether

Polarity in Amines In benzenamine, the R group is a benzene ring. The single lone electron pair on the nitrogen atom combined with the hydrogen atoms can result in hydrogen bonding.

Amine

Benzenamine

(17) **SEP Construct an Explanation** Menthol is responsible for the cooling sensation provided by many consumer products, such as aftershave. From the structural formula shown, determine whether it is an alcohol, ether, or amine. Would you expect the compound to be a solid, liquid, or gas at room temperature? Why? (Hint: Consider how hydrogen bonds affect the boiling point.) ✏️

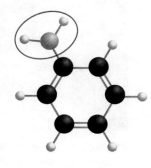

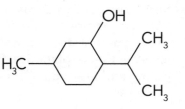

Aldehydes and Ketones

A **carbonyl group** is a functional group with the general structure C=O. An **aldehyde** is an organic compound in which the carbon of the carbonyl group is joined to at least one hydrogen. A **ketone** is an organic compound in which the carbon of the carbonyl group is joined to two other carbons. A carbonyl group does not form hydrogen bonds with other carbonyl groups because they lack —OH or —NH groups. However, a carbonyl group can form hydrogen bonds with water molecules in an aqueous solution.

Carbonyl Group The carbonyl group is polar. Therefore, aldehydes and ketones are attracted via polar-polar intermolecular forces.

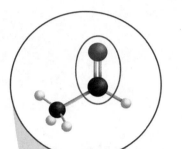

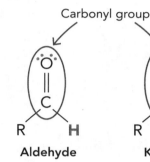

Carbonyl group

Aldehyde

Ketone

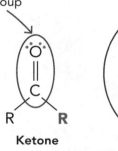

Also known as **ethanal,** acetaldehyde is produced in the liver. It's also found in coffee and other foods in small amounts.

Also known as **propanone,** acetone is used as a solvent. It is the active ingredient in nail polish remover and paint thinners.

(18) **SEP Construct an Explanation** The table shows a hydrocarbon, a ketone, and an alcohol having the same number of carbon atoms. Construct an explanation for the difference in boiling points. ✏️

Compound	Formula	Boiling Point (°C)	Primary Intermolecular Interactions
Propane	$CH_3CH_2CH_3$	−42	Dispersion forces
Propanone	CH_3COCH_3	56	Polar-polar interactions
1-Propanol	$CH_3CH_2CH_2OH$	97	Hydrogen bonding

Oranges and Bananas Citrus fruits like oranges and lemons have large concentrations of carboxylic acids, while aromatic fruits like bananas and strawberries contain esters.

Citric acid is a common carboxylic acid that is found in lemons, limes, and oranges.

Isopentyl acetate is an ester found in bananas that gives them their characteristic aroma.

Carboxylic Acids and Esters

A **carboxylic acid** is an organic compound with a carbonyl group and a hydroxy group. This combination of carbonyl and hydroxy groups is called a **carboxyl group.** Carboxylic acids are acids because they can lose a hydrogen ion in water, but they are weak acids. Similar to alcohols, carboxylic acids can form hydrogen bonds.

An **ester** is similar to a carboxylic acid, but the —OH hydroxy group has been replaced with the —OR group from an alcohol. The replacement of the hydrogen atom in the hydroxy group with an R group means that esters do not form hydrogen bonds with each other.

Similar Shapes Carboxylic acids and esters have similar shapes but very different properties due to the replacement of the hydrogen with an R group in the hydroxy group.

Carbonyl group

Hydroxy group

Alkyl or aryl group (from the alcohol)

Carboxylic acid

Ester

(19) **SEP Use a Model** Circle the carbonyl groups and draw rectangles around the hydroxy groups in the structures of the citric acid and isopentyl acetate shown. ✏️

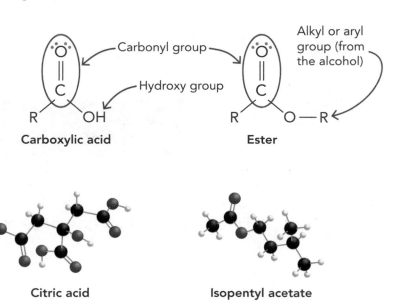

Citric acid

Isopentyl acetate

Identifying Functional Groups

This Learning Experience described six different functional groups that create eight different organic compound types. It can get confusing trying to identify everything, and these types only scratch the surface of organic chemistry. To help keep everything straight, use the Identification of Organic Compounds flowchart as a guide to identifying the functional group and the compound type for the basic organic compounds.

Identification of Organic Compounds

How do you identify functional groups and types of organic compounds?

Identify the Functional Group Your first step is to **look for atoms that are not hydrogen or carbon**—O, N, F, Br, Cl, and I. Then, follow the steps of the flowchart to identify the functional group and the compound type based on any other attachments.

The **amines** and **halocarbons** are the easiest to identify. They have either a nitrogen or halogen, respectively.

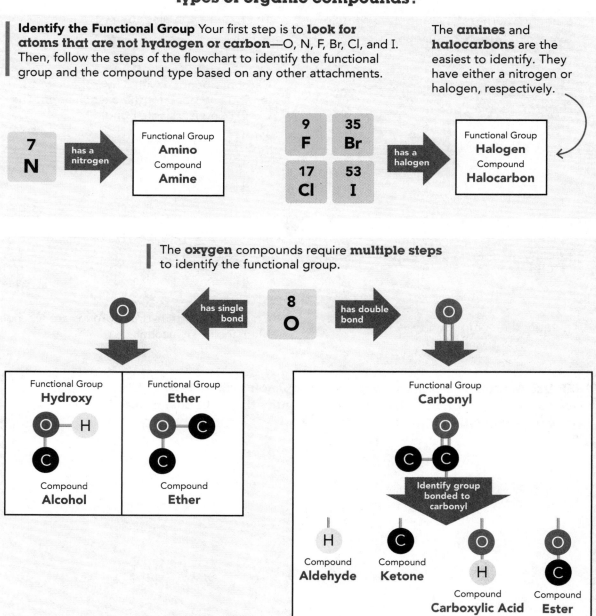

The **oxygen** compounds require **multiple steps** to identify the functional group.

Identifying Functional Groups

The organic compound methanol has the formula CH_3OH. Identify the functional group and compound type for methanol.

Analyze Identify the relevant concepts.

Functional groups contain either oxygen, nitrogen, or halogen atoms. Use the molecular formula to identify which attachment is present.

Solve Apply the concepts to the problem.

Identify whether the compound contains oxygen, nitrogen, or halogen atoms.	The formula contains an oxygen atom. $CH_3\mathbf{O}H$
Identify whether there is a C—O single bond or double bond.	Carbon is bonded with 3 hydrogen atoms, leaving one bond for the oxygen atom. The C—O bond is a single bond.
Identify the functional group.	Hydroxy group
Identify the compound type.	Compounds with hydroxy groups are alcohols. Methanol is an alcohol.

(20) **SEP Use Models** The organic compound propanoic acid, $CH_3CH_2CO_2H$, is used as a preservative in baked goods. Identify the functional group and compound type for propanoic acid. ✏️

GO ONLINE for more practice problems.

Organic Chemical Reactions

Substitution Reactions A common type of organic reaction is a **substitution reaction**, in which an atom or group of atoms replaces another atom or group. Substitution reactions can be used to introduce a new functional group to an organic compound.

Halogenation A halogen atom can replace a hydrogen atom on an alkane to produce a halocarbon. This type of substitution reaction is called halogenation.

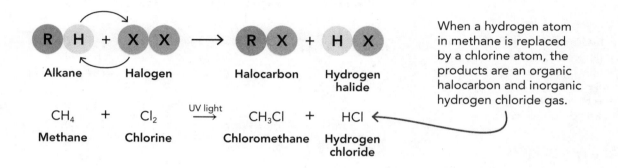

When a hydrogen atom in methane is replaced by a chlorine atom, the products are an organic halocarbon and inorganic hydrogen chloride gas.

Production of Alcohol A substitution reaction can produce an alcohol when the halogen group on a halocarbon is replaced with a hydroxide ion.

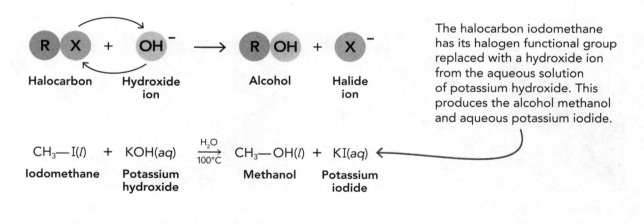

The halocarbon iodomethane has its halogen functional group replaced with a hydroxide ion from the aqueous solution of potassium hydroxide. This produces the alcohol methanol and aqueous potassium iodide.

(21) **SEP Use a Model** Bromoethane (CH_3CH_2Br) can react with sodium hydroxide (NaOH) to produce ethanol. Write the full substitution reaction equation for this process. ✏️

Addition Reactions In an **addition reaction,** a substance is added at the double or triple bond of an alkene or alkyne. These types of reactions can be used to add functional groups, like substitution reactions, or to convert alkenes to alkanes. An example of an addition reaction is a **hydration reaction,** where water is added to an alkene, resulting in the formation of an alcohol. A **hydrogenation reaction** is the addition of hydrogen to a C=C double bond to produce an alkane with single bonds.

Addition Reaction In the general addition reaction, X and Y represent the two parts of the reagent that are added to the alkene.

The **hydration** of the hydrocarbon ethene produces the alcohol ethanol. This reaction removes the double bond and adds a hydroxy group to the hydrocarbon along with an additional hydrogen.

The addition of two hydrogen atoms, or **hydrogenation,** turns unsaturated ethene into saturated ethane.

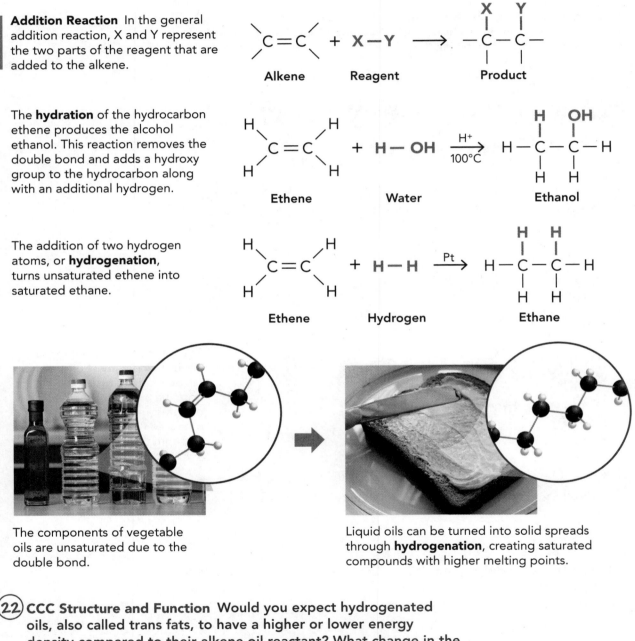

The components of vegetable oils are unsaturated due to the double bond.

Liquid oils can be turned into solid spreads through **hydrogenation**, creating saturated compounds with higher melting points.

22 **CCC Structure and Function** Would you expect hydrogenated oils, also called trans fats, to have a higher or lower energy density compared to their alkene oil reactant? What change in the molecular structure results in this macroscopic property change? 🖊

....

....

Holding Hands When a large group of people come together and hold hands, they form a continuous chain. Organic compounds can also form long chains of repeating units.

Polymers

A **polymer** is a large molecule formed by the covalent bonding of repeating smaller molecules. The smaller molecules that combine to form a polymer are called **monomers**.

Addition Polymers An **addition polymer** forms when unsaturated monomers react to form a polymer. The monomer-chain length, often represented as n, defines the properties of polymers.

Addition Polymer This sequence of reactions describes how multiple ethene units can form a polymer chain called polyethylene.

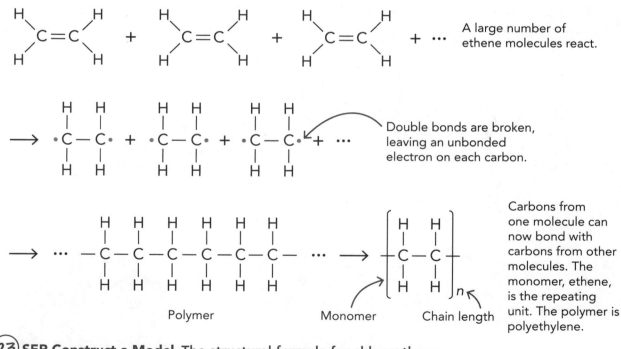

A large number of ethene molecules react.

Double bonds are broken, leaving an unbonded electron on each carbon.

Polymer   Monomer   Chain length

Carbons from one molecule can now bond with carbons from other molecules. The monomer, ethene, is the repeating unit. The polymer is polyethylene.

(23) **SEP Construct a Model** The structural formula for chloroethene is shown. Similar to the ethene polymerization, sketch how a polyvinyl chloride (PVC) addition polymer would be formed from chloroethene. Draw brackets around the monomer.

Condensation Polymers A **condensation polymer** forms when two monomers are joined with the loss of a small molecule such as water. Polyesters are polymers that consist of many repeating units of carboxylic acids and alcohols. The hydroxy groups from both combine to form a bond while releasing a water molecule. Polyamides are polymers in which carboxylic acid and amine monomer units are linked by amide bonds. Examples of polyamides are nylon and the proteins found in our food.

In order to form a continuing chain, condensation polymerization requires that there be at least two functional groups on each monomer molecule. Like addition polymers, chain length affects properties. The size and structure of the monomers can also have an effect. For example, polyamides containing aromatic rings result in tough and flame-resistant materials.

Condensation Polymerization This sequence of reactions describes how the condensation polymer polyethylene terephthalate (PET) forms.

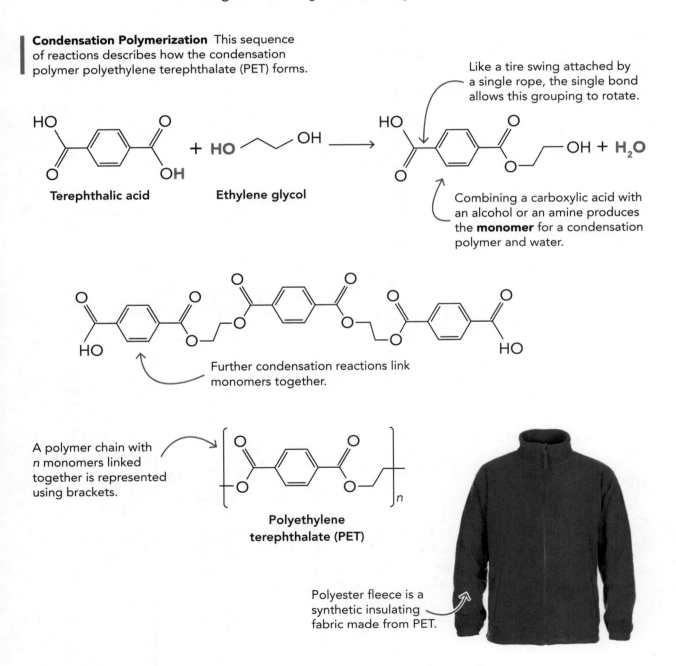

Like a tire swing attached by a single rope, the single bond allows this grouping to rotate.

Terephthalic acid

Ethylene glycol

Combining a carboxylic acid with an alcohol or an amine produces the **monomer** for a condensation polymer and water.

Further condensation reactions link monomers together.

A polymer chain with *n* monomers linked together is represented using brackets.

Polyethylene terephthalate (PET)

Polyester fleece is a synthetic insulating fabric made from PET.

(24) **SEP Obtain and Communicate Information** The fabric that makes up bulletproof vests can be made from terephthalic acid and an amine. Look up this reaction online and sketch it here. ✏

Revisit

INVESTIGATIVE PHENOMENON

GO ONLINE to Elaborate on and Evaluate your knowledge of how to identify functional groups and polymers by completing the peer review and engineering design activities.

In the CER worksheet, you drafted an explanation of why the combustion energy differs for two substances. With a partner, reevaluate the evidence cited in your arguments.

(25) **SEP Develop a Model** The acyclic structural formula for glucose, a carbohydrate our bodies use for fuel, is shown. Identify and circle the functional groups. If multiple glucose molecules were chained together, what type of polymer would be formed (addition or condensation)? Sketch the polymerization process. ✏

The Chemistry of Life

GO ONLINE to Explore and Explain the chemical composition of biomolecules such as starch, amino acids, and proteins.

Organic Macronutrients

The substances required by our bodies to survive are called **nutrients.** Our bodies synthesize only a small number of nutrients, so the rest we must get from the food that we eat. Nutrients provide us with energy, contribute to the structure of our bodies, and help regulate all of the important chemistry that happens inside our bodies. Nutrients that are required in small amounts and that regulate body chemistry are called **micronutrients.** Nutrients that we must consume in large amounts are called **macronutrients.**

The energy that a person consumes comes primarily from three macronutrients: carbohydrates, fats, and proteins. Energy from food is measured in units of **kilocalories.** European food labels use this unit to show the energy content of foods. However, in the United States, the unit **Calorie** is used, which is equivalent to one kilocalorie (1000 calories).

Macronutrients When we look at food labels, we're looking at how much energy the food contains (Calories) and the carbohydrate, fat, protein, and micronutrient content.

Nutrition Facts

8 servings per container

Serving size	**2/3 cup (46g)**

Amount per serving

Calories	**180**

	% Daily value*
Total Fat 8g	10%
Saturated Fat 1g	5%
Trans Fat 0g	
Cholesterol 0mg	0%
Sodium 110mg	4%
Total Carbohydrate 29g	11%
Dietary Fiber 4g	14%
Total Sugars 12g	
Includes 10g Added Sugars	20%
Protein 3g	
Vitamin D 2mcg	10%
Calcium 390mg	30%
Iron 8mg	45%
Potassium 235mg	6%

* The % Daily Value (DV) tells you how much a nutrient in a serving of food contributes to a daily diet. 2,000 calories a day is used for general nutrition advice.

Carbohydrates

Carbohydrates are the main source of energy for the body, and they are found in most foods. **Carbohydrates** are monomers and polymers of aldehydes and ketones that have numerous hydroxy groups attached. Most carbohydrates have the general formula $C_n(H_2O)_n$.

Monosaccharides and disaccharides The simplest carbohydrate molecules are called simple sugars, or **monosaccharides.** (The prefix *mono-* means "one.") Glucose and fructose are examples of monosaccharides. Glucose is the primary energy source for our bodies, and it is abundant in plants and animals. Fructose occurs in a large number of fruits and honey. A sugar that forms from the condensation reaction of two monosaccharides is known as a **disaccharide.** (The prefix *di-* means "two.")

Monosaccharides Both glucose and fructose have the same molecular formula, but glucose has an aldehyde functional group while fructose has a ketone group. The acyclic and cyclic structural formulas for both are shown.

Disaccharides Glucose and fructose molecules are linked together to form sucrose during a condensation reaction.

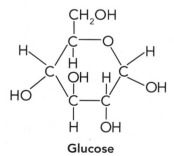

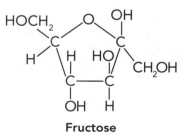

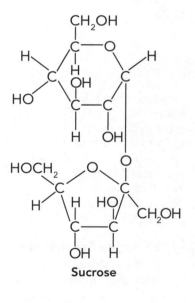

Sucrose

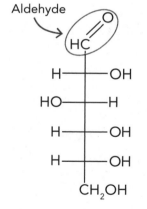

Glucose

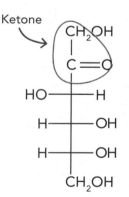

Fructose

Polysaccharides The formation of a disaccharide is sometimes the first step in a condensation polymerization reaction that produces extremely long molecules. The polymers produced by the linkage of many monosaccharide monomers are called **polysaccharides. Starches,** the major storage form of glucose in plants, are polysaccharide polymers that consist of glucose monomers linked in long chains. **Cellulose** is the main structural component of plant cell walls and is also a polymer made up of glucose monomers. Starches and cellulose are nearly identical. The only difference is the bond orientation between the glucose monomers. This simple difference makes starches digestible while cellulose is not. Your body gets most of the energy it needs to function by burning glucose obtained from starches. However, since cellulose isn't digested, it provides no energy.

Polymerization of Glucose Different orientations of the hydroxy groups in the glucose monomers within a polymer can result in structural isomers with very different properties, such as starch and cellulose.

Starch forms from glucose molecules linked together in the same orientation. It is ideal for **energy storage** as it is more easily formed and broken down.

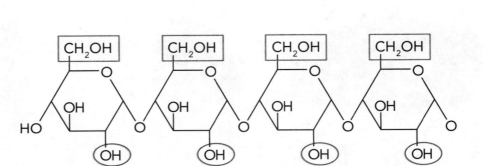

The alternating structure of **cellulose** allows for significantly more hydrogen bonds to form between chains, resulting in very strong and **insoluble** fibers. Your body cannot digest cellulose!

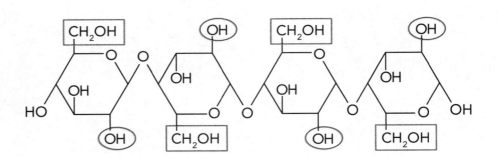

26 SEP Argue From Evidence Apples consist of cellulose as well as fructose. When juicing an apple, the cellulose is removed as pulp. Make a claim about the calorie content of apples compared to an equal mass of apple juice. Argue your claim from evidence.

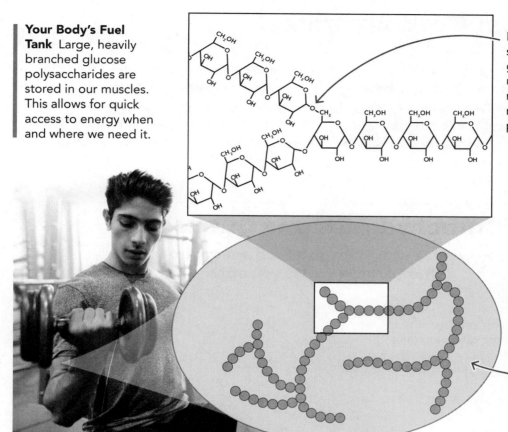

Your Body's Fuel Tank Large, heavily branched glucose polysaccharides are stored in our muscles. This allows for quick access to energy when and where we need it.

Because glucose has so many hydroxy groups, it can undergo condensation reactions that produce multiple branches per polymer chain.

These energy storage polysaccharides, called glycogen, are more heavily branched and compact than the starches we eat.

Carbohydrates Store Energy

When we eat food, not all of it is used immediately for energy. Some of the compounds in the food we eat are stored in the body for later use. When we eat simple sugars or starches, the glucose is extracted and either immediately combusted for energy in our cells, or stored in large branched polymers within the liver or skeletal muscles. These polymers are called glycogen, which is a heavily branched glucose polysaccharide our bodies use as one store of energy.

27) **SEP Construct an Explanation** Long-distance athletes often experience a phenomenon referred to as "hitting the wall," where they experience extreme muscular exhaustion. Construct an explanation for this phenomenon based on how energy is stored in the body. ✎

....

....

....

....

Energy from Carbohydrates

Your body requires energy to function. This energy is primarily obtained from the combustion of glucose. The complex process through which glucose is converted into energy is called **cellular respiration.** Cellular respiration takes place in and around the mitochondria in your body's cells, which is why mitochondria are often called the cell's "powerhouses." Although more complex in reality, we can model this process as a simple combustion reaction. Glucose reacts with the oxygen we breathe, producing carbon dioxide, water, and energy.

Carbohydrates and Our Body

How does your body produce energy from the carbohydrates you eat?

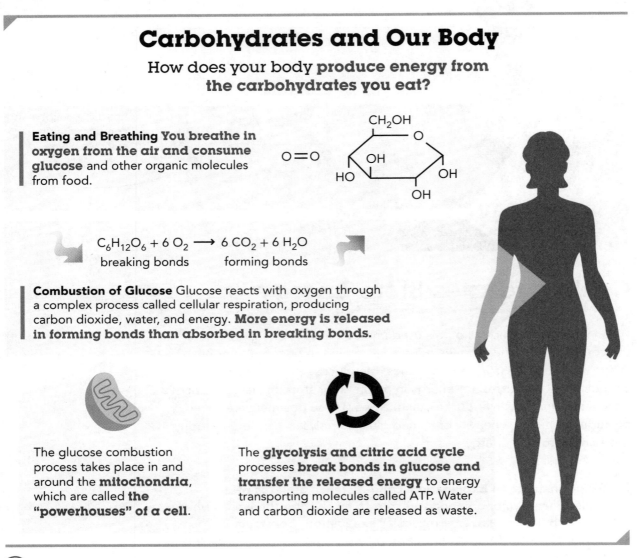

Eating and Breathing You breathe in oxygen from the air and consume glucose and other organic molecules from food.

$$C_6H_{12}O_6 + 6\,O_2 \longrightarrow 6\,CO_2 + 6\,H_2O$$
breaking bonds   forming bonds

Combustion of Glucose Glucose reacts with oxygen through a complex process called cellular respiration, producing carbon dioxide, water, and energy. **More energy is released in forming bonds than absorbed in breaking bonds.**

The glucose combustion process takes place in and around the **mitochondria,** which are called **the "powerhouses" of a cell**.

The **glycolysis and citric acid cycle** processes **break bonds in glucose and transfer the released energy** to energy transporting molecules called ATP. Water and carbon dioxide are released as waste.

28) **SEP Use Math** Breaking the bonds in oxygen molecules requires 498 kJ/mol. When the bonds in carbon dioxide are formed, 1,600 kJ/mol is released, and when the bonds in water are formed, 940 kJ/mol is released. The enthalpy of combustion for glucose is approximately −2,800 kJ/mol. Use this information and the chemical equation for cellular respiration to estimate how much energy it takes to break all of the bonds in a glucose molecule. ✏️

Amino Acids

Many organic compounds contain nitrogen in addition to carbon, hydrogen, and oxygen. Polymers of nitrogen-containing amino acids make up more than half the dry weight of your body. An **amino acid** is a compound that contains an amino group and a carboxyl group in the same molecule. There are 20 common amino acids used by your body. Nine of these, called essential amino acids, cannot be synthesized by your body and must be obtained from food.

Amino Acids All amino acids consist of a carboxyl group, an amino group, a hydrogen, and an R group side chain that are all covalently bonded to a central carbon atom.

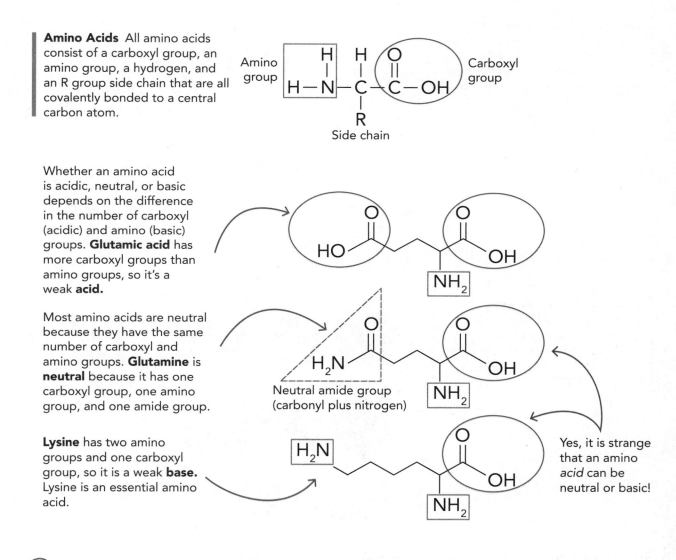

Whether an amino acid is acidic, neutral, or basic depends on the difference in the number of carboxyl (acidic) and amino (basic) groups. **Glutamic acid** has more carboxyl groups than amino groups, so it's a weak **acid.**

Most amino acids are neutral because they have the same number of carboxyl and amino groups. **Glutamine** is **neutral** because it has one carboxyl group, one amino group, and one amide group.

Lysine has two amino groups and one carboxyl group, so it is a weak **base.** Lysine is an essential amino acid.

Yes, it is strange that an amino *acid* can be neutral or basic!

(29) **SEP Use a Model** The structural formula for alanine is shown. Circle the carboxyl group, draw a box around the amino group, and underline the side chain. Will this amino acid be acidic, neutral, or basic? ✏️

Peptides

A **peptide** is any combination of amino acids in which the amino group of one is united with the carboxyl group of another. The bond between these two groups is called a **peptide bond.** Peptide bonds are formed during a condensation reaction, with water as the side product. Because all amino acids have two functional groups, condensation polymerization can result in long strings of peptides called **polypeptides.** A **protein** is a peptide polymer containing more than 100 amino acids.

Formation of a Peptide The hydroxyl in the carboxyl group reacts with hydrogen in the amino group, producing a C—N peptide bond and a water molecule.

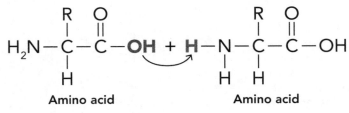

Amino acid   Amino acid

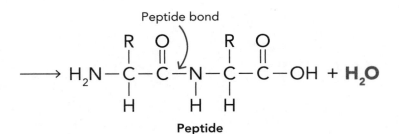

Peptide bond

Peptide

Polypeptides and Proteins A peptide with more than 10 but less than 100 amino acids is called a polypeptide. A peptide with more than 100 amino acids is called a protein.

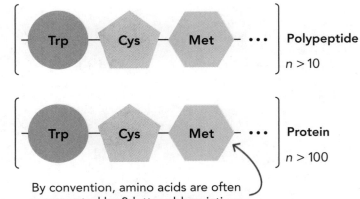

Polypeptide
$n > 10$

Protein
$n > 100$

By convention, amino acids are often represented by 3-letter abbreviations, such as Met for methionine.

(30) SEP Construct an Explanation The condensation reaction during peptide formation produces water as one of the products. Construct an explanation for where this water comes from.

....

....

....

Proteins

Structure of Proteins Proteins have a large number of amino acids strung together, resulting in very large, three-dimensional, and complicated molecules. Peptide chains can form long, straight chains called the **primary structure.** Hydrogen bonding with other close-by parts of the chain can cause the formation of a helix. Similarly, two peptide chains can cause hydrogen bonds to form a pleated, sheet-like structure. Both helices and sheets are called **secondary structures.** As the chains get longer they can begin to fold in very intricate ways, forming **tertiary structures,** due to side chain interactions. Finally, multiple proteins can combine and become tangled into a **quaternary structure,** with multiple types of intermolecular forces holding the entire macromolecule together.

Protein Structure The three-dimensional structure of a protein is determined by interactions among the amino acids in its peptide chains, mainly hydrogen bonding.

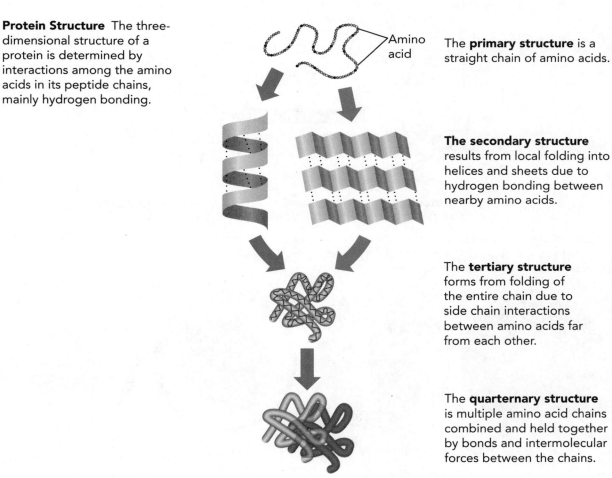

Amino acid

The **primary structure** is a straight chain of amino acids.

The secondary structure results from local folding into helices and sheets due to hydrogen bonding between nearby amino acids.

The **tertiary structure** forms from folding of the entire chain due to side chain interactions between amino acids far from each other.

The **quarternary structure** is multiple amino acid chains combined and held together by bonds and intermolecular forces between the chains.

31 **SEP Ask Questions** The structure of a large protein is very difficult to predict. What questions would you need to answer to begin determining the structure of a protein? ✎

....

....

....

Protein Denaturation Any process that disrupts or destroys the secondary, tertiary, and quaternary protein structure of a protein is called **denaturation.** Denaturation disrupts intermolecular forces but doesn't affect the significantly stronger covalent peptide bonds, so the primary structure of the protein remains. Proteins can be denatured by adding heat, acid, salt, or alcohol. Each of these additions results in a disruption of the intermolecular forces that provide the protein with its shape. Cooking meat begins the denaturing of proteins in the meat. Stomach acid and enzymes continue the process, eventually providing your body with access to the amino acids it needs.

Denaturation Interrupting the intermolecular forces between amino acids within proteins results in unfolding. You can interrupt these forces through the addition of heat, acid, salt, or alcohol.

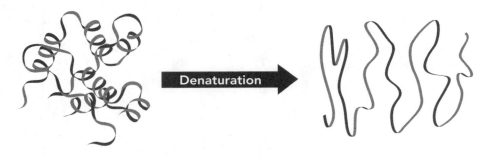

Folded protein   Denaturation   Unfolded protein

Boiled Eggs The photos show how the inside of an egg changes as you cook it. The protein albumin undergoes denaturation as it is heated.

0 minutes   1 minute   3 minutes   5 minutes

(32) **SEP Develop a Model** Egg white proteins start out as individual quaternary structures. When you denature them, they unfold. After unfolding, all of the stretched-out proteins coagulate into a mesh. Sketch a model of the egg white proteins during this process that explains why they go from transparent to opaque when cooking. ✎

Lipids

Fats, oils, and other water-insoluble compounds are called **lipids.** Most fats are obtained from animals, while most oils are obtained from plants. Although excessive dietary fat is harmful, you do need lipids in your diet to stay healthy. There are two main types of lipids that are necessary for your body to function: triglycerides are a long-term store of energy, and phospholipids make up the cell walls in your body.

Triglycerides Carboxylic acids with long side chains (12–24 carbons) are called **fatty acids.** When three fatty acids undergo a condensation reaction with glycerol, a compound with three hydroxy groups, the result is a **triglyceride.** Natural fats and oils are triglycerides, also called triesters of glycerol.

Triglycerides A condensation reaction of a glycerol alcohol compound with three carboxylic acids (fatty acids) produces a lipid called a triglyceride.

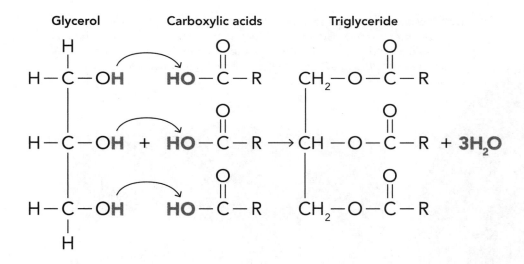

Solubility The presence of O—H and N—H bonds and lone electron pairs results in most carbohydrates and some proteins being polar and, therefore, soluble in water. Fats are not soluble in water because they are nonpolar.

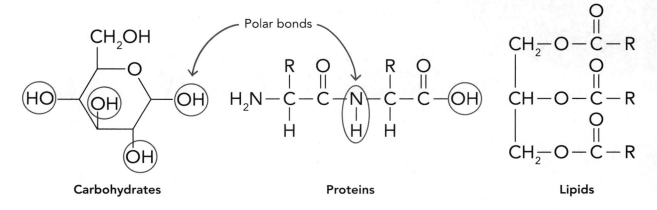

Carbohydrates · Proteins · Lipids

Phospholipids Lipids are called **phospholipids** when they contain phosphate groups. Phospholipid molecules have hydrophilic (water-loving) ionic heads and oily hydrophobic (water-hating) hydrocarbon tails. In water, half of the phospholipid behaves like a soluble ionic compound, and the other half behaves like an insoluble hydrocarbon. When placed in water, phospholipids spontaneously form a spherical double layer called a lipid bilayer. Lipid bilayers form the outsides of the cells in your body.

Phospholipid The representational diagram of a phospholipid shows the hydrophilic head as a sphere and the hydrophobic tails as wavy lines. The space-filling model shows the phospholipid lecithin.

Hydrophobic tail

Hydrophilic head

Cell Membranes Lipids spontaneously form spherical bilayers, which form cell membranes. The bilayer protects the cell, while protein channels allow select nutrients to pass through the cell membrane. Carbohydrates sit on the outside and act as a cell-to-cell recognition system.

Carbohydrate chain

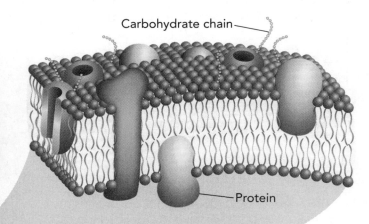

Protein

(33) SEP Construct an Explanation Based on the construction of just the cell membranes within your body, construct an explanation for why your diet should include a mixture of carbohydrates, protein, and fat.

....

....

....

Structure and Energy in Lipids The foods that we eat contain fats and oils in the form of both triglycerides and phospholipids. Both triglycerides and phospholipids have long hydrocarbon "tails" whose structures determine whether they are a fat or an oil. At room temperature, lipids with saturated chains are solids, or fats, and lipids with unsaturated chains are liquids, or oils. Saturated lipids also have a slightly larger energy density due to their larger H/C ratio.

> ▶ **Fats and oils have different melting points due to differences in their molecular structures.**

Saturation Triglycerides are composed of fatty acids, which are carboxylic acids with long side chains. The presence of a double bond changes the structure.

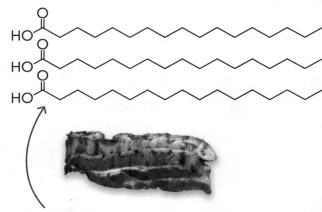

Stearic acids in animal fats, such as bacon fat, are saturated with no double bonds. The long chains experience greater intermolecular attraction, resulting in a higher melting point.

Oleic acid found in olive oil is unsaturated with one double bond. The bent structure reduces intermolecular attraction, resulting in a lower melting point.

(34) SEP Argue From Evidence Monounsaturated lipids are composed of fatty acids with one double bond. Polyunsaturated lipids are composed of fatty acids with multiple double bonds, like linoleic acid found in sunflower oil. Make a claim about which type of lipid would have a lower melting point and support your argument with evidence. ✎

....

....

....

Nucleic Acids

Nitrogen-containing polymers found in the nuclei of cells are called **nucleic acids.** Two types of nucleic acids are found in cells, deoxyribonucleic acid (DNA) and ribonucleic acid (RNA). The monomers that make up DNA and RNA polymers are called **nucleotides.** Each nucleotide consists of a phosphate group, a five-carbon sugar, and a nitrogen-containing unit called a nitrogen base. A difference in the sugar is what distinguishes DNA from RNA. The sugar in DNA is called deoxyribose, and the sugar in RNA is called ribose, which has one extra oxygen atom. There are four different nitrogen bases in DNA: adenine, guanine, thymine, and cytosine. These are abbreviated A, G, T, and C, respectively.

Nucleotides are composed of a phosphate, a sugar, and a nitrogen base. For DNA, the phosphate and sugar are the same in every nucleotide. The nitrogen base is one of four possible compounds.

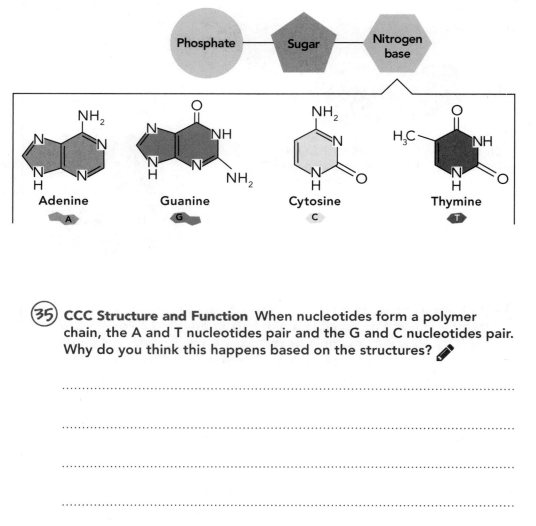

35 **CCC Structure and Function** When nucleotides form a polymer chain, the A and T nucleotides pair and the G and C nucleotides pair. Why do you think this happens based on the structures? ✏

....

....

....

....

DNA

Deoxyribonucleic acid (DNA) stores the information needed to make proteins and governs the reproduction and growth of new cells and new organisms. The structure of DNA consists of two nucleotide polymer chains wrapped into a spiral shape called a double helix. **Chromosomes** are large, tightly packed DNA molecules that contain all or part of the information needed for the construction of an organism.

DNA Double Helix For the nitrogen bases to fit neatly into the double helix, every double-ringed base (A and G) must pair with a single-ringed base (T and C) on the other strand.

Key

P   Phosphate group
S   Simple sugar
A   Adenine
G   Guanine
C   Cytosine
T   Thymine

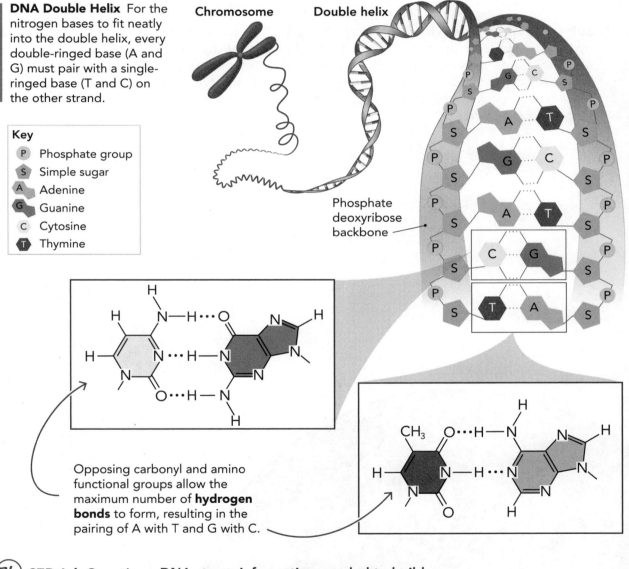

Chromosome

Double helix

Phosphate deoxyribose backbone

Opposing carbonyl and amino functional groups allow the maximum number of **hydrogen bonds** to form, resulting in the pairing of A with T and G with C.

36) **SEP Ask Questions** DNA stores information needed to build new proteins and cells. This information must be accessed and used in some way. What questions could you ask to help determine how the information is used? ✏

....

....

INVESTIGATIVE PHENOMENON

GO ONLINE to Elaborate on and Evaluate your knowledge of the structure and function of organic biomolecules by completing the class discussion and writing activities.

In the CER worksheet, you drafted an explanation about how to use mass ratios to identify biomolecules. With a partner, reevaluate the evidence cited in your arguments.

(37) **SEP Develop a Model** The food we eat is mostly made of carbon, hydrogen, and oxygen atoms. Sketch a flowchart model showing how these atoms are ingested, how more complicated organic molecules are formed in the body using these atoms, the types of reactions that occur, and how energy is stored and released from their rearrangement. ✎

GO ONLINE to Evaluate what you learned about organic chemistry and the chemistry of life by using the available assessment resources.

In the Performance Task, you produced your own biodiesel and measured its heat of combustion. Wrap up your experiment by answering the following questions.

38 **Construct an Explanation** How do you expect the measured heat of combustion for your biodiesel fuel to compare to the theoretical heat of combustion for the chemical compounds in your biodiesel? Explain your reasoning. ✏

....

....

....

....

39 **Construct an Explanation** How is the saturation level of the hydrocarbons in your biodiesel related to its heat of combustion? Explain your reasoning. ✏

....

....

....

....

40 **Revisit the Anchoring Phenomenon** How does what you learned in this investigation help explain the chemistry of organic molecules? ✏

....

....

....

....

GO ONLINE to Engage with real-world phenomena by watching a video and to complete reading and modeling activities.

What gives robots enough energy to explore Mars for many years?

Nuclear Processes

Most chemical reactions involve the interactions of electrons among atoms and molecules. In this investigation, however, we focus on reactions that involve the particles that make up atomic nuclei (protons and neutrons) and the smaller particles that they are made of. These reactions are the result of forces within nuclei and they are responsible for the energy released by nuclear fusion within stars, the generation of electricity by nuclear fission, and the radioactive decay of unstable atoms. Once you have viewed the Investigative Phenomenon video and worked on a first draft of a modeling exercise to explain how energy is transferred from the sun to Earth, discuss with a partner the following questions.

1) **CCC Energy and Matter** What are two ways that energy from nuclear processes might be used to power a robot on Mars, and what is an advantage and disadvantage of each? 🖉

....

....

....

....

2) **SEP Stability and Change** For these nuclear processes, why is it important for engineers to know the rates at which they occur? 🖉

....

....

....

....

Radioactivity and Half-Life

GO ONLINE to Explore and Explain radioactive decay chains and how to model radioactive decay processes.

Radioactivity

For centuries, alchemists, who were the first chemists, tried to transmute, or change, ordinary elements such as lead into precious elements such as gold. They never succeeded, of course, because it takes enormous amounts of energy to alter the nuclei of atoms—energies that humans achieved with powerful machines such as particle accelerators. It turns out, however, that humans now can create gold from other elements, such as mercury. This conversion of an atom of one element into an atom of another element is called **transmutation.** It also turns out that transmutation naturally occurs all the time, all around us, through the processes of radioactive decay, or radioactivity. **Radioactivity** is the process by which nuclei emit particles and rays.

Most isotopes are not stable, and their nuclei will naturally change or "decay" into other isotopes, releasing energy in the process. Radioactivity takes several forms that all involve changes to the nuclei of atoms and sometimes even changes to the neutrons and protons in the nuclei. This radioactivity can be used for many important applications, such as in medicine, but it can also pose serious hazards and risks to human health.

Glowing Nuclear Reactor Fuel Rods Once the uranium fuel rods in a nuclear fission reactor are finished with their useful life, they must be stored and left alone for many years because they are still highly radioactive. Some of this radioactivity causes a blue glow called Cherenkov radiation as it passes through matter.

The Standard Model

To study radioactivity, scientists must understand the smallest particles that make up matter. This set of fundamental particles and how they interact is known as the Standard Model. Electrons are fundamental particles: they cannot be divided into smaller particles. Neutrons and protons can be sub-divided, so they are not fundamental particles.

> **The Standard Model of Fundamental Particles** The four categories of fundamental particles are quarks, leptons, gauge bosons, and scalar bosons. Masses are given in electron volts (eV), millions of eV (MeV), or billions of eV (GeV), divided by the square of the speed of light (eV/c^2 or MeV/c^2 or GeV/c^2, respectively).

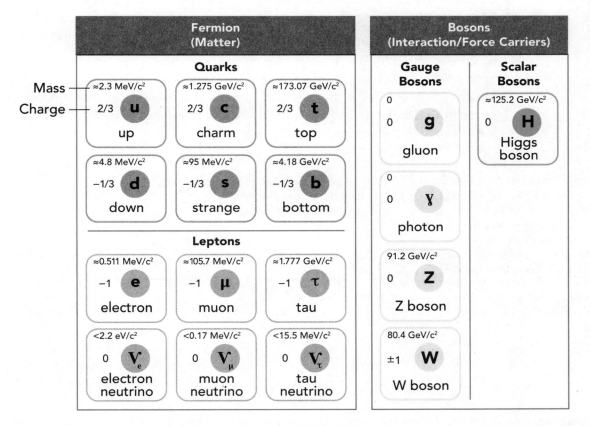

Quarks Quarks bind together to form larger particles called hadrons; a quark and an antiquark form a meson, and three quarks form a baryon. Neutrons and protons are examples of baryons. There are six different types of quarks, each with a different mass and charge. A neutron has two down quarks and one up quark. A proton has one down quark and two up quarks.

Leptons Leptons are small particles with either a negative charge or no charge. Muons and tau particles have substantial mass but only exist for fractions of a second. Electrons are much smaller in size, but are stable. All have associated neutrinos, which travel at extremely high speeds and have infinitesimal but non-zero masses that are still unknown.

Bosons The gauge bosons are particles that govern the ways that the quarks and leptons behave through different forces. Massless photons determine the ways that electromagnetic forces between electrically charged particles interact. Similarly, massless gluons determine the ways that forces hold particles such as quarks together in neutrons and protons. The W and Z bosons determine the ways particles interact through weak nuclear forces. The Higgs boson, not observed until 2012, is responsible for generating the masses of the quarks and leptons.

Matter and Antimatter There are other particles in addition to the 17 shown in the Standard Model chart. Most of the particles (quarks, leptons, W bosons) exist with antimatter particle equivalents. These are similar in mass but have an opposite charge. However, antiparticles do not last long because when they collide with their particle equivalent both particles are destroyed and a burst of electromagnetic radiation (photons) is produced.

Some of the particles (quarks and gluons) come in different "colors," or species (three for quarks, eight for gluons). Altogether, including antiparticles and different colors, there are a total of 61 different fundamental particles in the Standard Model. All of the interactions among particles that make up ordinary matter are ultimately explained by the particles and forces of the Standard Model.

Electron-Positron Annihilation
Positrons can be created by certain kinds of radioactive decay, but they nearly instantaneously attract an electron and both particles are annihilated when they collide. The released gamma rays are a major source of the energy given off by the sun's nuclear fusion.

Two high-energy gamma rays are released that exit the annihilation in opposite directions.

Gamma ray

e⁻ Electron

Gamma ray

Gamma ray

e⁺ Positron

The antimatter version of an electron is a positron, which has a similar mass but a charge of +1.

(3) **SEP Use Models** A neutron consists of two down quarks and one up quark. A proton consists of one down quark and two up quarks. When a down quark in a neutron changes to an up quark, the neutron changes into a proton. Use the charges of quarks listed in the Standard Model to calculate the charge of a neutron and proton and explain why this change occurs. 🖉

....

....

....

....

Strong and Weak Nuclear Forces

There are only four fundamental forces in the universe: gravity, electromagnetism, the strong nuclear force, and the weak nuclear force. Gravity acts between all particles of mass, but is extraordinarily weak, so it is only significant between objects that are more than about 1 kilometer in size. Gravity plays no role in most of chemistry, but it dominates forces at planetary and galactic scales. Electromagnetism is a much stronger force, but it only acts between negatively or positively charged particles. So, it plays no role at planetary scales, where net charges are balanced. However, no atoms would exist without it because electromagnetic (EM) forces hold the negatively charged electrons around the positively charged nuclei.

Strong Nuclear Force The strong interaction is an attractive force that holds quarks together to form neutrons and protons, which are both also called nucleons. Outside of a nucleon, the strong interaction is known as the **strong nuclear force,** which holds neutrons and protons together within atomic nuclei. The strong nuclear force is the strongest force. Consider an atom of the element lead, which has a large nucleus with 82 protons. The nucleus does not explode even though all of these positively charged protons are packed together because the strong nuclear force overcomes the EM force of repulsion. At the scale of a small helium nucleus (approximately 10^{-15} m), the strong force is about 100 times larger than the EM force. However, the strong force decreases more quickly with distance than the EM force. Thus, as the size of nuclei increases, the strong force is less able to hold the nucleons together.

> **Strong Force and Atomic Nuclei** The strong force is responsible for holding atomic nuclei together. However, the strong force decreases quickly with distance, so large nuclei become increasingly unstable.

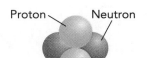

Proton — Neutron

A **small nucleus** has very few protons, so electrical repulsion is low. Nucleons are all close, so the strong nuclear force is large.

An **intermediate nucleus** with a larger number of protons has a greater electrical repulsion. There are many nucleons, but some are distant; so the strong force is moderate.

A **large nucleus** that has many protons has very high electrical repulsion. Having many nucleons means an increasing number are beyond the range of the strong nuclear force, and the strong nuclear force is weak. No nuclei with more than 208 nucleons are stable.

Weak Nuclear Force The force through which certain fundamental particles interact resulting in some forms of radioactive decay is the **weak nuclear force,** or weak interaction. The weak nuclear force is only about one-ten-millionth the strength of the strong nuclear force at the scale of nucleons. But the weak nuclear force allows quarks to change into other quarks, and this allows some particles to change into other particles. The most significant of these happens during **beta (β) decay,** which is a type of radioactivity involving the conversion between neutrons and protons with the emission of a beta particle. Electrons and positrons are beta particles. For example, in the form of radioactivity known as beta-minus (β^-) decay, or neutron decay, a down quark changes to an up quark, changing the neutron into a proton and releasing an electron and an electron antineutrino.

Weak Nuclear Force and β^- Decay This diagram is a graphical way to show radioactive decay, such as β^- decay. Time is on the vertical axis and the decay begins with the neutron.

The change of the down quark to an up quark means that the neutron changes to a proton and the atom changes into a new element.

The arrow for the electron antineutrino seems to suggest it is going backward in time. This does not seem to actually happen. It is a result of the fact that many of the characteristics of an antineutrino resemble a neutrino if it were going backward in time.

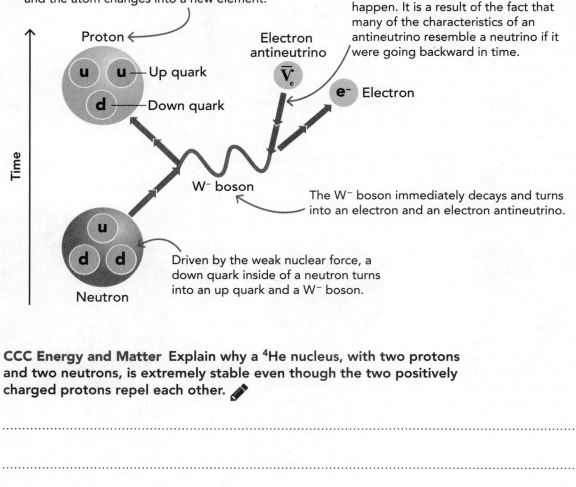

The W⁻ boson immediately decays and turns into an electron and an electron antineutrino.

Driven by the weak nuclear force, a down quark inside of a neutron turns into an up quark and a W⁻ boson.

(4) **CCC Energy and Matter** Explain why a ⁴He nucleus, with two protons and two neutrons, is extremely stable even though the two positively charged protons repel each other. ✏

....

....

....

....

Radioactive Processes

What are some of the major forms of radioactive decay?

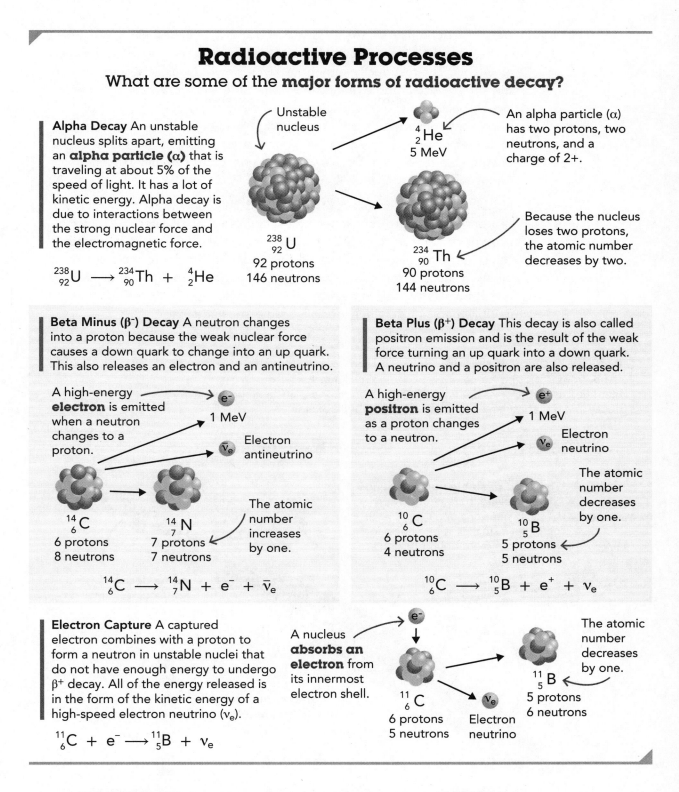

Alpha Decay An unstable nucleus splits apart, emitting an **alpha particle (α)** that is traveling at about 5% of the speed of light. It has a lot of kinetic energy. Alpha decay is due to interactions between the strong nuclear force and the electromagnetic force.

Unstable nucleus

$^{238}_{92}U$
92 protons
146 neutrons

$^{4}_{2}He$
5 MeV

An alpha particle (α) has two protons, two neutrons, and a charge of 2+.

$^{234}_{90}Th$
90 protons
144 neutrons

Because the nucleus loses two protons, the atomic number decreases by two.

$$^{238}_{92}U \longrightarrow \ ^{234}_{90}Th + \ ^{4}_{2}He$$

Beta Minus (β⁻) Decay A neutron changes into a proton because the weak nuclear force causes a down quark to change into an up quark. This also releases an electron and an antineutrino.

A high-energy **electron** is emitted when a neutron changes to a proton.

e^-
1 MeV

$\bar{\nu}_e$
Electron antineutrino

$^{14}_{6}C$
6 protons
8 neutrons

$^{14}_{7}N$
7 protons
7 neutrons

The atomic number increases by one.

$$^{14}_{6}C \longrightarrow \ ^{14}_{7}N + e^- + \bar{\nu}_e$$

Beta Plus (β⁺) Decay This decay is also called positron emission and is the result of the weak force turning an up quark into a down quark. A neutrino and a positron are also released.

A high-energy **positron** is emitted as a proton changes to a neutron.

e^+
1 MeV

ν_e
Electron neutrino

$^{10}_{6}C$
6 protons
4 neutrons

$^{10}_{5}B$
5 protons
5 neutrons

The atomic number decreases by one.

$$^{10}_{6}C \longrightarrow \ ^{10}_{5}B + e^+ + \nu_e$$

Electron Capture A captured electron combines with a proton to form a neutron in unstable nuclei that do not have enough energy to undergo β⁺ decay. All of the energy released is in the form of the kinetic energy of a high-speed electron neutrino (ν_e).

A nucleus **absorbs an electron** from its innermost electron shell.

e^-

$^{11}_{6}C$
6 protons
5 neutrons

ν_e
Electron neutrino

$^{11}_{5}B$
5 protons
6 neutrons

The atomic number decreases by one.

$$^{11}_{6}C + e^- \longrightarrow \ ^{11}_{5}B + \nu_e$$

During **alpha (α) decay** an unstable nucleus emits an alpha particle. **Electron capture** occurs when a nucleus absorbs an electron from its innermost electron shell. All forms of radioactive decay shown here share two things in common: they involve a change in the number of protons in the nucleus, changing the atom from one element to another. They also release a large amount of energy in the form of the kinetic energy of fast-moving particles, high-energy electromagnetic radiation such as gamma rays, and/or high-energy neutrinos.

Band of Stability Of the roughly 3,300 known nuclides, which are atoms whose nuclei have specific numbers of protons and neutrons, less than 300 are stable. The rest decay, either quickly or slowly. Nuclei are stable when the strong nuclear force greatly overcomes the electric repulsion of the closely packed protons. The locations of these stable nuclides on a plot of protons versus neutrons form a **band of stability,** which extends from hydrogen (a single proton) to very large atoms. When nuclei are too big or when the ratio of neutrons and protons becomes too unbalanced, radioactive decay occurs.

Nuclei with certain numbers (2, 8, 20, 28, 50, 82, and 126) of neutrons, protons, or both are very stable against nuclear decay. These numbers of protons or neutrons are called magic numbers and they make complete shells in the nucleus. Complete nuclear shells are similar to the stable electron shells of the noble gases. Nuclei are doubly magic if they have magic numbers for both neutrons and protons, such as ^4_2He, $^{16}_8O$, and $^{40}_{20}Ca$. Doubly magic nuclei are especially stable against decay.

Radioactive Decay of Nuclides The number of protons vs. the number of neutrons is plotted for naturally occurring nuclides. Each isotope is identified as stable or as the type of decay it undergoes. Unstable nuclei decay in a way that moves them closer to the band of stability.

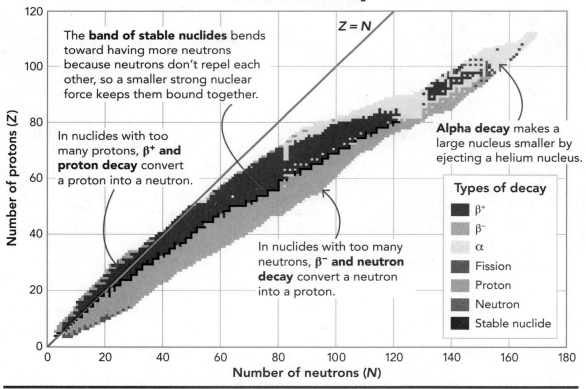

Band of Stability

The **band of stable nuclides** bends toward having more neutrons because neutrons don't repel each other, so a smaller strong nuclear force keeps them bound together.

$Z = N$

In nuclides with too many protons, **β⁺ and proton decay** convert a proton into a neutron.

Alpha decay makes a large nucleus smaller by ejecting a helium nucleus.

In nuclides with too many neutrons, **β⁻ and neutron decay** convert a neutron into a proton.

Number of protons (Z)

Number of neutrons (N)

Types of decay
- β⁺
- β⁻
- α
- Fission
- Proton
- Neutron
- Stable nuclide

5 **SEP Develop Models** Balanced equations are used to model reactions. In a chemical reaction, mass is conserved. In a nuclear reaction, baryons are conserved. During any nuclear process, the total number of neutrons plus protons does not change. Write an equation describing the beta-minus decay of $^{239}_{93}$Np.

Radioactive Half-Lives

Probability of Decaying An unstable nucleus will eventually decay through one of the radioactive decay processes. The radioactive decay of any single unstable nucleus is an unpredictable event, governed by quantum fluctuations. However, when dealing with large numbers of a particular isotope, the rate of decay of the initial isotopes, known as the parent isotopes, into new isotopes, known as the daughter isotopes, occurs in a very predictable probabilistic way. The decay occurs as a negative exponential function as shown in the graph. Another way to describe the radioactive decay is through a quantity called the **half-life** ($t_{1/2}$), which is the amount of time it takes for half of a radioactive isotope to be likely to decay. For large numbers of parent isotopes, this is basically the median lifetime of the parent, and it is related to the mean lifetime by $t_{1/2} = \tau \ln(2) \cong 0.693\tau$, where τ is the mean lifetime of a parent before decaying.

> **Half-Lives of Radioactive Decay** Any form of decay of a large number of unstable parent isotopes into a new isotope can be described using the half-life of the isotope.

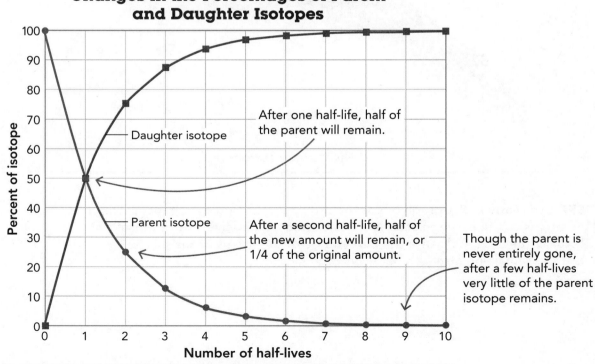

Changes in the Percentages of Parent and Daughter Isotopes

After one half-life, half of the parent will remain.

After a second half-life, half of the new amount will remain, or 1/4 of the original amount.

Though the parent is never entirely gone, after a few half-lives very little of the parent isotope remains.

Half-life Durations Some nuclei are extremely unstable and decay quickly. For example, ^{5}He has such a short half-life that samples usually completely decay in less than 10^{-21} seconds. Some nuclei are very stable and decay slowly. The half-life of ^{232}Th is 14.1 billion years, more than the age of the universe. These lifetimes are not random but are a function of the particular characteristics of the nucleus, and most importantly, how close the nucleus is to the band of nuclide stability. Nuclides that have neutron-to-proton ratios that put them adjacent to stable nuclides tend to have very long half-lives, as much as millions or billions of years. Very unbalanced nuclei can exist for just fractions of a second. For example, ^{7}H, with one proton and six neutrons, has a half-life of just 2.3×10^{-23} s.

Half-Lives of Nuclei The lifetimes of nuclei are largely a function of their distance from the band of stable nuclides.

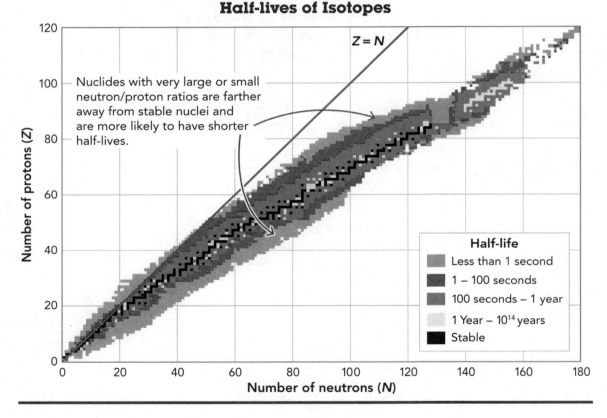

Half-lives of Isotopes

Nuclides with very large or small neutron/proton ratios are farther away from stable nuclei and are more likely to have shorter half-lives.

Z = N

Number of protons (Z)

Number of neutrons (N)

Half-life
- Less than 1 second
- 1 – 100 seconds
- 100 seconds – 1 year
- 1 Year – 10^{14} years
- Stable

(6) **SEP Use Math** In the graph of parent and daughter isotopes, it looks like no atoms of the parent isotopes are left after ten half-lives, but this isn't actually the case. Calculate the percentage of the atoms of the parent isotope remaining after ten half-lives.

Radioactive Decay Chains

For most unstable nuclei, especially large ones, many separate radioactive decays, each with its own half-life, must occur before a stable daughter product is finally reached. The largest stable nuclei are of lead, so decay chains of very large nuclei end at ^{206}Pb, ^{207}Pb, or ^{208}Pb. The most common radioactive decays are through α-decay, β-decay, and electron capture, and they occur in such a way as to keep the nuclei on track to reach the band of stable nuclei.

Thorium-232 Decay Chain The isotope ^{232}Th is unstable and decays to ^{238}Ra through an alpha decay. After a long series of successive α and β$^-$ decays, the decay chain ends with stable ^{208}Pb. Each time one of the isotopes in the decay chain decays to the next isotope, energy is released. One atom of ^{232}Th eventually releases six alpha particles, five electrons, five antineutrinos, and a total energy of 42.6 MeV.

The **half-life of ^{232}Th is 14.1 billion years.** However, the half-life times for the successive decays are much shorter, so it only takes on average another 11 years to decay to ^{208}Pb.

All of the isotopes in the chain are solid except for **^{220}Rn, which is a gas with a half-life of 56 seconds.** That means that for about a minute, ^{220}Rn can travel through the air and lodge in your lungs, where it will decay several times, releasing ionizing radiation, before ending as ^{208}Pb.

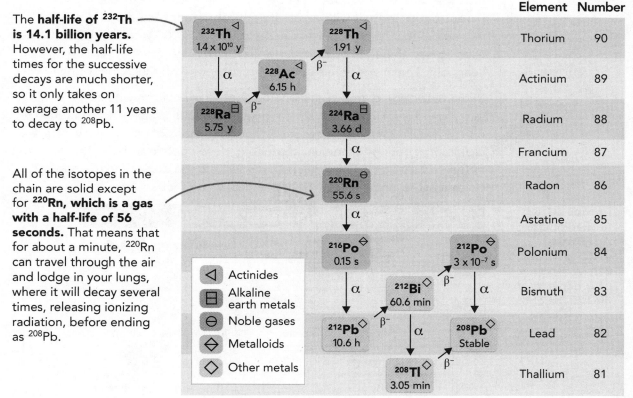

Data from: USGS

(7) **CCC Stability and Change** The decay chain of ^{238}U passes through a different isotope of radon, ^{222}Rn, which has a half-life of 3.8 days. Like ^{220}Rn, ^{222}Rn is the only isotope in the decay chain that is a gas. Explain why the natural underground decay of ^{238}U poses a much greater threat of lung cancer than the decay of ^{232}Th.

....

....

....

Radiometric Dating

A useful outcome of the decay rates of unstable nuclei is their ability to determine the ages of old objects. **Radiometric age dating** provides an estimate of the age of a material by comparing the relative amounts of a radioactive isotope and its daughter isotope. Scientists use this method to determine the ages of ancient archaeological remains, dinosaur bones, and even the age of Earth. If a rock formed with some amount of a parent isotope (*P*) and none of the daughter isotope (*D*), you can count the relative numbers of parent and daughter isotopes in that rock today. Then you can use the half-life ($t_{1/2}$) to calculate the age of the rock using the following formula.

$$\text{Age} = 1.44 \, t_{1/2} \ln\left(1 + \frac{D}{P}\right)$$

Because different nuclides have different half-lives, scientists choose the parent/daughter pair with a half-life appropriate for the material's age. For example, most carbon-14 has decayed after 100,000 years, so it cannot be used to find the ages of dinosaur bones, which are greater than 66 milllion years old. These ages are found using isotopes with much longer half-lives.

Radiometric age dating is challenging. Not all rocks form with all elements (e.g., igneous rocks contain almost no carbon) and not all rocks can retain the parent and daughter isotopes for millions or billions of years. Many different radiometric dating techniques have been developed in order to handle some of these challenges. The result is that scientists can determine the ages of objects and events from Earth's deep past with great accuracy.

Isotopes Used for Radiometric Age Dating The useful range of parent/daughter pairs depends on the half-life of the parent isotope.

Parent/Daughter Isotope Pairs			
Parent Isotope	**Daughter Isotope**	**Half-life of Parent (Years)**	**Useful Range (Years)**
^{14}C	^{14}N	5,730	100 – 50,000
^{234}U	^{230}Th	245,000	1000 – 350,000
^{40}K	^{40}Ar	1.3 billion	100,000 – 4.6 billion+
^{235}U	^{207}Pb	710 million	10 million – 4.6 billion+
^{238}U	^{206}Pb	4.5 billion	10 million – 4.6 billion+
^{87}Rb	^{87}Sr	47 billion	10 million – 4.6 billion+

(8) **SEP Construct Explanations** The age of the bones of this fossil of *Cynognathus*, a 250-million-year-old mammal-like reptile, was found using $^{40}K/^{40}Ar$ isotope ratios. What must be true about the bones of this fossil for its age to be determined? ✏️

....

....

Determining Age Using ^{14}C

Suppose that a treasure hunter comes to you, selling a wooden sarcophagus that she claims belonged to an ancient Egyptian pharaoh. You are able to take a sample and test it using ^{14}C dating. You find that 1 part in 101 of the ^{14}C has decayed to ^{14}N. How old in years (rounded to the nearest integer) is the sarcophagus? (And could it have been the pharaoh's?)

ANALYZE List the knowns and unknown.

Knowns	Unknown
$t_{1/2}$ (^{14}C) = 5,730 years	Age = ? years
ratio $\frac{D}{P} = \frac{^{14}N}{^{14}C} = \frac{1}{100}$	

CALCULATE Solve for the unknown.

Write the age equation.

$$\text{Age} = 1.44 \times t_{1/2} \ln\left(1 + \frac{D}{P}\right)$$

Substitute the knowns into the equation.

$$\text{Age} = 1.44 \times 5{,}730 \text{ yr} \times \ln\left(1 + \frac{1}{100}\right)$$

Solve the equation.

$$\begin{aligned}
\text{Age} &= 1.44 \times 5{,}730 \text{ yr} \times \ln(1.01) \\
&= 1.44 \times 5{,}730 \text{ yr} \times 0.00995 \\
&= 82.1 \text{ yr}
\end{aligned}$$

The sarcophagus is much too young to belong to an ancient pharaoh.

Make sure to use the natural log *ln* function on your calculator and not the *log* function to calculate ln(1.01).

EVALUATE Does the result make sense?

The half-life of ^{14}C is 5,730 years, which means that 50.5 out of 101 parts would have decayed in 5,730 years. Only 1 out 101 parts decayed in the sample, so the wood must be much younger than 5,730 years.

9 **SEP Calculate** Suppose that an early human cave site contains cutting stones, charcoal, and a pile of clam shells. Explain why you can use the charcoal and clam shells but not the stones for age dating the cave site. If only 5.00% of the original ^{14}C is left in the charcoal and shells, calculate how old the cave site is. ✎

GO ONLINE for more practice problems.

Carbon-14 Age Dating

Carbon-14 is one of the most useful isotopes for radiometric age dating because carbon is very plentiful and its intermediate half-life makes it ideal for dating objects and events in human history going back many thousands of years. Radiocarbon dating, or ^{14}C age dating, has some challenges: the starting amount of ^{14}C and the starting and ending amounts of the abundant daughter isotope ^{14}N are unknown. However, plants and animals indiscriminately absorb ^{14}C and stable ^{12}C, so the $^{14}C/^{12}C$ ratio is used to determine the age of old organic objects: this ratio decreases over time because the amount of ^{12}C in an object stays constant while the amount of ^{14}C decreases.

Another challenge is that ^{14}C is produced in the atmosphere from the bombardment of ^{14}N atoms by cosmic rays, but the amount produced varies. To determine accurate ages using ^{14}C, scientists use a calibration curve that takes this into account.

Carbon-14 Calibration Curve The amount of atmospheric ^{14}C varies over time, so using uncorrected $^{14}C/^{12}C$ ratios gives the wrong age. A ^{14}C calibration curve corrects this.

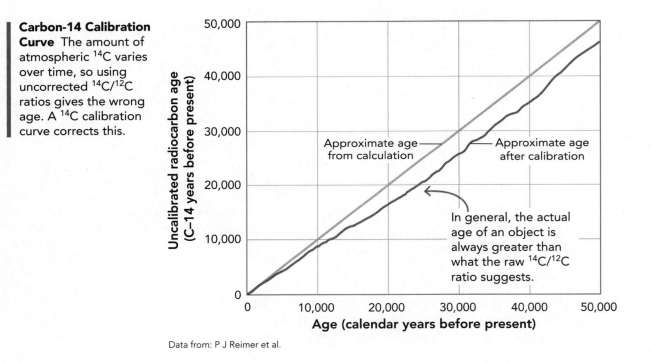

Data from: P J Reimer et al.

10) **SEP Analyze and Interpret Data** On the previous page, you calculated the age of an early human cave site. Because of the changing amounts of ^{14}C in the atmosphere, this age is not correct. Explain how to use the calibration curve to get the correct age. What is the correct age? ✎

....

....

....

Radiometric Dating of Old Materials

Radiometric dating has provided dates for our planet's history, both in terms of geology and biology. The Earth and solar system formed 4.568 billion years ago, the ocean formed at least 4.41 billion years ago, and life evolved very soon afterward (though the oldest single fossil dates to 3.465 billion years ago). Dinosaurs evolved 243 million years ago and became extinct 66 million years ago. Both ^{238}U to ^{206}Pb and ^{235}U to ^{207}Pb are used simultaneously to determine these dates. For many of these old dates, we rely upon sturdy crystals such as zircon to store the parent uranium and daughter lead atoms that are used in the age dating process. For early human fossils, however, the decay of ^{40}K to ^{40}Ar is a better tool because bones contain significant amounts of potassium.

Radiometric Dating Isotopes In the process of radiometric dating, the best isotope pair is chosen to match the age and material of the object being dated.

The oldest **Earth rocks** discovered so far are zircon crystals that have remained unchanged for 4.4 billion years. **Zircon** is a very hardy mineral and very resistant to weathering and melting. It can even remain intact when rock around it melts. This zircon crystal trapped atoms of uranium within it when it formed.

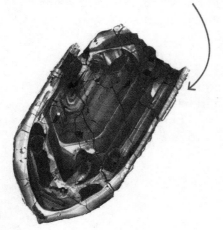

Radiometric dating using the $^{40}K/^{40}Ar$ method has shown that the earliest **hominid ancestors of modern humans** evolved about 7 million to 6 million years ago. This skull is from an early human that lived 80,000 years ago.

Age of Earth Scientists argued about the age of Earth for centuries and used a variety of methods (saltiness of the ocean, rate of heat flow out of Earth's surface, the numbers of sedimentary rock layers) with poor results. Radiocarbon dating finally gave the answer, 4.568 billion years, though not from Earth rocks. Certain meteorites called carbonaceous chondrites, which contain tiny spherical carbon-rich nodules and CAIs (calcium-aluminum-rich inclusions), are the oldest known objects from the start of the solar system. They formed at the same time as Earth and the rest of the solar system, so their ages are the same as Earth's.

11) **SEP Construct an Explanation** This Allende meteorite, a piece of the largest carbonaceous chondrite ever found, landed in Mexico in 1969. The small, spherical grains visible in the meteorite were some of the first particles to form in the earliest times of the solar system. Radiometric dating using the ratios of three lead isotopes— ^{204}Pb, ^{206}Pb, and ^{207}Pb— provided an age for this rock of more than 4.567 billion years. How can radiometric dating be used to construct a timeline of Earth's early history? Where does the Allende meteorite fit within Earth's history?

....

....

....

....

Revisit

INVESTIGATIVE PHENOMENON

GO ONLINE to Elaborate on and Evaluate your knowledge of radioactive decay and half-lives by completing the data analysis and discussion activities.

12) **SEP Energy and Matter** The latest Mars rover uses about 5 kilograms of plutonium-238 (^{238}Pu), which undergoes alpha decay and has a half-life of 88 years, as a heat source for producing electricity. What changes happen as ^{238}Pu decays? Why is its long half-life important for a rover?

....

....

....

....

....

....

Fission and Fusion

Conservation of Mass and Energy

Mass and Energy The law of conservation of mass works well for chemical reactions but not for nuclear reactions. The reason is that mass is a form of energy. So, the law of conservation of energy is true, but only if it includes mass as a form of energy. The connection between mass and energy is expressed by the equation $E = mc^2$, where E is energy, m is mass, and c is the speed of light (3.00×10^8 m/s). When a small amount of mass is destroyed, it creates a great amount of energy.

Nuclear Binding Energy An example of the equivalence of mass and energy is in the binding energy of groups of nucleons (protons and neutrons) in a nucleus. For example, the mass of the helium atom at rest is significantly less than the sum of the masses of its protons, neutrons, and electrons. The difference in the mass of an atom and the total mass of its nucleons and electrons is called the **mass defect.** This missing mass is the energy, called binding energy, released when the nucleus forms. **Nuclear binding energy** is the minimum energy required to break apart an atomic nucleus into its component nucleons. The binding energy is positive because energy is required to move the nucleons apart against the attractive force of the strong nuclear force.

Helium Binding Energy The mass of a ^{4}He atom is 4.00260 atomic mass units (amu). This is considerably less than the total mass of two protons, two neutrons, and two electrons.

	Particle			
	Helium Atom	**Proton**	**Neutron**	**Electron**
Mass (amu)	4.00260	1.00728	1.00867	0.00055
Mass (kg)	6.64644×10^{-27}	1.67262×10^{-27}	1.67493×10^{-27}	9.1094×10^{-31}
Mass (MeV/c^2)	3,710	934	936	0.509

For nuclear interactions, million electron-volts (MeV) is often used as the unit of energy: 1 MeV = 1.609×10^{-13} J. The mass unit is 1 MeV/c^2, where c is the speed of light; 1 MeV/c^2 = 1.79×10^{-30} kg.

Chemical Binding Energy All chemical bonds have a binding energy. A small amount of mass is also destroyed and converted into energy during chemical reactions, according to $E = mc^2$, but the amount is immeasurably small. For example, the binding energy released by the formation of a ^{2}H deuterium nucleus (from a proton and neutron) is 2.2 MeV, but the binding energy released by the electrostatic attraction of a hydrogen's proton and electron is only 13.6 eV, almost a million times smaller. The hydrogen's atomic mass is less than the sum of its proton and electron masses, but only by 2.4×10^{-35} kg, too small to measure.

Curve of Binding Energy The energies released when some nuclei combine (nuclear fusion) and others split apart (nuclear fission) are explained by their binding energies. Plotting the binding energies per nucleon versus the number of nucleons gives the curve of binding energy. Small nuclei release energy when they fuse because adding nucleons creates a greater strong force per nucleon. The resulting atomic masses are smaller than the sum of their components, and binding energy is released (as particles or radiation) when they fuse. Because of the relative strengths of the strong and electromagnetic forces, ^{62}Ni, ^{58}Fe, and ^{56}Fe have the most tightly bound nuclei with the highest binding energy per nucleon. For isotopes larger than ^{56}Fe, fission results in a net decrease in mass, releasing energy.

Curve of Binding Energy
A graph of the average binding energy per nucleon versus number of nucleons in a nucleus defines two separate regions for isotopes.

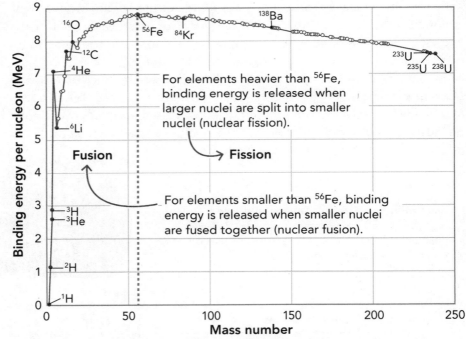

Data Source: National Nuclear Data Center, Brookhaven National Laboratory based on ENSDF and the Nuclear Wallet Cards

(13) **CCC Scale, Proportion, and Quantity** Describe how nuclear binding energy and chemical binding energy can be used to explain why nuclear processes are able to produce much larger amounts of energy than chemical processes. ✎

....

....

Nuclear Binding Energy of Helium

Energy is released when a helium atom forms from protons, neutrons, and electrons. What is the mass defect of a ^{4}He isotope? How much energy is released by this missing mass, and how does it relate to the binding energy of ^{4}He?

ANALYZE List the knowns and unknowns.

Knowns	Unknowns
Mass of proton (m_p) = 934 MeV/c^2	Mass defect of ^{4}He = ? MeV/c^2
Mass of neutron (m_n) = 936 MeV/c^2	Energy released = ? J
Mass of electron (m_e) = 0.509 MeV/c^2	Binding energy = ? J
Mass of ^{4}He atom (m_{He}) = 3710 MeV/c^2	
1 MeV = 1.609×10^{-13} J	

CALCULATE Solve for the unknowns.

Calculate the mass defect by subtracting the total mass of the particles from the mass of the isotope.

$$\text{Mass defect} = m_{He} - (2m_p + 2m_n + 2m_e) =$$
$$= 3710 \text{ MeV}/c^2 - (2(934 \text{ MeV}/c^2) + 2(936 \text{ MeV}/c^2)$$
$$+ 2(0.509 \text{ MeV}/c^2))$$
$$= 3710 \text{ MeV}/c^2 - 3741 \text{ MeV}/c^2$$
$$= -31.0 \text{ MeV}/c^2$$

Write the equation that relates energy to mass.

$$E = mc^2$$

Substitute in the values and solve for the energy released.

$$E = \left(-31.0 \frac{\text{MeV}}{c^2}\right)c^2 = -31.0 \text{ MeV}$$

Convert MeV to joules.

$$-31.0 \text{ MeV}\left(\frac{1.609 \times 10^{-13} \text{ J}}{1 \text{ MeV}}\right) = -4.99 \times 10^{-12} \text{ J}$$

The energy released is -4.99×10^{-12} J.
The binding energy is positive 4.99×10^{-12} J.

EVALUATE Does the result make sense?

A mass defect of 31.0 MeV/c^2 is about 1/100 of the mass of the ^{4}He atom, so this is reasonable.

14) **CCC Energy and Matter** A 1-gigawatt coal-fired power plant burns about 900 metric tons of coal per day to generate 8.6×10^{13} J of energy. Using $E = mc^2$, how much atomic mass (in grams) would need to be converted into energy to generate 8.6×10^{13} J of energy? (Hint: 1 J = 1 kg·m^2/s^2) ✎

GO ONLINE for more practice problems.

Mass and Energy at the Big Bang

The Big Bang theory explains all available data about the formation, structure, and composition of the universe. This includes its bulk composition (76% H, 24% He), the rapid motions of galaxies away from each other, and the temperature of outer space (2.7 K).

Big Bang Our universe began about 13.8 billion years ago, infinitesimally small and infinitely hot. It immediately began expanding at the speed of light and started cooling.

The universe became a **soup of quarks, antiquarks, and gluons**. The quarks and antiquarks collided and mostly annihilated each other, leaving a slight excess of quarks.

Big Bang

First quarks and leptons

First bosons

Quark soup

First protons and neutrons

0 s 10^{-36} s 10^{-32} s 10^{-12} s 10^{-6} s   10 s

Time after the Big Bang

Pure radiation

The universe, centimeters in size, expanded faster than the speed of light during the **inflationary period**. The **first fundamental particles** (quarks, electrons, neutrinos) formed from the radiation.

Boson particles began to form, including the Higgs boson, which provided mass to other particles. The universe, which now had four distinct forces, was about the size of our solar system.

Quarks combined to form **hadrons** (protons and neutrons) and their antimatter equivalents. Collisions of protons and electrons released neutrinos. Annihilation of hadrons and antihadrons left **a universe dominated by leptons** (electrons and positrons), which largely annihilated each other.

As the early universe expanded, it cooled, and radiation energy began to convert into mass according to $E = mc^2$. The universe went through a sequence of stages as different particles formed and were annihilated. The early universe contained vast numbers of both particles and antimatter particles, which mostly collided and annihilated. However, the universe had a tiny amount of matter left over, which forms the materials of our world.

Matter is found in several different forms in the present universe. The matter seems to be 0.01% photons (background microwave energy), 0.1% neutrinos, and 4.84% ordinary matter (mostly protons, neutrons, and electrons). Only about 6% of this ordinary matter is in the form of stars, planets, and visible gas clouds. The rest is invisible to us, perhaps in black holes. Most of the mass of the universe is in the form of dark matter (25.8%) and dark energy (69.2%). Astronomers continue to make more discoveries about matter in the present universe, which can lead to refinements to the Big Bang, and our understanding of the early universe.

Nuclear fusion of neutrons and protons created lots of ^{4}He and small amounts of ^{2}H, ^{3}He, and ^{7}Li. By 20 minutes, the universe had cooled enough that **nucleosynthesis** stopped, leaving a universe mostly 76% H and 24% He.

Stars and galaxies began forming, carrying out stellar nucleosynthetic processes that create larger elements. Galaxies formed large clusters.

First atomic nuclei | First neutral atoms | Dark ages | First stars and galaxies | Expansion accelerates

380,000 y   3 million y   300 million y   9.8 billion y   Today
Time after the Big Bang

During recombination and decoupling, temperatures cooled enough for electrically **neutral H and He** atoms to form (with electrons around nuclei), allowing photons to travel without being scattered by plasma and giving the universe an orange glow.

As the universe expanded, the wavelengths of this orange light were stretched into the microwave range, known as the Cosmic Microwave Background, and were no longer visible. The **universe went dark again**, now because there were no sources of light.

The universe's **expansion began to accelerate**, and is still increasing today. The eventual fate of the universe is not understood.

(15) **SEP Construct Explanations** The early universe was dark during two time periods, which included most of the first 300 million years. Explain the differences between these time periods that resulted in darkness. ✏️

....

....

....

Particle Accelerators and Transmutation

Humans can now summon the enormous energies needed to carry out the high-velocity particle collisions that can cause the transmutation of one element into another. Instruments called particle accelerators are able to make artificial radioisotopes, including ones that do not occur in nature. Of the 118 named elements, only 94 occur naturally, and six of these are extremely scarce. The other elements have been produced through artificial transmutation, though they usually only last for fractions of a second. Although it is not economically viable, particle accelerators can now create gold from the transmutation of mercury by bombarding it with neutrons, fulfilling the alchemists' ancient dream of making gold.

Particle Accelerator Particle accelerators have many current and potential uses, including the production of medical and industrial radioisotopes and accelerating the decay of radioactive wastes, as well as examining the nature of matter and the origins of the universe.

Particle source

Particles

Electromagnet

Electric field generator

Large numbers of powerful magnetic and electric fields are used to accelerate particles within a large ring, so that they reach speeds sufficient to achieve nuclear reactions with other particles upon collision.

A worker rides a bike around the 27-kilometer long particle accelerator ring of the CERN Large Hadron Collider.

16 **CCC Connect to Technology** It is possible to make many rare metals through artificially induced transmutation. Explain why it is rarely cost-effective to do so now but might become more so in the future. ✏️

....

....

....

Nuclear Fission

Large, unstable nuclei can undergo nuclear fission through the bombardment of neutrons. **Nuclear fission** is the splitting of a nucleus into smaller fragments, with the release of neutrons and a large amount of energy. Large nuclei that are unstable would eventually transmute naturally through radioactive decay, but the added neutron destabilizes them and triggers an immediate fission into two new elements. The particular daughter products can vary, but one is usually much larger than the other. Most actinide isotopes with an odd number of neutrons are **fissile,** meaning that they can undergo nuclear fission. However, certain isotopes are good for use as nuclear fuel in nuclear power reactors. These isotopes are plentiful, have long half-lives, will usually split upon neutron capture, and release multiple neutrons during fission. The released neutrons then fly off and split other nuclei, creating continuous chain reactions. The most common nuclear fuel is the naturally abundant uranium-235.

Uranium-235 Fission Neutron bombardment of a ^{235}U nucleus causes it to become unstable and begin to split into two separate nuclei. This releases 203 MeV of energy in the form of gamma rays (3.5%), three fast neutrons (2.5%), and the kinetic energy of the two new nuclei (94%) that fly off at 3% of the speed of light.

One neutron starts one fission event of ^{235}U that releases three new neutrons. They can start new fission events, leading to a chain reaction.

Neutron

Uranium-235

Uranium-236

Krypton-92

Gamma rays

Neutrons

Gamma rays

Barium-141

Of the two nuclei that are formed by the fission process, one is always much larger than the other.

(17) **CCC Use Models** Sketch a model, including an equation, for the alpha decay of ^{222}Ra. Then, use your model to explain why alpha decay is considered a type of nuclear fission. ✏️

Nuclear Fusion

Nuclear fusion is the process of combining nuclei to produce a nucleus of greater mass. For lighter nuclei, up to about ^{56}Fe, this process releases energy. The fused nucleus has less mass than the sum of the initial particles, with the mass defect converting into kinetic energy according to $E = mc^2$.

Nuclear fusion reactions have a very large energy barrier because particles must first overcome strong electrical repulsions between protons: fusing just two protons has a 1.1 MeV energy barrier. Once they do closely approach, the strong nuclear force takes over, and the nucleus becomes tightly bonded. These high-energy barriers have so far prevented humans from building nuclear fusion power plants. However, fusion reactions power the life cycles of stars because the intense temperatures and pressures within the cores of stars allow particles to overcome these energy barriers.

Fusion of Deuterium and Tritium Two hydrogen isotopes collide with enough energy to overcome the electrical repulsion of their protons. The fusion has a total energy release of 17.6 MeV in the form of the kinetic energy of the ^{4}He atom (3.5 MeV) and neutron (14.1 MeV).

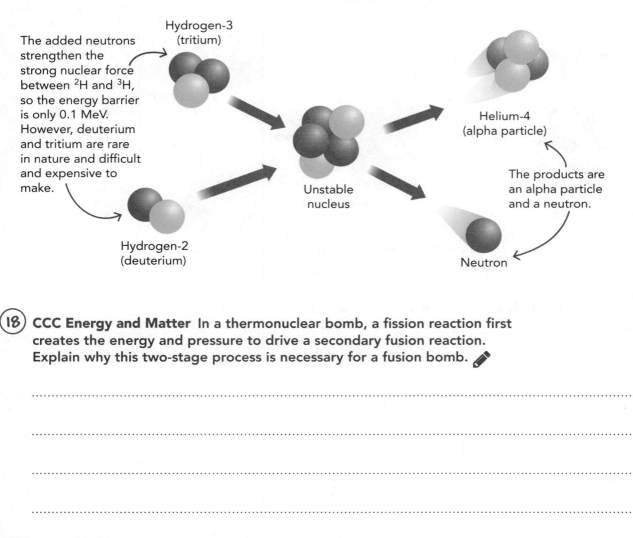

The added neutrons strengthen the strong nuclear force between ^{2}H and ^{3}H, so the energy barrier is only 0.1 MeV. However, deuterium and tritium are rare in nature and difficult and expensive to make.

Hydrogen-3 (tritium)

Hydrogen-2 (deuterium)

Unstable nucleus

Helium-4 (alpha particle)

The products are an alpha particle and a neutron.

Neutron

(18) **CCC Energy and Matter** In a thermonuclear bomb, a fission reaction first creates the energy and pressure to drive a secondary fusion reaction. Explain why this two-stage process is necessary for a fusion bomb. ✏️

....

....

....

....

Solar Fusion

For most of a star's lifetime, hydrogen fuses into helium, releasing vast amounts of energy that powers the star and is the original source of a star's light. Each second, 620 million metric tons of protons undergo nuclear fusion within our sun. The kind of fusion processes that occur depend on the size and age of the star, which determine its temperature and pressure.

Fusion in Small Stars For small stars, including and up to stars 1.3 times larger than the sun, the most common fusion process is a proton-proton chain. Six protons fuse to form a ^{4}He nucleus, two high-speed protons, and gamma rays. The process takes several steps because the sun contains no free neutrons. The neutrons have to be made from protons. Our sun is made of a high-temperature plasma of about 10^{57} protons and electrons. The proton-proton chain releases gamma rays, which provide the energy that we see as sunlight.

> **Solar Proton-Proton Chain Fusion** In this fusion within small stars, 0.7% of the proton masses is converted into 26.7 MeV of energy as gamma rays, neutrinos, and the kinetic energies of particles.

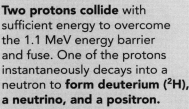

Two protons collide with sufficient energy to overcome the 1.1 MeV energy barrier and fuse. One of the protons instantaneously decays into a neutron to **form deuterium (^{2}H), a neutrino, and a positron.**

The **positron** formed by the proton decay instantly interacts with an electron and **annihilates,** releasing a burst of gamma rays. The proton fusion, including the **gamma rays,** releases 1.44 MeV of energy.

The deuterium nucleus can collide and fuse with a proton to form ^{3}He in **proton-deuterium fusion.** This process releases 5.45 MeV of energy, some in the form of additional gamma rays.

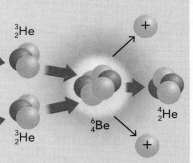

Helium fusion can occur in several different ways. Here, two ^{3}He nuclei are driven by the strong nuclear force to fuse into a ^{6}Be nucleus.

Immediately, **^{6}Be decays** to a stable alpha particle and two protons, which can then all engage in more fusion reactions.

Fusion in Large Stars

Large stars, greater than 1.3 times the mass of the sun, have higher temperatures and pressures within their cores. So, even though they have much greater mass, they "burn" through their hydrogen, producing helium, much faster than small stars do. Large stars primarily fuse hydrogen through the carbon-nitrogen-oxygen (CNO) cycle, in which a large nucleus fluctuates in size among carbon, nitrogen, and oxygen nuclei. The nucleus acts as a catalyst, absorbing hydrogen and emitting helium. The total amount of energy released when four protons are converted into ^{4}He in the CNO cycle is 26.7 MeV. This energy is exactly the same as the amount released by the proton-proton chain for small stars. However, the fusion process occurs much faster at the higher temperatures within large stars.

CNO Fusion Cycle If a large star forms with some carbon, it can act as a catalyst in the process of converting hydrogen to helium. The net reaction through all versions of the cycle is given by the following equation:

$4 {}^1_1H + 2e^- \rightarrow$
${}^4He + 2e^+ + 2e^- + 2\nu_e + 3\gamma + 24.7$ MeV $\rightarrow$
${}^4He + 2\nu_e + 7\gamma + 26.7$ MeV

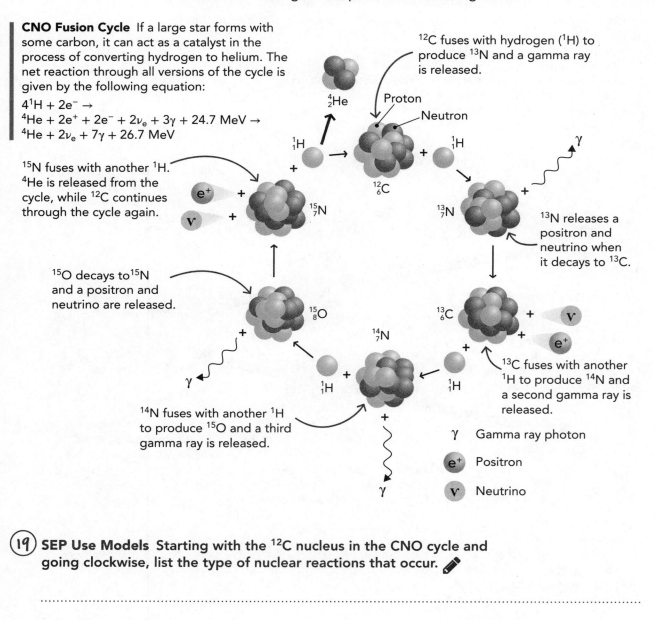

^{12}C fuses with hydrogen (^{1}H) to produce ^{13}N and a gamma ray is released.

^{15}N fuses with another ^{1}H. ^{4}He is released from the cycle, while ^{12}C continues through the cycle again.

^{15}O decays to ^{15}N and a positron and neutrino are released.

^{13}N releases a positron and neutrino when it decays to ^{13}C.

^{13}C fuses with another ^{1}H to produce ^{14}N and a second gamma ray is released.

^{14}N fuses with another ^{1}H to produce ^{15}O and a third gamma ray is released.

γ   Gamma ray photon

e⁺   Positron

v   Neutrino

(19) **SEP Use Models** Starting with the ^{12}C nucleus in the CNO cycle and going clockwise, list the type of nuclear reactions that occur. ✏️

....

....

Nucleosynthesis

For most of the life of a star, fusion reproduces what happened in the first 20 minutes after the Big Bang: hydrogen fuses into helium. However, when the star begins to run low on hydrogen, it starts fusing helium to make larger nuclei. This happens quickly at the end of a star's life because the temperatures and pressures increase rapidly, making fusion reactions easier. **Nucleosynthesis** is the process of making new elements within a star's core. Nucleosynthesis makes all of the elements our planet is made of other than the hydrogen and helium left over from the Big Bang.

Stellar Nucleosynthesis The elements made inside a star and released to the universe vary according to the star's size and composition. For small stars, nucleosynthesis does not produce very large elements. Stars that are eight times smaller than our sun can only create elements up to carbon and oxygen. In a very large star, the ^{4}He nuclei make increasingly larger elements by fusing with themselves and nuclei that are multiples of alpha particles, called *alpha elements* (C, O, Ne, Mg, Si, etc.). Alpha elements are very abundant in our solar system. Only very large stars can produce elements all the way up to the size of iron through fusion.

Stellar Nucleosynthesis This occurs during the red supergiant phase for a star with a mass 10 times greater than the sun's, with multiple shells of fusion occurring for different elements at different temperatures and pressures. This occurs for about 1,000 years before collapsing into a supernova.

Nonburning hydrogen

Hydrogen fusion

Helium fusion

Carbon fusion
$^{12}C + {}^4He \longrightarrow {}^{16}O + \gamma$

Oxygen fusion
$^{16}O + {}^4He \longrightarrow {}^{20}Ne + \gamma$

Neon fusion
$^{20}Ne + {}^4He \longrightarrow {}^{24}Mg + \gamma$

Magnesium fusion
$^{24}Mg + {}^4He \longrightarrow {}^{28}Si + \gamma$

Silicon fusion
$^{28}Si + {}^4He \longrightarrow {}^{32}S + \gamma$

Iron ash

Nuclei repeatedly fuse with alpha particles to create nuclides up to ^{56}Fe, each time releasing gamma rays. The fusion reactions within different shells are dominated by the fusion of ^{4}He with a different alpha element.

Elements Larger than Nickel Fusion reactions within stars can generate elements up to ^{56}Fe and ^{62}Ni, which are then ejected into space by a star's solar wind, seeding the universe. Larger elements only form during a star's supernova phase or during the collisions between neutron stars.

Many atoms larger than iron form in the thousands of years before a supernova from high-energy neutron impacts. The sequence of neutron captures and beta decays creates increasingly larger elements that go up the band of stable nuclides. Other large nuclides form in the last seconds of a star, during the supernova explosion. Free neutrons shoot throughout the star, causing neutron absorption with no time for radioactive decay.

White dwarfs, formed from smaller stars, also undergo supernova explosions, seeding the universe with heavier elements, but most large nuclei in space may be the result of massive neutron star collisions.

Nucleosynthesis Periodic Table This shows the astrophysical processes that can create elements for a sample of eight elements selected from the periodic table.

The Big Bang made most of the universe's H and He. Everything else, other than human lab-created elements, was made inside stars.

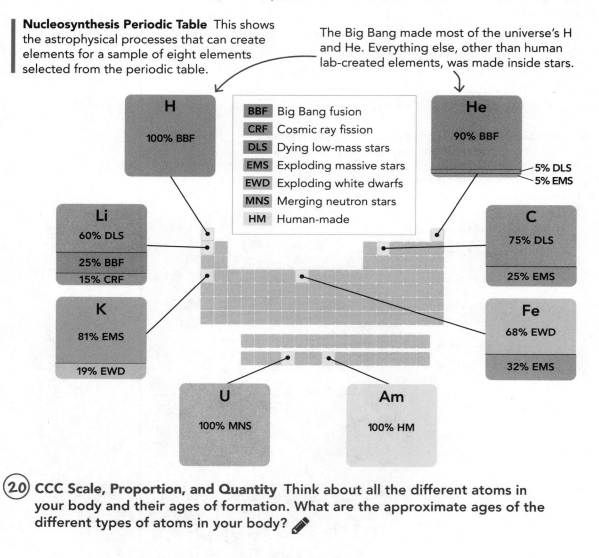

BBF	Big Bang fusion
CRF	Cosmic ray fission
DLS	Dying low-mass stars
EMS	Exploding massive stars
EWD	Exploding white dwarfs
MNS	Merging neutron stars
HM	Human-made

H 100% BBF

He 90% BBF — 5% DLS — 5% EMS

Li 60% DLS / 25% BBF / 15% CRF

C 75% DLS / 25% EMS

K 81% EMS / 19% EWD

Fe 68% EWD / 32% EMS

U 100% MNS

Am 100% HM

20. **CCC Scale, Proportion, and Quantity** Think about all the different atoms in your body and their ages of formation. What are the approximate ages of the different types of atoms in your body? ✏

....

....

....

Star Life Cycle

Star Formation All stars form from the gravitational collapse of a star-forming nebula of gas and dust into a rotating disk-shaped protostar. After that, there is surprising variety in the types and sizes of stars that form. Smaller stars last much longer than larger stars, up to tens of billions of years. Some of the universe's original small stars, formed just from hydrogen and helium, still shine. The largest stars last just millions of years, so their remains, including elements up to plutonium, are what new stars form from. The starting composition and size of a star determines which fusion processes occur and, therefore, the star's temperature, color, and brightness. Large stars are usually brighter than smaller stars, but a star's brightness changes over time.

The Life Cycle of Smaller and Larger Stars The lifetimes of stars are often divided into two simplified pathways, depending on the star's size.

In the **life cycle of smaller stars,** small stars (97% of all stars) slowly get hotter as they become denser and eventually swell into a red giant when the core runs out of hydrogen.

In the **life cycle of larger stars,** large stars (more than eight times our sun's mass) last at most tens of millions of years before briefly becoming a supergiant, swelling to the size of Jupiter's orbit.

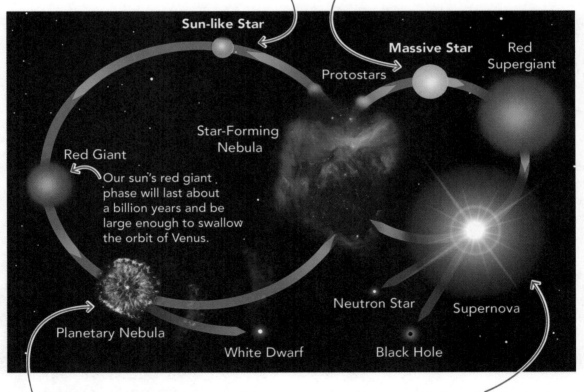

Sun-like Star

Massive Star

Red Supergiant

Protostars

Star-Forming Nebula

Red Giant

Our sun's red giant phase will last about a billion years and be large enough to swallow the orbit of Venus.

Planetary Nebula

White Dwarf

Neutron Star

Supernova

Black Hole

A small star sheds its outer layers to become a beautiful planetary nebula (misnamed and not related to planets), leaving its core behind as a white dwarf, which sometimes explodes as a supernova.

In a supergiant, fusion quickly burns elements up to iron and then either contracts into a black hole or violently explodes as a supernova more than 100,000 times brighter than a small star. The remaining star collapses into either a neutron star or black hole, both made of neutrons so dense that a teaspoon's mass is more than a billion tons.

Reincarnation of Stars Ironically, it is often the supernova explosion of a dying star that triggers the birth of new stars. The supernova or neutron star collision blasts heavier elements into space, seeding it with elements other than just hydrogen and helium. This also can cause a shock wave that accelerates the collapse of a star-forming nebula into a protostar. The fact that elements as large as the actinides exist naturally in our planet requires that our solar system formed from the remnants of cataclysmic astronomical phenomena from the deaths of other stars. There is evidence that both a supernova explosion and the collision of two neutron stars occurred soon before the birth of our solar system. These stars might have had their own planets, but they exist now as the heavier elements of our planets and of our bodies. Your body is then, literally, made from stardust.

(21) **SEP Construct an Explanation** Explain how the composition of the universe is changing over time. ✏️

....

....

....

Revisit

INVESTIGATIVE PHENOMENON

GO ONLINE to Elaborate on and Evaluate your knowledge of the properties of stars and the energy released by fission and fusion by completing the data analysis and discussion activities.

(22) **SEP Matter and Energy** The Mars Curiosity rover uses ^{238}Pu to provide its energy. This isotope is produced artificially from the transmutation of uranium. Describe what astronomical phenomenon must have happened before our solar system formed for Earth to contain uranium. ✏️

....

....

....

....

....

Nuclear Technologies

 GO ONLINE to Explore and Explain the health risks of nuclear radiation.

Radiation Penetration

Radiation has many medical and industrial uses but also poses risks to humans because of its ability to damage living tissue. **Radiation** is a term used to describe both electromagnetic radiation and high-energy particles. Of particular risk is ionizing radiation, which includes both high-energy particles—mainly α and β particles and neutrons—and high-frequency electromagnetic waves—gamma rays and X-rays. Higher-energy ultraviolet waves are also ionizing radiation. **Ionizing radiation** has the ability to knock electrons off of atoms to produce ions, which is damaging to living organisms. These particles and rays are the by-products of the processes of radioactivity, nuclear fission, and nuclear fusion. Fortunately, it is possible for people to shield themselves from ionizing radiation.

Radiation Penetration Depths The different forms of ionizing radiation pose differing risks and also penetrate different materials to different depths.

Alpha particles are the most dangerous but also the easiest to shield, blocked by a sheet of paper.

High-energy β particles (electrons) are ionizing and can also generate X-rays upon impact.

Gamma rays and X-rays are very ionizing, and the knocked-off high-energy electrons can cause additional ionization. They can be stopped by lead.

Neutrons are the most penetrating. They can knock protons off of nuclei, causing neutron capture and radioactivity.

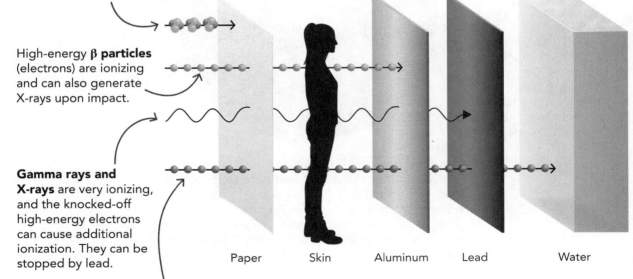

Paper   Skin   Aluminum   Lead   Water

Radiation Hazards and Units

Half of an average American's annual radiation exposure, ~6.2 millisieverts per year (mSv/yr), occurs naturally. The other half comes from medical procedures. A small amount comes from work-place hazards and consumer products. The largest risk is from inhaling the gaseous isotopes ^{222}Rn, generically called *radon*, and ^{220}Rn, which is called *thoron*, made from the radioactive decay chains of ^{238}U and ^{232}Th in underground rocks and water. Other natural radiation sources include secondary decay particles from cosmic rays, radioactive isotopes consumed in food (mostly ^{14}C and ^{40}K) and water (^{238}U and ^{232}Th), and the radioactive decay of minerals in the ground. Medical sources of radiation vary greatly, depending on a person's health, but include X-rays, CT scans, PET scans, and targeting radioisotopes.

Typical Sources of Radiation Exposure The amount of radiation a person is exposed to varies. In the United States, most of the exposure is split between natural background sources and medical sources.

Certain rocks such as phosphates, used for soaps and fertilizers, contain higher levels of the **radioactive minerals** uranium and thorium.

Americans benefit from many advanced medical technologies, but these also pose radiation exposures five times the global average.

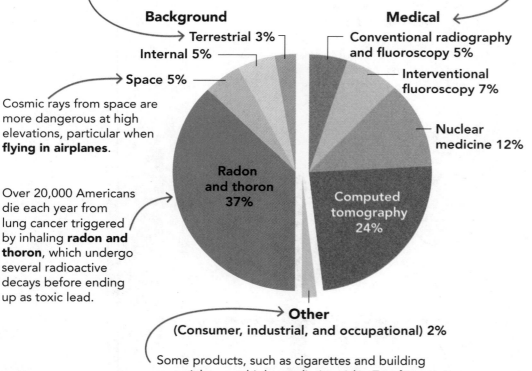

Background

Terrestrial 3%
Internal 5%
Space 5%

Cosmic rays from space are more dangerous at high elevations, particular when **flying in airplanes**.

Over 20,000 Americans die each year from lung cancer triggered by inhaling **radon and thoron**, which undergo several radioactive decays before ending up as toxic lead.

Radon and thoron 37%

Medical

Conventional radiography and fluoroscopy 5%

Interventional fluoroscopy 7%

Nuclear medicine 12%

Computed tomography 24%

Other
(Consumer, industrial, and occupational) 2%

Some products, such as cigarettes and building materials, pose higher radiation risks. **Foods** contain trace amounts of radioactive ^{40}K and ^{14}C, and **water** supplies can contain ^{235}U and ^{232}Th.

Measuring Ionizing Radiation

How is the amount of ionizing radiation quantified?

The way that ionizing radiation is absorbed by human tissue is a health hazard, but the radioactive decay itself is not. To complicate matters, not all dangerous radiation comes from radioactive decay, and some types of radioactive decay are more dangerous than others. So, there are several different ways to measure radiation risks that address radioactivity, exposure, absorption, and biological dose.

Radioactive material

The number of atoms undergoing **radioactive decay per second** is a measure of **radioactivity**. The SI unit for radioactivity is the **becquerel (Bq)**, which is decays/sec. Another commonly used unit is the curie (Ci), which is the radioactivity from 1 gram of ^{226}R (1 Ci = 3.7×10^{10} Bq).

The amount of **radiation received through the air** is known as exposure, which is measured as **electric charge per mass (Coulomb/kg.)** It is also commonly measured in roentgens (R) (1 R = 2.58×10^{-4} Coulomb/kg).

The amount of **radiation energy absorbed by an object** is the **absorbed dose**, which is measured in **grays (Gy)**, which are J/kg, or commonly in rads (1 rad = 0.01 Gy).

The biological risk from ionizing radiation is the **dose equivalent**, or **effective dose**. It combines both the amount of radiation absorbed and the damaging effects on living tissue. The SI unit is **sieverts (Sv)**, but it is measured in roentgen equivalent man (rem) in the U.S. (1 Sv = 100 rem). A 1 rem effective dose has a 0.05% chance of eventually causing cancer.

On average, 1 R of exposure $\cong$ 1 rad absorbed $\cong$ 1 rem of biological dose equivalent.

(23) **SEP Construct an Explanation** Home remediation for radon exposure should be taken if radioactivity levels exceed 150 Bq/m³. Home radon values across the country vary greatly, from close to zero to more than 100,000 Bq/m³. Explain why values might vary so greatly. Design a solution to reduce indoor radon radioactivity levels. ✎

....

....

....

....

Detecting Radiation

Several technologies are used to measure radioactivity and its dose equivalent. The most common is a dosimeter, which is worn by professionals in places where ionizing radiation is used or generated. The best-known ionizing radiation detector is a Geiger counter, which uses a chamber of inert gas (helium, neon, or argon) with a voltage across it. If the gas is hit by α particles, β particles, or gamma rays, the ionization creates an electric current that can be recorded. Geiger counters have a limitation in that they do not record the amount of energy received, just the number of hits. Another device, called a scintillation counter, is able to measure both intensity and energy. It generates light when hit by ionizing radiation and converts the light into an electric signal.

Dosimeters People in professions who are routinely exposed to ionizing radiation wear dosimeters to track their effective dose. Modern devices are usually electronic personal dosimeters, which record exposure and can be reset at any time. In the past, people used film badge dosimeters to record exposure.

As the name suggests, a film badge dosimeter consists of a piece of film with several different materials that are barriers to different kinds of ionizing radiation.

Detector

Radiologist
University Medical Center

The film behind the different materials gets exposed at different rates according to the varying amounts of α particles, β particles, X-rays, and gamma rays. These badges are use-once devices because once the film is exposed, the effects of radiation cannot be removed or erased.

Radiologist
University Medical Center

Alpha Beta Gamma   Alpha Beta Gamma   Alpha Beta Gamma   Alpha Beta Gamma

(24) **CCC Energy and Matter** Based on the penetration depth of different forms of ionizing radiation, what three materials do you think are in the windows of the dosimeter? 🖊

....

....

....

Cosmic Rays

Cosmic rays are high-energy protons and atomic nuclei that travel through space at nearly the speed of light. Cosmic rays come from supernovae within our galaxy, the black hole at the center of our galaxy, and sources from outside of our galaxy. Cosmic rays pose a health hazard from the showers of secondary particles ejected when cosmic rays hit nitrogen and oxygen molecules in the atmosphere. The energy of one incoming cosmic ray proton is great enough to generate up to 50 new particles.

Cosmic Rays
These particles travel across space with such high energies that they can generate dozens of ionizing particles and rays when they hit atoms in the atmosphere, in this case, a nitrogen atom.

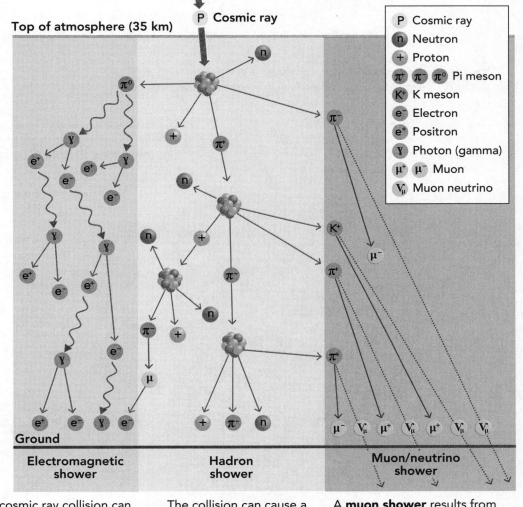

A cosmic ray collision can produce an **electromagnetic shower** of dangerous X-rays, gamma rays, electrons, and positrons.

The collision can cause a **hadron shower** of high-energy protons, neutrons, and π and K mesons (pions and kaons).

A **muon shower** results from the instantaneous decay of pions and kaons into muons and neutrinos.

(25) **SEP Design Your Solution** Mars has a very thin atmosphere and no global magnetic field. If humans were to live there, design a solution for how they could reduce their high risk from cosmic rays. ✏️

Nuclear Fission Power

Nuclear Reactors As of 2019, nuclear fission provided about 10% of the world's electricity from more than 450 nuclear reactors. Most involved the splitting of ^{235}U atoms, which releases 3 million times the energy of coal by mass. Though there are many different designs, nuclear reactors all work on the same principle. The heat from the fission reaction, from gamma rays and the kinetic energy and radioactive decay of the products, is used to turn water into steam in order to run turbines. These turbines either turn the shafts of electric power generators or the propellers of large ocean ships and submarines. Nuclear generators also produce unstable radioisotopes for medical and industrial applications and plutonium needed for nuclear bombs.

Nuclear Reactor Design Nuclear reactors are designed to convert the heat released by a controlled fission reaction to electricity.

The **reactor core** is where nuclear fuel undergoes fission, heating a fluid such as liquid salt. Chain reactions are controlled with neutron-absorbing control rods.

The **containment shell** protects the outside from potential nuclear accidents and the reactor from outside damage.

The **turbine** uses the steam to generate electricity.

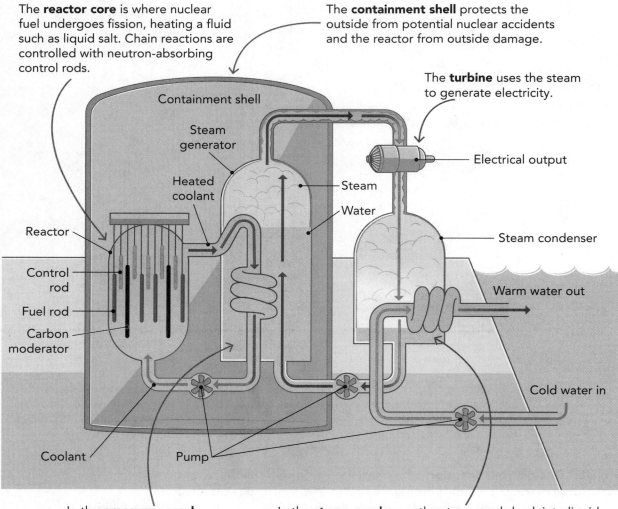

In the **pressure vessel** heat from the reactor core fluid is transferred to water, creating steam.

In the **steam condenser** the steam cools back into liquid water. The extra heat is transferred to a separate cycle of cold water that is taken from and then returned to a lake, stream, or the ocean. This heat loss means that nuclear power plants run at energy efficiencies of about 33%.

Breeding Plutonium The plentiful ^{238}U can be converted into the fissile nuclear fuel ^{239}Pu by a transmutation process called breeding.

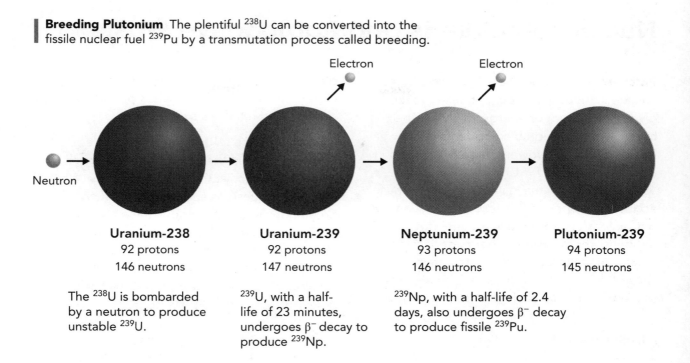

Uranium-238	Uranium-239	Neptunium-239	Plutonium-239
92 protons	92 protons	93 protons	94 protons
146 neutrons	147 neutrons	146 neutrons	145 neutrons

The ^{238}U is bombarded by a neutron to produce unstable ^{239}U.

^{239}U, with a half-life of 23 minutes, undergoes β^- decay to produce ^{239}Np.

^{239}Np, with a half-life of 2.4 days, also undergoes β^- decay to produce fissile ^{239}Pu.

Breeder Reactors Other fissile isotopes for nuclear power plants include ^{233}U, ^{239}Pu, and ^{241}Pu; and although these are not abundant in nature, they can be created by nuclear breeding. **Nuclear breeding** is the process of producing fissile isotopes by bombarding non-fissile isotopes with neutrons. The non-fissile isotopes used for breeding, such as ^{232}Th, ^{238}U, and ^{240}Pu, are known as fertile isotopes. They can become fissile isotopes when they undergo neutron capture.

For example, the only naturally occurring fissile uranium isotope is ^{235}U, but it is only 0.7% of geologically available uranium. The other 99.3% is ^{238}U, which is not fissile. However, ^{238}U can be used to produce the fissile ^{239}Pu. The use of breeding also reduces the expensive cost of uranium separation. Currently, reactors that use ^{235}U must first concentrate ^{235}U to be at least 4% of the uranium, through a time-consuming process that uses centrifuges to separate ^{235}U from ^{238}U. Breeder reactors can also be used to process some nuclear wastes into fissionable products. Another common breeding process turns the plentiful ^{232}Th into ^{233}U, going through ^{233}Th and ^{233}Pa along the way. However, the half-life of ^{233}Pa is 27 days, so this process takes months to occur.

26) **SEP Use Models** Examine the model of the fission reactor, and research how a coal combustion power plant works. Then, explain two ways that a nuclear power plant is similar to a coal combustion power plant and two ways that it is different. ✏️

....

....

....

Nuclear Accidents and Radioactive Waste

Nuclear Accidents There have long been concerns about the safety of nuclear reactors, given the amount of energy involved. There have been three notable accidents in the history of nuclear power: Three-Mile Island in Pennsylvania in 1979; Chernobyl in Ukraine in 1986; and Fukushima in Japan in 2011. These accidents happened because the reactions went out of control and there was a meltdown, which happens when extremely hot material in the reactor melts through the containment vessel. Given this record, compared to the millions of people who die each year from coal power plant pollution, and the increased safety of current reactor designs, nuclear power has been shown to be relatively safe.

Nuclear Waste A greater safety concern is the waste from the spent fuel rods, which remains radioactive for millions of years. While new reactor designs and processes, such as breeding, can greatly reduce the amount of nuclear waste from fission reactions, some will always be left over. Its disposal is a serious challenge. Nuclear wastes are currently accumulating on-site at American nuclear power plants, with no place to go.

Radioactivity of Nuclear Waste The radioactivity of 1,000 kg of waste from the fission of ^{235}U, measured in terabecquerels (TBq), or trillion decays per second, changes over time.

About 6.5% of the total energy from the uranium fission occurs from the radioactive decay chains of the fission products and other actinide isotopes made in the nuclear reactor.

Therefore, it takes thousands of years before the radioactivity of the waste decays to the level of the original uranium ore.

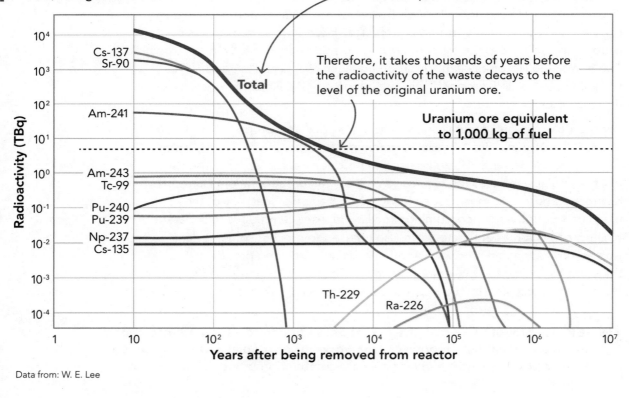

Data from: W. E. Lee

(27) **CCC Energy and Matter** After the creation of radioactive waste from nuclear fission, the amount of ^{240}Pu temporarily increases. Explain why.

....

....

Nuclear Fusion Power

Nuclear power from fusion has been extremely difficult to obtain. Fundamentally, this is because reproducing the temperatures and pressures of the central cores of stars is not easy. An enormous amount of energy is needed to do this, often exceeding the energy obtained from the fusion. So far, the most promising fusion reactor design is that of a circular donut-shaped tokamak reactor, which contains a rotating plasma. Containing the plasma is very difficult, however, and has been likened to squeezing water within your fist. The plasma just squirts out wherever it can. Radiation is also a problem. The most favorable fusion reactions produce lots of free neutrons, and these can irradiate the containment vessel so that it must be frequently replaced and rebuilt. Obtaining electricity from the fusion of hydrogen would be remarkable, but we are still a long way from determining if it can ever be done economically.

International Thermonuclear Experimental Reactor (ITER)
The most promising experiment in nuclear fusion power is an international project, ITER, being built in France by 35 nations. Completion is expected in 2035.

ITER will carry out the fusion reaction of deuterium (^{2}H) and tritium (^{3}H) to make helium (^{4}He) and a neutron, releasing 17.6 MeV per fusion event in the process.

The main part of the reactor is a donut-shaped vacuum vessel where the deuterium-tritium plasma will be squeezed and heated by powerful magnetic fields to temperatures of over 100 million K. Outside the vessel, cooling will be required to keep the tokamak from melting.

The ITER is represented here by a model cutaway to show the interior. The relative size of this figurine of a person helps convey the ITER's large size.

(28) **CCC Energy and Matter** Nuclear fusion happens naturally inside our sun. Explain why it is difficult to replicate this on Earth. 🖊

....

....

....

Radiation and Medicine

X-ray Images Recall that different forms of ionizing radiation will penetrate different materials to differing degrees. This property of X-rays has made them very useful for medical imaging. In the past, if a medical doctor wanted to know what was wrong with a person or other animal, they would have to cut them open and look. With X-rays, the structures of bones and other organs can be imaged and diagnosed without surgery. An X-ray radiograph is a single image, so the body appears flattened out. It cannot distinguish 3D structures. The 3D structure can be better seen using fluoroscopy, where a continuous X-ray emitter and plate can be moved, examining different parts of the body in real time.

CT scan A computer tomography (CT) scan creates a 3D image of a body by taking a large number of X-rays from many different angles and then using computer processing to create a 3D image that best matches all of the different X-rays.

Medicine also uses other imaging methods that do not use ionizing radiation. Ultrasound uses high-frequency sound waves. Magnetic resonance imaging (MRI) involves radio waves within a strong magnetic field to make hydrogen atoms resonate, which highlights any body parts with water or fat in them.

X-ray This X-ray of a human indicates a fracture in a thumb bone. X-rays show bones very well because bones absorb more of the X-rays than the soft body tissues.

CT scan This CT scan of a brain indicates blood is collecting on the left side of the image.

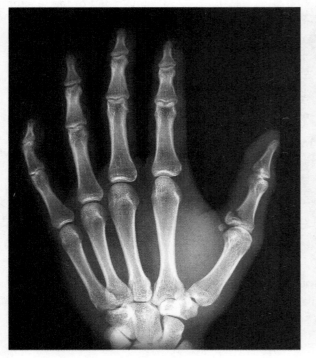

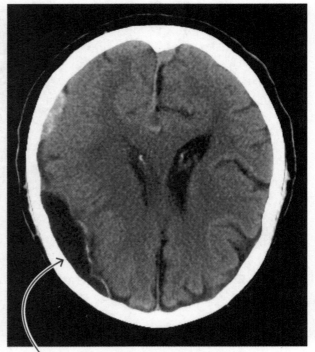

This darker, red area is false color used to help see the affected area.

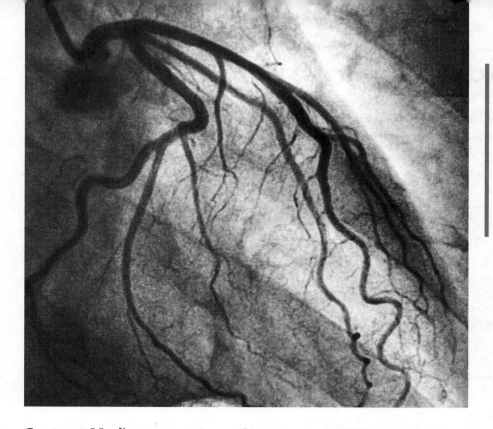

Angiogram with Contrast Media Before this X-ray was taken, the patient was injected with iodinated contrast. This contrast medium makes it easier to distinguish blood vessels from the surrounding tissue. Then a radiologist can determine if there are any areas where blood isn't flowing properly.

Contrast Media In some X-rays, fluoroscopy, and CT scans, an internal contrast medium is used to help image certain body parts. These contrast media are very effective at absorbing X-rays, so any place that the contrast medium flows is highlighted within the radiograph. Two common contrast media are iodine, which is injected into arteries to identify blood flow, and barium sulfate, which is swallowed and allows X-rays to sharply image the digestive tract.

Nuclear Medicine Medical imaging can also be done by injecting short-lived radioisotopes directly into the body in order to see how organs are functioning. As a general rule, the radiation from a radioisotope is distinguishable from background radiation until about ten half-lives. A common method of imaging is the positron emission tomography (PET) scan, where a radioisotope such as ^{18}F, which undergoes a β^+ decay, is injected into a particular part of the body. The ^{18}F decays with a half-life of 1.8 hours to safe and stable ^{18}O by emitting positrons. The positrons immediately decay in contact with electrons to release gamma rays. A gamma ray detector can therefore identify where the injected ^{18}F traveled.

(29) **SEP Construct an Explanation** Explain why the half-life of ^{18}F is optimal for doing PET scans of internal human organs. How long does it take for the ^{18}F to decay to background levels? ✎

....

....

....

....

Radiation and Living Tissue

Ionizing radiation can destroy living tissue, with many different effects depending on the rate, amount of the dose (rem), and the kind of radiation. The effects of radiation are greater in cells that reproduce rapidly, such as cancer cells, the stomach lining, hair follicles, bone marrow, and embryos. This is why ionizing radiation can be used to destroy certain cancerous tumors, either through the focused bombardment of X-rays or protons or through the targeted injection of radioactive substances such as ^{125}I or ^{131}Cs. It is also why patients undergoing radiation therapy often feel nauseated or sick to their stomach, lose their hair, and have bone aches, and why pregnant women need to limit radiation exposure.

Radiation exposures of greater than 400 rem can cause death within a couple of months. Exposures of greater than 2000 rem can cause death in a matter of hours. This has been observed in workplace accidents involving radioactive materials and in the two cases where nuclear bombs were used on the Japanese cities of Hiroshima and Nagasaki during WWII. Radiation can also alter the genetic structure of cells, which can trigger the growth of cancerous tumor cells.

Radiation Therapy
This patient is receiving radiation therapy for a brain tumor. A narrow beam of X-rays, gamma rays, or protons is targeted at the tumor in the brain to kill the cancerous cells.

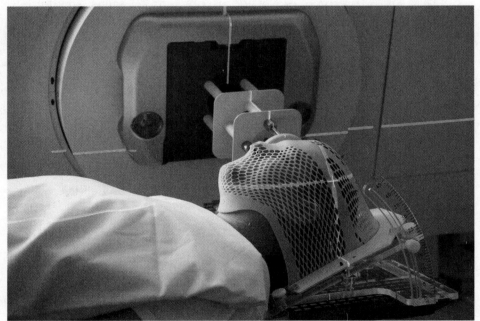

(30) **SEP Construct an Explanation** Explain why it is very difficult to determine the exact number of people who have died from later-developing cancers from a radiation accident such as the Chernobyl nuclear reactor meltdown.

....

....

....

Radiation and Gene Mutation

Gene Mutation Radioactive damage to cells can also involve damage to the structures of DNA. This can occur through external ionizing radiation that penetrates the body or through internal radioactive decay. If this DNA damage occurs to either sperm or egg cells, or to embryos, the result can be a mutation that is passed on to offspring. These mutations often lead to an inviable embryo, but sometimes the offspring is born with a mutation. These mutations are usually not helpful to the individual, and result in early death. Such mutations are not passed on to future generations. However, occasionally, a mutation helps the organism survive. Such mutations allow for the continual evolution of species. If genetic mutations didn't occur, new species could never evolve. This is critically important because Earth's environments have been consistently changing over the past 3.5 billion years, and life has had to continually adapt all the while.

Radiation Damage to DNA Damage to DNA can occur from either external ionizing radiation or from the decay of ^{14}C atoms within the DNA. For example, some of the carbon atoms within genes are ^{14}C atoms, and about 50 ^{14}C atoms decay inside a person's DNA each second, changing a carbon atom to nitrogen. There are several places within the DNA molecule that can be damaged from radiation.

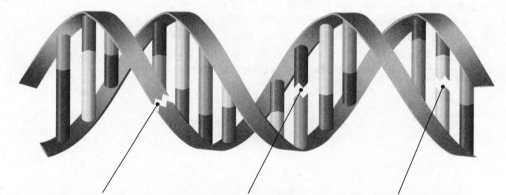

Break in strand of DNA backbone

Break in hydrogen bonds between base pairs

Damage to DNA base

Evolution Gene mutations combined with environmentally driven natural selection allows some offspring to thrive and reproduce better than others. Over time, this can cause genetic drift and new species to evolve, such as in this famous example of Darwin's finches.

Genetic Drift, Natural Selection, and Speciation New species evolve in many ways. In some cases, populations get spread out and the gradual genetic drift, or change in the frequency of specific genes, causes them to eventually become separate species, no longer able to reproduce together. Genetic drift happens particularly quickly in single-celled organisms such as bacteria. In other cases, a change of environment (climate change, habitat destruction, a new habitat, introduction of new predators or prey) changes the natural selection pressures, and mutations that provide individuals with newly beneficial characteristics may survive when others may not. Ironically, the continual genetic mutations within living organisms resulting from cosmic rays and radioactive radon gases throughout Earth's history are the reason why humans and all of their ancestor species were ever able to evolve.

Revisit

INVESTIGATIVE PHENOMENON

GO ONLINE to Elaborate on and Evaluate your knowledge of the effects of nuclear radiation and nuclear technologies by completing the discussion and writing activities.

(31) **SEP Engage in Argument** On Mars, the thermal energy released by the alpha decay of ^{238}Pu fuel is transformed to electricity in a radioisotope thermoelectric generator (RTG). Why did engineers design an RTG for the rovers instead of using a fusion or fission reactor, and why did they use a fuel that generates alpha particles instead of beta particles or gamma rays?

GO ONLINE to Evaluate what you learned about nuclear processes by using the available assessment resources.

In the Performance-Based Assessment, you estimated your radiation exposure and measured the radioactivity of potassium-40. Wrap up your analysis by answering the following questions.

(32) **SEP Construct an Explanation** Why is your exposure to natural and artificial radiation likely to vary from year to year over your lifetime, even though the background radiation from potassium-40 is relatively stable? ✏

....

....

....

....

....

....

(33) **SEP Apply Scientific Reasoning** Explain whether you could use your procedure to measure the radioactivity of other isotopes, such as calcium-40 or radon-222. What adjustments might you need to make? ✏

....

....

....

....

....

....

INVESTIGATIVE PHENOMENON

GO ONLINE to Engage with real-world phenomena by watching a video and to complete a CER interactive worksheet.

Can algae be used as a renewable energy source?

Green Chemistry

When underground petroleum is no longer cost efficient to use, society might rely on other materials as the foundation for making plastics, synthetic clothing, fertilizers, pharmaceuticals, fuels, and other organic materials. One of these potential materials is microscopic algae, also called microalgae. Once you have viewed the Investigative Phenomenon video and completed the claim-evidence-reasoning exercise to explain the phenomenon you observed, answer these reflection questions about evaluating energy choices.

1) CCC Energy and Matter Explain why fuels made from microalgae might be more important for powering future planes compared to homes. ✏️

....

....

....

....

2) SEP Design Solutions Microalgae are one of many organisms, such as food crops, grasses, and trees, that carry out photosynthesis and can be used to generate biofuels. If you had to choose between algae and these other choices, what kind of model would you make to help you in your decision? ✏️

....

....

....

....

Industrial Chemicals and the Environment

GO ONLINE to Explore and Explain industrial chemical processes and why the field of green chemistry began.

Chemicals All Around Us

Chemicals, or chemical substances, can be natural or human-made. Examples of natural chemicals are water, sugars, minerals, DNA, and pheromones. Examples of human-made, or synthetic, chemicals include pharmaceuticals, plastics, glues, and detergents. Scientists even make synthetic chemicals that are indistinguishable from their natural counterparts. Synthetic chemicals are used for many aspects of life, and huge industries are built around them.

Some chemicals, particularly when produced in large quantities, are harmful to the environment and have had negative impacts on plant and animal life and human health. The awareness of these impacts has led to the development of a new field of environmentally friendly "green" chemistry.

Chemicals in Everyday Life Chemistry is used to make materials that people depend on in their daily lives. These materials can make life easier or more enjoyable.

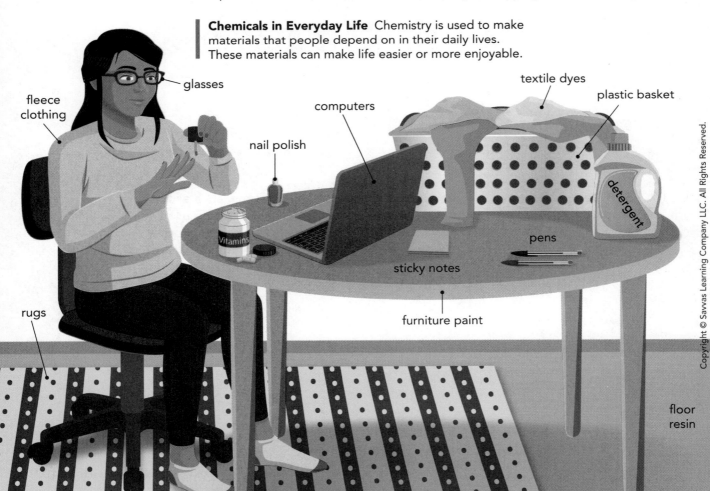

glasses

fleece clothing

textile dyes

plastic basket

computers

nail polish

detergent

Vitamins

pens

sticky notes

rugs

furniture paint

floor resin

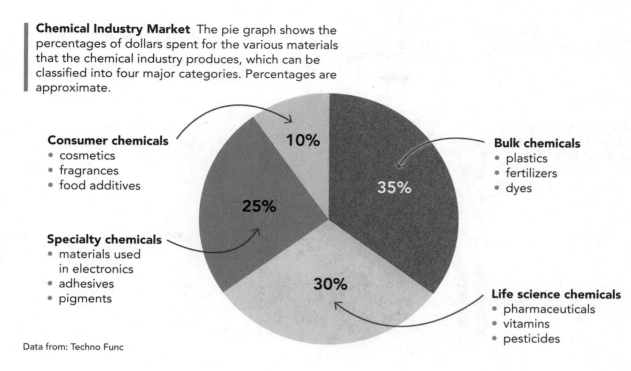

Chemical Industry Market The pie graph shows the percentages of dollars spent for the various materials that the chemical industry produces, which can be classified into four major categories. Percentages are approximate.

Consumer chemicals
- cosmetics
- fragrances
- food additives

10%

Bulk chemicals
- plastics
- fertilizers
- dyes

35%

25%

Specialty chemicals
- materials used in electronics
- adhesives
- pigments

30%

Life science chemicals
- pharmaceuticals
- vitamins
- pesticides

Data from: Techno Func

The Chemical Industry

The chemical industry converts raw materials, such as fossil fuels, atmospheric gases, minerals, and water, into products. A resulting product can be classified as primary, secondary, or tertiary, depending on how far removed the product is from the consumer. Primary products are furthest from the consumer and are sold to other factories within the industry. The products made from the primary products are often passed from factory to factory before they are finally converted into products intended for consumers.

Research and Development New substances and chemical processes are discovered and optimized through a process called research and development (R&D), in which different reactions, reaction conditions, and product candidates are investigated. In the R&D phase, companies also optimize for such factors as efficiency, cost, environmental impact, and safety. There is a financial trade-off in considering how much time to devote to the R&D phase. Products and processes can be improved further with longer R&D time periods, but R&D is expensive and brings no short-term income. Therefore, it is advantageous to transition to the production phase as soon as possible.

(3) SEP Evaluate A company spends $10 million on R&D to develop a process with a annual operating cost of $3 million. Suppose investing $10 million more in R&D would reduce the annual operating cost to $2 million. After how many years would the investment pay off? ✏️

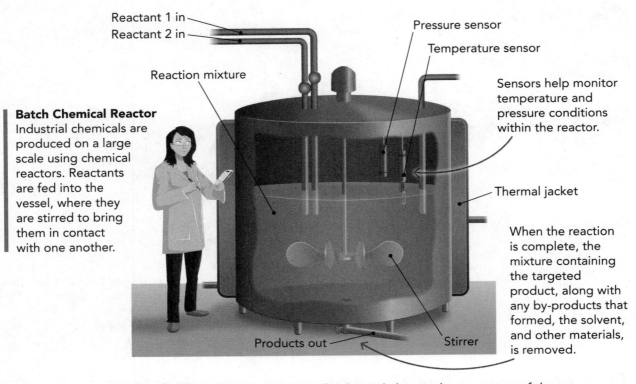

Batch Chemical Reactor
Industrial chemicals are produced on a large scale using chemical reactors. Reactants are fed into the vessel, where they are stirred to bring them in contact with one another.

Reactant 1 in
Reactant 2 in
Reaction mixture

Pressure sensor
Temperature sensor
Sensors help monitor temperature and pressure conditions within the reactor.

Thermal jacket

When the reaction is complete, the mixture containing the targeted product, along with any by-products that formed, the solvent, and other materials, is removed.

Products out   Stirrer

Production The production of industrial chemicals uses many of the same fundamental chemistry concepts as your chemistry lab, but the reactions and other processes are scaled up to serve the needs of society. Most chemicals are produced in a sequence of steps, each of which requires energy. The sequence begins with the input materials for the process. These input materials, which include starting materials, or reactants, as well as any solvents and catalysts needed to increase reaction efficiency, are added to reactors that can be the size of rooms. The reactions are then carried out at temperatures and pressures that were optimized in the R&D phase. Often, the temperatures used in reactors are much warmer than room temperature. Maintaining these elevated temperatures requires large inputs of energy.

Once a product is formed, it often must be isolated from a mixture that may contain a solvent, catalyst, excess reagent, and one or more by-products. A **by-product** is a product of a chemical reaction that is not the targeted product. Next, the product may be refined further with methods such as crystallization, washing, filtering, drying, and pulverizing into a fine powder.

④ **SEP Construct an Explanation** Use your knowledge of collision theory to explain why solvents and elevated temperatures are often used in the production of industrial chemicals. ✏

....

....

....

....

Challenges for Chemical Production

In the past, the chemical industry thrived while providing people with the materials they needed. The four main reasons for this were high demand, inexpensive feedstocks, inexpensive energy, and the freedom to dispose of the resulting waste without treatment. **Feedstocks** are the raw materials that are fed into an industrial process for conversion into something different. **Waste** is any material that is unwanted and must be disposed of.

Although the demand for industrial chemicals remains high, the production costs have increased significantly. The chemical industry currently faces three main challenges. First, many feedstocks are becoming increasingly expensive because of the limited availability of petroleum and minerals. Companies must pay the extra cost or find suitable replacements. Second, energy costs have become more expensive. Third, governmental regulations, such as the Clean Water Act and the Clean Air Act, now more seriously protect natural resources by limiting industrial pollution. As companies and society have become more aware of how chemical production can affect the environment, many companies have begun looking for ways to make goods using environmentally friendly methods. A major component of this shift involves changing the way companies manage their waste.

Changing the Status Quo In the past, companies didn't reuse or recycle many materials, and little effort was made to reduce waste. Now, companies strive for the opposite. This inverted waste-management hierarchy is more environmentally friendly and economically beneficial.

The best way to manage waste is to design chemical processes to avoid producing waste in the first place.

In the past, most industrial wastes were simply thrown out.

Eliminate waste

Reduce waste

Reuse materials

Recover/recycle materials

Disposal

Desirability

(5) **SEP Engage in Argument** How can focusing efforts on reducing waste and on reusing and recycling materials save the chemical industry money? 🖉

....

....

....

....

Elements at Risk of Running Out Many elements are abundant at Earth's surface and show no indications of running out soon. Others are either rare or not naturally well concentrated. The less that remain, or the harder they are to obtain, the more expensive they become.

Liquid helium is extremely cold and is used to cool magnets in medical devices, such as MRIs.

- ● Limited availability
- ■ Increasing threat
- ▲ Serious threat

Cobalt is used in rechargeable batteries and many alloys.

Data from: Innovate UK

Supply: Finite Resources

Mineral Resources Mining is an important source of feedstocks for the chemical industry. The minerals that humans mine from the ground are finite resources—that is, Earth contains a limited amount of them. Humans also use these resources at an alarming rate, causing the resources to become increasingly expensive. Currently, people in the United States use about 9 metric tons of nonfuel minerals per person per year, which is a total of about 3 billion metric tons per year.

Important minerals often exist in very low concentrations and are only economically minable where past geologic processes have concentrated them. For example, platinum, which is used as a catalyst, exists in Earth's crust at a low concentration, making it rare and expensive. However, past volcanic activity has concentrated it in places such as Finland and South Africa. Once these regions have been mined, the remaining supplies may be harder to find and more expensive to obtain. Because valuable minerals are not found everywhere, some countries have more than others. For example, China contains large deposits of rare earth elements and controls approximately 85 percent of their global market. Rare earth elements, such as neodymium, are used for many industrial applications, including in the manufacture of catalysts, electronic devices, and computers.

Reserves and Resources The amount of minerals left in the ground is hard to determine. **Mineral resources** are estimated amounts of minerals in Earth's crust that have the potential to be extracted for profit either now or in the future. For example, the United States has about 21 billion cubic meters of helium resources. **Mineral reserves** are the estimated amounts of mineral resources that are fairly certain and can be currently mined for profit. The United States has about 4 billion cubic meters of helium reserves. The years that remain for a mineral depend on the estimated amount remaining and how quickly humans use it.

Petroleum Resources Currently, hydrocarbons are the largest single feedstock for the chemical industry. Hydrocarbons such as methane, butane, propane, and benzene are used as the starting materials for making many different products, including paints, adhesives, and plastics. Hydrocarbons are primarily obtained from the distillation of petroleum that is pumped out of the ground. Like minerals, petroleum is a finite resource. Petroleum is likely to become more expensive as the large and easily accessed reserves are drained. To obtain future petroleum resources, humans will need to dig deeper, use more energy, and go to inhospitable regions such as the deep ocean or Arctic.

6 **SEP Evaluate Solutions** Suppose there is a push to replace many gasoline-powered vehicles with vehicles that are powered by Li-ion batteries. How would you expect this initiative to affect the demands and costs for lithium and petroleum? ✎

....

....

....

Petrochemical Plant Petrochemical plants, such as this one in Thailand, convert crude oil and other materials into petrochemical feedstocks for industrial use as well other products humans use.

Consumerism in the United States An average consumer in the United States currently requires more than 18,000 kg of minerals, metals, and fuels in one year to make the products he or she uses. The table shows the average consumption rates in 2019 for a few of these materials.

Average U.S. Consumption Rates for Some Materials	
Material	Amount an average consumer uses in one year
Petroleum	3130 kg
Phosphate rock	83 kg
Zinc	2.7 kg
Salt	174 kg
Sand, stone, gravel, and cement	8140 kg
Iron ore	116 kg
Other minerals and metals	405 kg

Data from: Minerals Education Coalition

Demand: Human Population and Consumerism

The need for more environmentally friendly chemistry might not be as important if there weren't so many people in the world. The chemical industry has to use a lot of natural resources to produce goods for billions of people, and industrial production processes can generate a lot of waste. Although the annual growth rate of the global human population (r_1) is only about 1 percent, another billion people are added to the world every 15 years. The resulting environmental impacts are not just from the number of people, however, but also from an increase in the global standard of living (r_2). This increases by approximately 2 percent each year, as measured by global gross domestic product. To estimate the annual increase in total consumption for a material, multiply the two rates together.

$$\text{Annual growth in consumption} = (1 + r_1)(1 + r_2)$$
$$= (1 + 0.01)(1 + 0.02)$$
$$= 1.01 \times 1.02$$
$$= 1.03 \ (3\% \text{ increase per year})$$

Estimating Resource Lifetime

The estimated available copper resource is 5600 million metric tons, and the rate of consumption of new copper resources is 21 million metric tons per year. Dividing the available resource by the use rate gives the projected resource lifetime—approximately 270 years. However, the rate of consumption increases each year. How many years (t) is it likely to be before copper resources are used up?

Use the equation for compounding increase, $A = P(1 + r)^t$, where P is the starting amount, A is the ending amount, r is the annual rate of increase in consumption, and t is the number of years. Assume $r = 3.0\%$.

ANALYZE List the knowns and the unknown.

Knowns	Unknown
Starting amount (P) = 21 million metric tons	$t = ?$ years
Ending amount (A) = 5600 million metric tons	
Annual rate of increase (r) = 3.0% = 0.030	

CALCULATE Solve for the unknown.

Start with the equation.

$$A = P(1 + r)^t$$

Rearrange the equation to solve for t. Divide both sides by P. Next, take the log of both sides. Then, divide both sides by $\ln(1 + r)$.

$$\frac{A}{P} = (1 + r)^t$$

$$\ln\left(\frac{A}{P}\right) = (t)\ln(1 + r)$$

$$t = \frac{\ln\left(\frac{A}{P}\right)}{\ln(1 + r)}$$

Substitute the knowns into the equation and solve.

$$t = \frac{\ln\left(\frac{5600 \text{ million tons}}{21 \text{ million tons}}\right)}{\ln(1 + 0.030)} = \frac{\ln(267)}{\ln(1.03)} = \frac{5.587}{0.02956}$$

$$t = 190 \text{ years}$$

EVALUATE Does the result make sense?

The answer has two significant figures. The calculated value is sooner than the original 270 years by almost a century, which seems reasonable.

7. Suppose that in addition to the growth in consumption, there is an annual increase in the amount of copper that gets recycled and reused, at the level of 3 percent per year. In this case, how long will it take to use up the 5600 million metric tons of copper resources?

....

....

GO ONLINE for more practice problems.

Waste and Unintended Impacts

Waste For centuries, wastes from chemical reactions were simply dumped on land or in bodies of water. However, human populations and the amounts of wastes were low. So, after the wastes were dumped, they often became sufficiently diluted. In the early 1700s, Philadelphia's waterways were polluted by tanneries and public waste. In 1739, Ben Franklin and other city residents petitioned to get the tanneries removed from the city. Decades later, he led efforts to limit water pollution and waste dumping.

As the human population and the demand for chemicals increased, so did the impacts on the environment. The chemical processes needed to provide goods for billions of people generated enormous wastes that impacted the environment. By the 1960s, some major rivers in the Unites States were too polluted from the dumping of industrial wastes to drink, swim in, or fish in. Organisms in rivers began dying from a combination of water pollution and acid rain resulting from air pollution.

Environmental Impacts of Chemical Industries

How does producing chemical substances **affect the planet?**

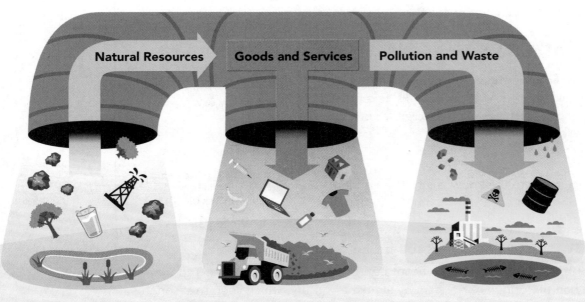

Natural Resources → **Goods and Services** → **Pollution and Waste**

Consumption of Natural Resources Chemical processes require **raw materials from the earth.** Pumping petroleum and natural gas, mining minerals, and growing crops all have negative impacts on Earth's systems, including plants and animals.

Goods and Services Materials made by the chemical industry are used in the production of food, clothes, and other products. However, **products are thrown out when people are done with them.** Plastics used in food packaging may be thrown out immediately, while house paint can last for years. In the end, all products become part of humans' waste.

Pollution and Waste From Chemical Processes Because traditional chemical processes are not very efficient, **the waste a process generates can be more than 100 times greater than the mass of the products.** This waste has had many negative environmental impacts.

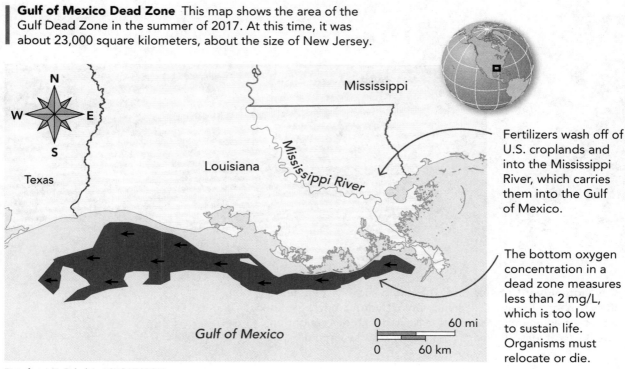

Gulf of Mexico Dead Zone This map shows the area of the Gulf Dead Zone in the summer of 2017. At this time, it was about 23,000 square kilometers, about the size of New Jersey.

Mississippi

Louisiana

Mississippi River

Texas

Gulf of Mexico

Fertilizers wash off of U.S. croplands and into the Mississippi River, which carries them into the Gulf of Mexico.

The bottom oxygen concentration in a dead zone measures less than 2 mg/L, which is too low to sustain life. Organisms must relocate or die.

0   60 mi

0   60 km

Data from: N. Rabalais, LSU/LUMCON

Unintended Impacts Sometimes, products that are designed and produced by the chemical industry have unintended effects on the biosphere. An example is synthetic fertilizers. Such fertilizers allow current agricultural practices, which are used to feed 7.5 billion humans. However, precipitation carries the fertilizers from the fields and into bodies of water. The fertilizers can cause dead zones, which are large areas of water that are depleted of oxygen. Dead zones are often associated with the overgrowth of algae, as a result of the influx of nutrients from fertilizer runoff. When the algae die, the oxygen needed to support life is used up in the decomposition of the algae by bacteria and other organisms.

Another example is dichloro-diphenyl-trichloroethane (DDT). This substance was introduced in the 1940s as the first synthetic pesticide, and it was very effective at fighting malaria and other diseases spread by insects. DDT is not very soluble in water, but it is very soluble in fats and quickly crosses cell membranes. As a result, its concentration in the fatty tissues of organisms increases moving up the food chain. In affected regions, concentrations might be 0.000003 ppm in water, 0.04 ppm in zooplankton, 0.5 ppm in small fish that eat the zooplankton, 2 ppm in large fish that eat the small fish, and 25 ppm in fish-eating birds. Evidence linked DDT to thinning eggshells of affected birds, which caused the eggs to crumble, killing the chicks and causing bird populations to decrease.

8 **SEP Use Math** The concentration of DDT in fish-eating birds is how many times greater than the concentration of DDT in water? 🖊

Cuyahoga River Catches Fire The photo shows a 1952 fire on the Cuyahoga River in Cleveland, Ohio. Hydrocarbon pollution from petroleum refineries, steel mills, and factories caught on fire. It was at least the ninth time the river had caught fire.

Chemical Disasters

Disasters within the chemical industry have been significant in bringing public awareness to the dangers of certain substances and the need for governmental regulation. These events take two forms: factory accidents and environmental releases of pollution by factories. Some events were sudden, such as the explosion of ammonium nitrate in Toulouse, France, in 2001, which killed at least 29 people. Other events were gradual, such as the long-term dumping of mercury-contaminated wastewater into the sea from 1932 to 1968 by a chemical factory in Minimata, Japan. This dumping caused mercury poisoning in more than 3000 people.

Some substances, such as mercury and pesticides, are inherently toxic, and some substances are explosive. In the United States, governmental regulations, such as the Occupational Safety and Health Act and the Resource Conservation and Recovery Act, can help ensure employee safety and proper waste disposal. In addition, regulatory bodies such as the Environmental Protection Agency and the Department of Transportation regulate the generation, disposal, and transportation of hazardous waste.

(9) SEP Construct an Explanation Why do you think different countries would reach the point of adopting antipollution laws at different times in their histories? ✏️

....

....

....

A Greener Vision for Chemistry

Green chemistry is the "design of chemical products and processes to reduce or eliminate the use and generation of hazardous substances." The concept was introduced and defined by Paul Anastas of the U.S. Environmental Protection Agency (EPA) soon after Congress passed the Pollution Prevention Act in 1990. The act called for a shift in focus from after-the-fact solutions for pollution to preventing pollution at the source. Recognizing that "design" is an important aspect of green chemistry, Paul Anastas and John Warner wrote the book *Green Chemistry: Theory and Practice* in 1998. In this book, the authors laid out the 12 Principles of Green Chemistry, which are suggested guidelines for all chemists to follow.

Green chemistry involves a different way of thinking when designing a product or process. Achieving a good design requires careful planning and consideration of many interacting components.

> In green chemistry, the design criteria and constraints include both technical and environmental considerations.

For example, the design for a new product is not only about its function and how to mass produce it in a way that is economically feasible, but also about how to make the product and its production as environmentally friendly as possible.

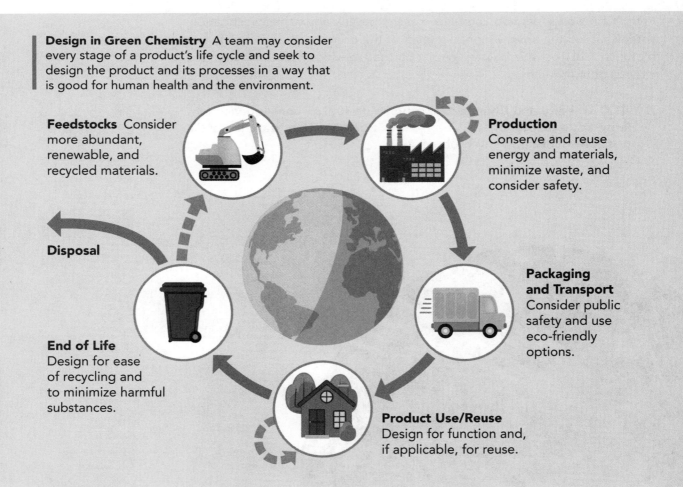

Design in Green Chemistry A team may consider every stage of a product's life cycle and seek to design the product and its processes in a way that is good for human health and the environment.

Feedstocks Consider more abundant, renewable, and recycled materials.

Production Conserve and reuse energy and materials, minimize waste, and consider safety.

Packaging and Transport Consider public safety and use eco-friendly options.

Product Use/Reuse Design for function and, if applicable, for reuse.

End of Life Design for ease of recycling and to minimize harmful substances.

Disposal

10 **CCC Systems and System Models** You saw how fertilizers from crops were washing into rivers and causing dead zones in the ocean. Looking at the whole system, propose three different solutions to prevent this. ✏

....

....

....

....

Revisit

INVESTIGATIVE PHENOMENON

GO ONLINE to Elaborate on and Evaluate what you learned about the chemical industry and the environment by completing the class discussion and writing activities.

In the CER worksheet you completed at the beginning of the investigation, you evaluated the environmental impact of the production and use of biofuel made from microalgae. With a partner, reevaluate the evidence you cited in your arguments.

11 **CCC Stability and Change** Describe an unwanted consequence of large-scale biofuel production from microalgae. Then describe a possible solution to the problem. ✏

....

....

....

....

....

....

....

....

Principles of Green Chemistry

GO ONLINE to Explore and Explain the use of different types of catalysts and to revise a chemical process to make it greener.

The 12 Principles of Green Chemistry

The 12 Principles of Green Chemistry suggest changes to many practices within the chemical industry. Important themes of many of these principles include that chemical processes should be safer, use fewer raw materials and less energy, produce less waste, and produce waste that is less toxic. Chemical processes that can achieve these goals will have fewer environmental impacts and cost less.

Green Chemistry Principles			
Principle	**Emphasis**		
	Resources	**Waste**	**Safety**
1. Waste Prevention		✔	
2. Atom Economy	✔	✔	
3. Less Hazardous Synthesis		✔	✔
4. Designing Safer Chemicals			✔
5. Safer Solvents and Auxiliaries		✔	✔
6. Design for Energy Efficiency	✔		
7. Use of Renewable Feedstocks	✔		
8. Reduce Derivatives	✔	✔	
9. Catalysis	✔	✔	
10. Design for Degradation		✔	✔
11. Real-Time Analysis		✔	✔
12. Accident Prevention			✔

1. Waste Prevention

"It is better to prevent waste than to treat or clean up waste after it is formed."

Waste can include goods that no longer serve a need or by-products left over when making the goods. Waste is costly, pollutes the land and water, and can cause human health problems.

For a chemical process, there are two common metrics for measuring the amount of waste generated, the environmental impact factor (E-factor) and process mass intensity (PMI). The **E-factor** for a process is the mass of waste generated divided by the mass of the targeted product. It varies greatly by industry. The E-factor is about 0.1 for oil refining, 1–5 for bulk chemicals, 5–50 for specialty chemicals, and 25–100 for pharmaceuticals. A similar metric, the **PMI,** is the mass of raw materials divided by the mass of targeted products. Reducing the E-factor and PMI makes the process not only greener but also cheaper, by reducing costs for resources, waste treatment, and disposal.

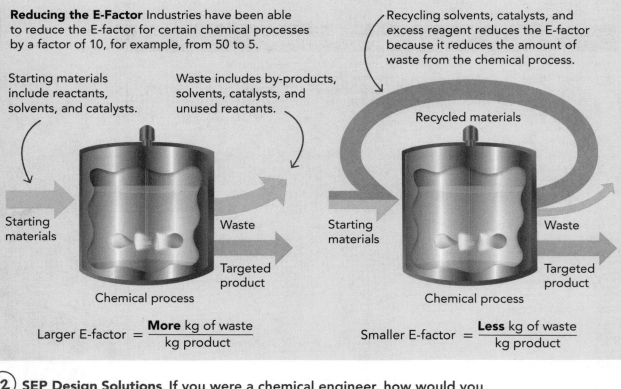

Reducing the E-Factor Industries have been able to reduce the E-factor for certain chemical processes by a factor of 10, for example, from 50 to 5.

Starting materials include reactants, solvents, and catalysts.

Waste includes by-products, solvents, catalysts, and unused reactants.

Recycling solvents, catalysts, and excess reagent reduces the E-factor because it reduces the amount of waste from the chemical process.

Recycled materials

Starting materials

Waste

Targeted product

Chemical process

$$\text{Larger E-factor} = \frac{\textbf{More} \text{ kg of waste}}{\text{kg product}}$$

Starting materials

Waste

Targeted product

Chemical process

$$\text{Smaller E-factor} = \frac{\textbf{Less} \text{ kg of waste}}{\text{kg product}}$$

(12) **SEP Design Solutions** If you were a chemical engineer, how would you apply the concepts of stoichiometry and equilibrium to minimize the E-factor for a reaction?

....

....

....

2. Atom Economy

"Synthetic methods should be designed to maximize incorporation of all materials used in the process into the final product."

Industrial chemical processes are often very inefficient in terms of numbers of atoms used that become part of the targeted product. Many atoms instead become part of the by-products, which are the substances that are produced in addition to the targeted product.

The efficiency of a chemical process can be measured in terms of the actual numbers of atoms. **Atom economy** (AE) is the mass of the desired product divided by the mass of the starting materials multiplied by 100. The molar mass of each substance is used to calculate the atom economy. For a single reaction step, if m_A and m_B are the masses of the reactants, and m_C is the mass of the product, the atom economy is given by the following equation.

$$AE = \frac{m_C}{m_A + m_B} \times 100$$

Certain types of chemical reactions have a high atom economy, such as addition reactions. Other reactions have a low atom economy, such as substitution reactions. For example, the following substitution reaction is used to produce the element titanium: $TiO_2(s) + 2Mg(s) \rightarrow Ti(s) + 2MgO(s)$. The atom economy of the substitution reaction is quite low:

$$AE = \frac{47.9 \text{ g/mol}}{[47.9 \text{ g/mol} + 2(16.0 \text{ g/mol})] + 2(24.3 \text{ g/mol})} \times 100 = 37.3\%$$

Efficiency of Producing Titanium Rutile, the mineral form of titanium dioxide, is a raw material used to obtain titanium. Using a substitution reaction to produce titanium from rutile has a low atom economy because magnesium and oxygen are not part of the desired product, titanium.

(13) **SEP Use Math** Calculate the atom economy for extracting titanium from titanium dioxide using electrolysis: $TiO_2(s) \rightarrow Ti(s) + O_2(g)$. ✏️

3. Less Hazardous Chemical Synthesis

"When practicable, synthetic methodologies should be designed to use or generate substances that pose little or no toxicity to human health and the environment."

Many chemical processes use or produce substances that are toxic in some way. **Toxicity** is the risk of damage to living organisms through the effects of a substance on individual organs or bodily systems.

The targeted product, the substances used during the chemical process, and the by-products may be toxic. It is important for chemists to be aware of the potential hazards of the substances they use and make because those substances can cause unintended harm when used or discarded as waste. During the Vietnam War, Agent Orange was used as an herbicide to kill plants. In addition to the substances that acted as herbicides, the mixture also contained an extremely toxic by-product of the reaction—the dioxin known as TCDD. This dioxin causes cancer and other diseases in humans. Scientists can now use computational tools to predict the health and environmental impacts of the substances involved in their syntheses and also to design processes that use and produce less-toxic substances.

Redesigning Chemical Synthesis The starting materials and solvents used to make cadmium selenide particles were toxic. Scientists developed a new way to make the particles that uses less-toxic starting materials. The new method of making the particles reduces the amount of toxic waste that is produced.

Cadmium selenide particles are made to glow different colors and are used in television and phone screens.

(14) **SEP Construct an Explanation** How can understanding biochemical mechanisms that make substances toxic help chemists predict the toxicity of the substances they make?

....

....

....

Safer Ship Coatings Scientists designed a ship-coating material that kills plants and animals that grow on ships but causes less harm to the marine environment.

4. Designing Safer Chemicals

"Chemical products should be designed to preserve efficacy of the function while reducing toxicity."

It is impossible to make all substances nontoxic, because sometimes the toxicity is part of the desired function of the substance. For example, herbicides are toxic to plants, and antibiotics are toxic to bacteria. Many medicines are also toxic at certain doses.

Understanding how the structure of a molecule leads to its toxic effects helps scientists design safer substances that have the same function. Plants and shellfish can grow on the outside of ships, requiring the ships to use more fuel. To prevent this, ships are coated with substances that are toxic to plants and animals. One such substance, tributyltin oxide (TBTO), was banned because it stays in the marine environment for a long time and builds up in organisms, causing long-term harmful effects. Scientists developed a new substance to replace TBTO that breaks down quickly in the environment and does not build up in living things.

(15) **Connect to Technology** Describe a product or process used in daily life that used to use toxic materials but no longer does. 🖋

....

....

....

5. Safer Solvents and Auxiliaries

"The use of auxiliary substances (e.g. solvents, separation agents, etc.) should be made unnecessary wherever possible and, when used, innocuous."

Auxiliaries are substances used to help with the reaction, but they do not become part of the final products. The most common auxiliaries are solvents, which usually become waste after the reaction. Some solvents, such as benzene, are toxic and should be avoided if possible. Other solvents, such as water, are not toxic.

One way to reduce the amount of solvents is to reduce the number of reaction steps. Pharmaceutical syntheses can have more than five steps with each using its own solvents. Chemical industries have also developed solvent selection guides to help chemists choose safer solvents that will work for their syntheses. For example, benzene can cause cancer and is classified as a carcinogen. For some reactions, toluene, which is not a carcinogen, can be used as the solvent instead of benzene. For some processes, solvents can be removed entirely by using technologies such as milling.

Rotating drum

Ball Mill Instead of using solvents to bring reactants into contact, ball mills use ball bearings that can be reused many times.

Not to scale

The circle shows a cross section of the spinning drum. The ball bearings pulverize solid reactants, allowing them to react together without the use of liquid solvents.

⑯ CCC Structure and Function Why would it be difficult for chemists to replace solvents such as benzene with water? ✏️

....

....

....

6. Design for Energy Efficiency

"Energy requirements of chemical processes should be recognized for their environmental and economic impacts and should be minimized. If possible, synthetic methods should be conducted at ambient temperature and pressure."

Chemical processes often use large amounts of energy, which can be expensive. Energy-intensive processes also impact the environment because most energy comes from fossil fuels. Energy is used when reactions are heated and cooled. Processes, such as distillation, that are used to separate and purify water and other substances also require energy. Distilled water is often used to make aqueous solutions because it does not contain impurities.

Designing reactions to run at or near ambient pressures and temperatures will usually significantly reduce energy consumption, but it often reduces reaction rates. A catalyst is often required to form product in a reasonable time frame. Energy efficiency can also be gained by eliminating or combining reaction steps and by avoiding processes such as distillation when possible.

Two Ways to Desalinate Water Salts can be removed from water by distillation or reverse osmosis. Reverse osmosis is more energy efficient than distillation.

During reverse osmosis, water is forced through a semipermeable membrane that blocks the larger ions that make up the salts.

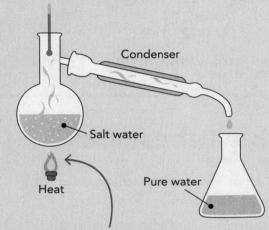

Condenser

Salt water

Heat

Pure water

Water must be heated to its boiling point during distillation. Then, cold water must be pumped through the condenser to cool the steam.

Energy requirement = $\dfrac{\text{about 90 kJ}}{\text{1 L}}$

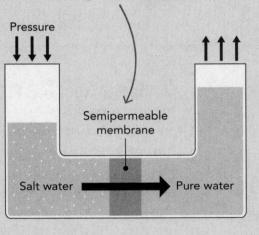

Pressure

Semipermeable membrane

Salt water → Pure water

Energy requirement = $\dfrac{\text{about 11 kJ}}{\text{1 L}}$

(17) **SEP Construct an Explanation** Identify two properties of water that makes its distillation so energy intensive. Explain. ✏️

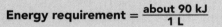

....

....

....

Renewable Feedstocks

What types of **biomass** can be used to make **chemical products?**

Different types of biomass can be used as **renewable feedstocks** to provide **carbon- and nitrogen-based starting materials.**

Chemical processes turn the biomass into **different substances** that the chemical industry can use **to make a variety of products.**

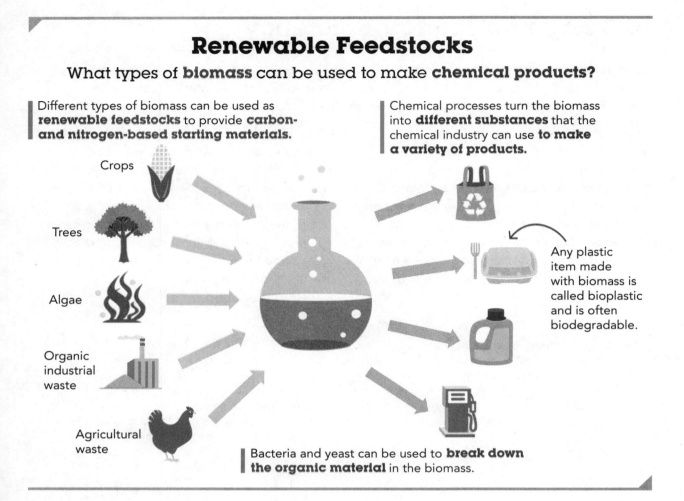

Crops

Trees

Algae

Organic industrial waste

Agricultural waste

Any plastic item made with biomass is called bioplastic and is often biodegradable.

Bacteria and yeast can be used to **break down the organic material** in the biomass.

7. Use of Renewable Feedstocks

"A raw material or feedstock should be renewable rather than depleting whenever technically and economically practicable."

Petroleum refining provides many feedstocks for the chemical industry. It provides the raw materials for pharmaceuticals, fertilizers, polymers, plastics, and other materials. However, petroleum is not renewable and can be replaced by renewable biomass, including trees, crops, and algae. Various chemical conversion processes, such as fermentation, combustion, and pyrolysis, are used to convert the biomass into various carbon- and nitrogen-based starting materials.

(18) **SEP Evaluate Solutions** Biodiesel fuels can be made from leftover cooking fats, such as from fast-food industries. Explain the environmental attraction of this in terms of Principle 1 (Waste Prevention). ✏

....

....

....

8. Reduce Derivatives

"Unnecessary derivatization (use of blocking groups, protection/deprotection, temporary modification of physical/chemical processes) should be minimized or avoided if possible, because such steps require additional reagents and can generate waste."

To make the desired products, chemists need to control which parts of the reactant molecules change. For example, a molecule may have two hydroxy groups, but only one of these groups is supposed to react. A protecting group, or blocking group, can be added to the molecule to get the targeted product. A protecting group is temporarily added to specific parts of a molecule to block certain atoms from participating in particular reactions. Synthetic chemists add and remove protecting groups in order to add different functional groups to the same molecule. Complex syntheses may use multiple protection and deprotection steps, which significantly reduces the atom economy of the process.

In the future, synthetic biology may be able to help reduce the inefficiencies of reactions that require protecting groups. Microorganisms are able to carry out all kinds of highly selective reactions. The goal of synthetic biology is to harness the natural abilities of organisms to help with chemical transformations.

Protecting Groups Chemists add and remove protecting groups during syntheses to reduce or avoid unwanted products.

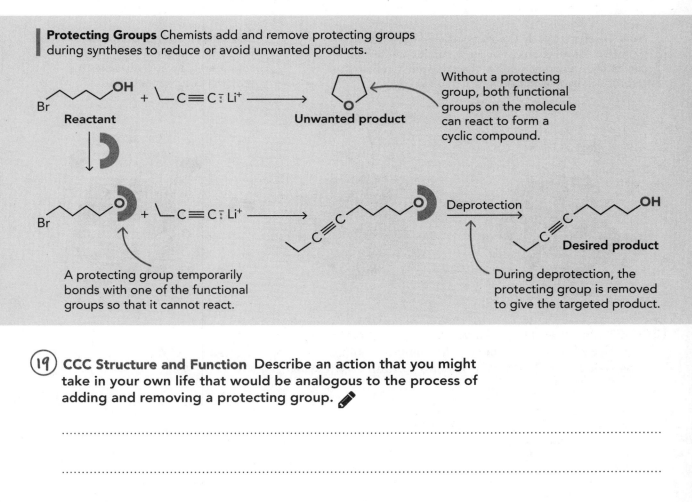

Without a protecting group, both functional groups on the molecule can react to form a cyclic compound.

A protecting group temporarily bonds with one of the functional groups so that it cannot react.

During deprotection, the protecting group is removed to give the targeted product.

⑲ **CCC Structure and Function** Describe an action that you might take in your own life that would be analogous to the process of adding and removing a protecting group. ✏️

....

....

9. Catalysis

"Catalytic reagents (as selective as possible) are superior to stoichiometric reagents."

A catalyst is a substance that increases reaction rates by providing a lower energy path for the reaction without being used up during the reaction. The way a catalyst increases a reaction rate is by reducing the activation energy for the reaction. As a result, a catalyst is able to reduce the energy requirements involved in the production of a chemical.

◼ **Catalysts are very important in green chemistry because they allow reactions to occur faster at lower temperatures.**

Catalysts can provide atom economies of up to 100% because they can reduce the need for other reagents and, unlike stoichiometric reagents, are not used up during the reaction. Some catalysts, such as enzymes, are highly selective, which means they catalyze specific reactions and thus produce the desired product and few, if any, by-products. Enzymes catalyze reactions in living organisms and work at low temperatures in aqueous solutions. Because they can work under mild conditions, enzymes make great green catalysts.

How Catalysts Work Catalysts provide lower energy pathways for reactions to occur. A surface of palladium can catalyze the reaction between oxygen and hydrogen to produce hydrogen peroxide in high yields.

The catalyst surface brings the reactants, oxygen and hydrogen, together in a way that makes the reaction occur more easily.

(20) **SEP Construct an Explanation** What is the atom economy of the catalyzed reaction shown in the diagram that produces hydrogen peroxide from hydrogen gas and oxygen gas? Explain. ✏️

....

....

....

Pesticide Selection Pesticides are needed to control the spread of mountain pine beetles, which have damaged large areas of western U.S. forests due to warming climates. This person is spraying a carbamate insecticide on a pine tree to protect it against the beetles.

10. Design for Degradation

"Chemical products should be designed so that at the end of their function they break down into innocuous degradation products and do not persist in the environment."

A major factor with toxicity and waste is a substance's persistence, which is how long the substance remains in the environment before it breaks down. Persistence is measured in terms of half-life, which is the time it takes for half of the substance to break down. For water, soil, and sediment, a half-life of less than 60 days is not persistent, between 60 and 180 days is persistent, and greater than 180 days is very persistent.

The insecticide DDT is a classic example of the perils of persistence. DDT has a very long half-life of up to 15 years in soil and 150 years in water. Scientists developed other insecticides, such as carbamates, that degrade more quickly. They can have half-lives as short as 4 days.

Substances can break down, or degrade, in many different ways, and the half-lives vary greatly for each of them. New substances need to be designed, keeping in mind how similar substances naturally break down. This is becoming increasingly important for plastics and related polymers, which often take more than 50 years to degrade. However, newer technologies are being used to develop plastics that degrade much faster.

(21) **Connect to Technology** Some substances break down in the presence of sunlight. Describe one possible advantage and one disadvantage of a plastic that rapidly degrades in this way. ✏️

....

....

....

11. Real-Time Analysis for Pollution Prevention

"Analytical methodologies need to be further developed to allow for real-time, in-process monitoring and control prior to the formation of hazardous substances."

Although chemists can often predict the products of chemical reactions, it is important that they also know how reactions are progressing. Chemists monitor reaction conditions, such as temperature, pressure, and acidity, to help maintain the optimum conditions for making the desired product. Monitoring the reaction in real time, while the reaction is taking place, allows chemists to adjust the reaction conditions as needed. Because chemical reactors are often closed systems, they often have different sensors to monitor the conditions inside. The sensors can be connected to computers that automatically adjust reaction conditions as needed.

Chemists also collect samples to test for relative amounts of products and unwanted by-products. This can help them maximize the yield of the desired product and reduce the amount of by-products that become waste. It also allows chemists to maintain safe conditions by controlling how quickly exothermic reactions occur, which can prevent explosions.

Monitoring Chemical Reactions Chemists use many techniques to monitor chemical reaction conditions and the substances that form to maximize their yields and reduce unwanted waste.

Samples are analyzed to track the reaction progress, such as how much of the product and by-products have formed.

- **High product yield**
- **Fewer by-products**

Reaction conditions, including temperature, are monitored with sensors.

Reaction conditions are adjusted to maintain the ideal conditions.

(22) **Apply Concepts** Explain whether you would use an acid-base indicator or a pH meter to monitor a neutralization reaction in real time. ✎

....

....

....

12. Safer Chemistry for Accident Prevention

"Substances and the form of a substance used in a chemical process should be chosen to minimize the potential for chemical accidents, including releases, explosions, and fires."

Sometimes, chemists have to make toxic or dangerous substances because it is the unsafe properties that makes them valuable, such as flammable gasoline and toxic chemotherapy drugs. However, it is vital to make chemical products and processes safer wherever possible. As an example, consider the 1984 accident that killed thousands of people at a plant in Bhopal, India. To synthesize a carbamate insecticide, the plant sometimes stored a highly toxic reaction intermediate, methyl isocyanate, in huge tanks. The intermediate would be used in a later step to make the final product. One day, a tank malfunctioned and released the toxic substance. To avoid this disaster, the plant could have matched the production and consumption

rates for the intermediate. Doing so would have eliminated the need for storing the substance.

Following some notable 20th-century accidents, such as the one in Bhopal, companies began using modern safety practices. These practices often involve making the process safe from the start, rather than relying on protective equipment that could possibly fail. For example, companies can avoid or minimize toxic materials in their processes, use safer solvents when possible, and use real-time monitoring to help ensure reactions go as planned. Explosions, which often result from runaway exothermic reactions in which the rate of heat generation exceeds the rate of heat removal, can be prevented with real-time monitoring.

(23) **SEP Interpret Data** The graph shows the relationship between heat production and removal for a reaction. For temperatures above the ignition temperature, heat is generated faster than it is removed, and an explosion can result. On the graph, indicate the temperature range where the reaction can occur safely. ✎

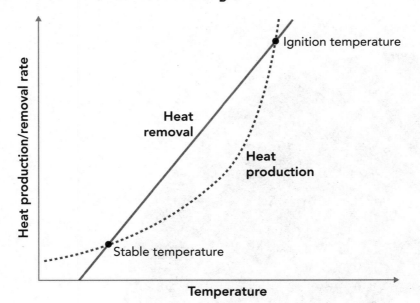

INVESTIGATIVE PHENOMENON

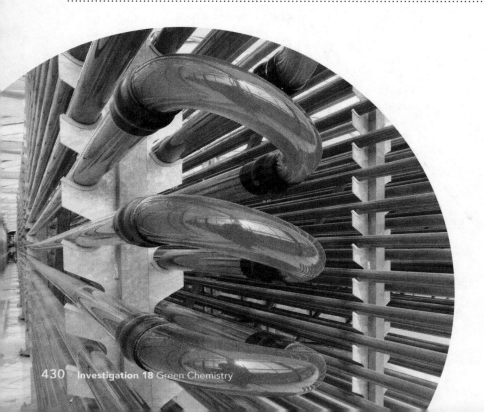

GO ONLINE to Elaborate on and Evaluate what you learned about the principles of green chemistry by completing the class discussion and engineering design activities.

In the CER worksheet you completed at the beginning of the investigation, you evaluated the environmental impact of the production and use of biofuel made from microalgae. With a partner, reevaluate the evidence you cited in your arguments.

24 **SEP Construct an Explanation** Both microalgae, which tend to be rich in fat, and wood can be used as renewable feedstocks. Explain why using wood might be less efficient than microalgae in making liquid biofuels. ✏

....

....

....

....

....

....

....

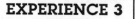
Designing Sustainable Chemical Processes

GO ONLINE to Explore and Explain how green chemistry can be applied to improve industrial processes and why waste prevention is advantageous for a company.

Tradeoffs and Synergies

Green chemistry can involve tradeoffs among feedstocks, waste volume, safety, environmental impacts, energy consumption, and cost. For example, a company may make trade-offs to ensure employee safety. Using a less hazardous solvent makes a reaction safer, but the revised reaction conditions may produce less of the targeted product and generate more waste.

However, when applying the 12 Principles of Green Chemistry, chemists deal with not only tradeoffs, but also synergies. For example, catalysts by their very nature reduce energy input requirements for a chemical reaction. Additionally, catalysts often offer improved product selectivity, which equates to less waste. In other words, applying Principle 9 (Catalysis) can offer synergies with Principle 1 (Waste Prevention) and Principle 6 (Energy Efficiency). Synergies also exist between cost savings and waste prevention because proper waste treatment and disposal are expensive.

Tradeoff Example A company may choose to use renewable feedstocks obtained from plants to make plastic. This choice would greatly reduce the company's dependence on petroleum-based feedstocks.

Pro: Bioplastic made from switchgrass can degrade more quickly than petroleum-based plastics.

Cons: Growing switchgrass takes up land and may require the use of fertilizers.

BIODEGRADABLE
OK compost
BIOBASED

431

Parts of the Triple Bottom Line
Greener chemical practices include factoring in the triple bottom line to business practices. This includes not only profits but also people and the planet.

Triple Bottom Line

SOCIAL (people)	**ENVIRONMENT** (planet)	**ECONOMIC** (profit)
Health and safety of employees	Waste production	Sales, profits, return on investment
Human rights	Energy usage	Jobs created
Employment	Air and water quality	Taxes paid
Fair labor practices	Biosphere impacts	Monetary flows
Community impacts	Climate impacts	Market stability

The Triple Bottom Line

Businesses that practice green chemistry usually measure their performance by more than how much money they make, traditionally called the bottom line. They also measure their performance with respect to their social and environmental impacts. These three areas combined, often called the 3Ps (people, planet, and profit), make up an accounting framework called the **Triple Bottom Line.** The Triple Bottom Line can help chemical companies pursue sustainable growth.

Measuring performance based on profits is fairly straightforward and is measured in dollars, but there is no standard way to measure performance based on people (social impact) and the planet (environmental impact). Things that are measured vary from company to company. Each company chooses a set of measurements that help quantify the company's performance against its goals. For social impact, a company that wants to improve employee safety may measure human toxicity potential for the substances used in its processes. A company that wishes to increase the number of women employed at the company may measure the ratio of women to men. For environmental impact, a company may measure tons of waste produced per ton of product and seek to decrease waste. A company may also measure CO_2 emissions and energy and water consumption.

(25) **Predict** A new chemical company has decided to use the Triple Bottom Line to measure their performance. How is the decision likely to affect its choice of energy sources? ✏️

....

....

....

Sustainable Resource Management

For the chemical industry to be sustainable, it needs to ensure that resources for raw materials are available for future generations. The minerals and fossil fuels that are used as feedstocks are nonrenewable resources and have a limited supply. Renewable feedstocks come from biological sources, such as plants and waste products from agriculture and forestry, and they are sustainable if they are managed well.

Minerals provide essential materials, including silicon and metals that are used as catalysts. Because easily obtainable minerals can be used up, they need to be carefully managed. Developing catalytic processes that use metals that are in greater supply or that use enzymes that come from renewable sources can extend the availability of platinum and other rare metals. Developing methods to recycle metals from electronics and other products will also make them more sustainable.

◗ Part of the focus of green chemistry is developing efficient chemical processes that use fewer materials that come from nonrenewable feedstocks.

Recycling Materials Computers, phones, other electronics, and rechargeable batteries contain many valuable metals that are in limited supply. Scientists are developing ways to recycle these materials so that they can be used as starting materials again.

(26) **SEP Construct Explanations** Most Li-ion batteries contain valuable metals but are not currently recycled. Why might designing improved recycling processes be important for the future? 🖉

....

....

....

Sustainable Energy Practices

Chemical processes still depend largely on energy that comes from the combustion of nonrenewable fossil fuels, which produces carbon dioxide and contributes to climate change. To reduce the energy consumption of the chemical industry, chemists and engineers are designing and improving processes to make them more energy efficient.

In addition, chemical processes can use sustainable energy sources, such as wind, solar, tidal, and biomass, instead of fossil fuels. Wind and solar power are becoming less expensive and more efficient. With batteries and other energy storage technologies, these sources can now provide energy when it is needed, even in the absence of wind and sunlight. Wind, solar, and tidal energy generate electricity, whereas biomass can be burned for heat. Many industrial chemical processes rely on heat from burning fossil fuels. To use solar and wind energy, engineers are designing new systems that can carry out the same processes using electricity.

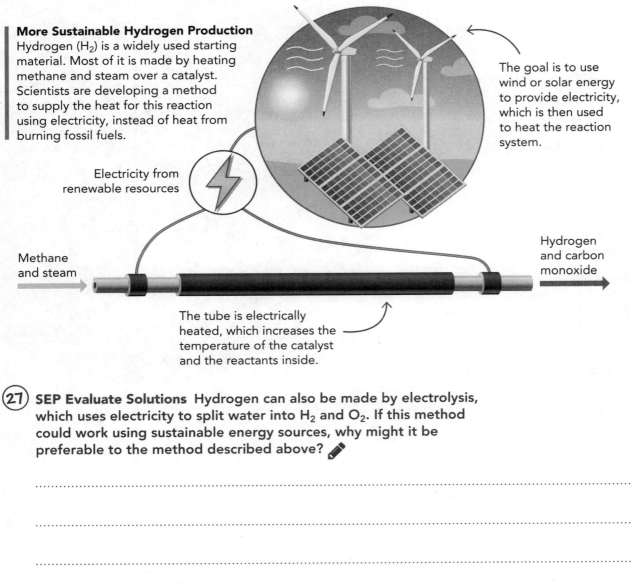

More Sustainable Hydrogen Production
Hydrogen (H_2) is a widely used starting material. Most of it is made by heating methane and steam over a catalyst. Scientists are developing a method to supply the heat for this reaction using electricity, instead of heat from burning fossil fuels.

The goal is to use wind or solar energy to provide electricity, which is then used to heat the reaction system.

Electricity from renewable resources

Methane and steam

Hydrogen and carbon monoxide

The tube is electrically heated, which increases the temperature of the catalyst and the reactants inside.

(27) **SEP Evaluate Solutions** Hydrogen can also be made by electrolysis, which uses electricity to split water into H_2 and O_2. If this method could work using sustainable energy sources, why might it be preferable to the method described above? ✎

....

....

....

Sustainable Waste Management

The chemical industry generates hazardous waste, which includes used solvents, excess reagents, by-products, and other materials used during production. These materials can be solids, liquids, or gases, and they must be treated and disposed of in specific ways, which can be costly. If they are not disposed of properly, they can contaminate soil, water, and air. Many solid and liquid wastes are incinerated, which destroys toxic compounds. However, the gas that is generated must be treated to remove contaminants before it is released into the air.

"Designing Out" Waste The most desirable way to manage waste is to produce less of it. Companies can redesign their chemical processes to achieve this goal. High atom economies, the use of catalysts, and reduced use of solvents can all help reduce waste. Waste-minimizing reactions involve fewer steps and produce the desired product along with few or no by-products.

Reuse and Recycle Catalysts can be reused only so many times before they are no longer effective and must be discarded. Catalysts that are dissolved in the reaction mixture need to be isolated before they can be reused. Most other materials need to be recycled before they can be used again because they are not pure. Impurities can cause problems, such as unwanted side reactions, in a chemical process. Solvents may be recyclable depending on the impurities they have dissolved in them. Solvents are separated from impurities by processes such as distillation and filtration.

Cutting Waste at the Source Ibuprofen was once made using a six-step synthetic method that did not involve a catalyst. This method produced a lot of waste. Chemists redesigned the method so that it involves three catalytic steps and produces a fraction of the waste.

The six-step method produces waste at four of the six steps.

2-methylpropylbenzene (starting material)

The first step of the redesigned three-step method produces acetic acid, a waste product that can be recycled.

Ibuprofen (product)

(28) **SEP Design Solutions** Suppose you are advising a start-up chemical company on waste management. Develop some brief guidelines you could share with them. ✏️

....

....

....

Achieving Sustainable Chemistry

Education and Collaboration Practitioners of green chemistry around the world have accomplished an impressive amount of work. However, these accomplishments represent the beginning stages. Green chemistry is a different philosophical approach to chemistry, which is often referred to as "benign by design." Implementing a new way of thinking into industry can be challenging. These challenges can be met by allowing students to practice and become skilled in this new way of thinking. Education of the general public is also needed in order for society to support and encourage the efforts of the chemical industry. For example, the support of the general public is crucial for recycling efforts that will help the industry manage Earth's nonrenewable resources more responsibly. Outreach, education, and on-the-job mentoring for groups in the chemical industry in nations that are not as aware of the potentials of green chemistry, or in industry sectors that are hesitant to implement change, can also help.

Chemists also need to work more closely with their colleagues in other fields and with collaborators in fields such as toxicology, engineering, manufacturing economics, computational modeling, and the geosciences. Close collaboration in interdisciplinary teams can lead to innovative processes for materials production that are efficient, environmentally friendly, and sustainable.

Education Green chemistry is a very new field, and there is tremendous room for future scientific discovery, so educating the next generation of scientists is a top priority.

Recognizing Innovators

How can government initiatives promote green chemistry?

One EPA initiative, the **Green Chemistry Challenge Awards,** recognizes about five innovative technologies per year. Winning technologies must have significant impacts and be transferable to other processes, factories, or industry sectors.

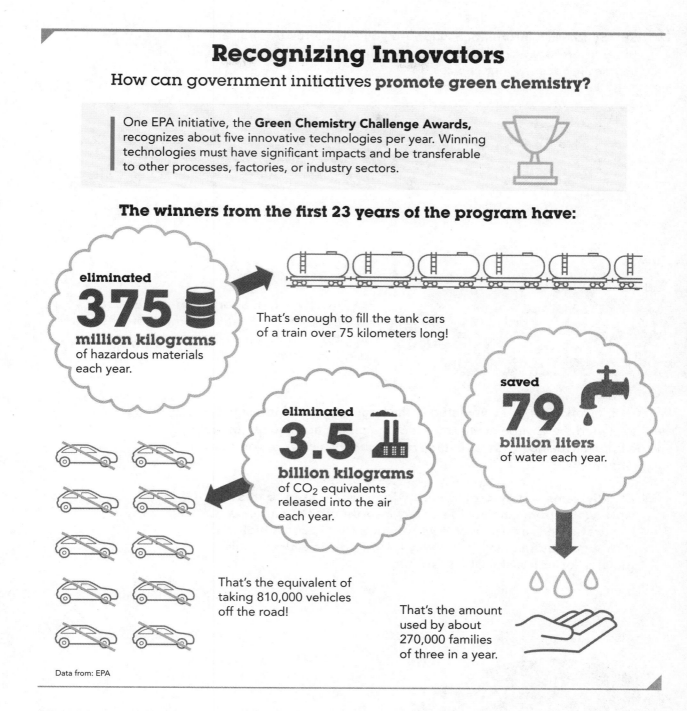

The winners from the first 23 years of the program have:

eliminated

375

million kilograms of hazardous materials each year.

That's enough to fill the tank cars of a train over 75 kilometers long!

eliminated

3.5

billion kilograms of CO₂ equivalents released into the air each year.

That's the equivalent of taking 810,000 vehicles off the road!

saved

79

billion liters of water each year.

That's the amount used by about 270,000 families of three in a year.

Data from: EPA

Government Role Governments play crucial roles in supporting green chemistry through enacting legislation that protects natural resources of land, air, and water. Laws and subsequent amendments levy fines for companies that pollute the air or water above acceptable levels. These actions have led to significant improvements in industrial practices and, as a result, to human health in many parts of the world. Government initiatives are also important. For example, the EPA's Green Chemistry Challenge recognizes and promotes "innovative chemical technologies that prevent pollution and have broad applicability in industry." This initiative facilitates both competition between and information sharing among companies and industry sectors, which can accelerate changes in the industry.

29 **SEP Synthesize Information** Suppose you are interested in a career in green chemistry. What fields of study other than chemistry would you take courses in? Justify your choices.

....

....

....

....

Revisit

INVESTIGATIVE PHENOMENON

GO ONLINE to Elaborate on and Evaluate your knowledge of sustainable chemical processes by completing the data analysis and engineering design activities.

In the CER worksheet you completed at the beginning of the investigation, you evaluated the environmental impact of the production and use of biofuel made from microalgae. With a partner, reevaluate the evidence you cited in your arguments.

30 **CCC Systems and System Models** Algae can be used to treat wastewater from communities. They incorporate the nutrients, such as nitrates, in the wastewater into the oils that become biofuels. How would using algae in this way be synergistic with multiple general societal sustainability strategies?

....

....

....

....

....

....

....

GO ONLINE to Evaluate what you learned about green chemistry by using the available assessment resources.

In the Performance-Based Assessment, you analyzed different solutions for making your chemistry laboratory curriculum greener. Wrap up your analysis by answering the following question.

(31) **SEP Evaluate Solutions** How does designing new experiments that serve the same function as existing experiments align with the goals of green chemistry? ✏️

....

....

....

....

....

Revisit
ANCHORING PHENOMENON

(32) Apply what you learned in Storyline 5 to answer the Anchoring Phenomenon question "How can we sustainably meet the world's energy needs?" ✏️

....

....

....

....

....

GO ONLINE for a problem-based learning activity that you can tackle after completing Storyline 5.

End-of-Book Resources

TABLE A.1	
PHYSICAL CONSTANTS	
Atomic mass unit	$1 \text{ amu} = 1.6605 \times 10^{-24}$ g
Avogadro's number	$N = 6.02 \times 10^{23}$ particles/mol
Gas constant	$R = 8.31$ L·kPa/(K·mol)
Ideal gas molar volume	$V_m = 22.4$ L/mol
Masses of subatomic particles	
Electron (e^-)	$m_e = 0.000549 \text{ amu} = 9.1094 \times 10^{-28}$ g
Proton (p^+)	$m_p = 1.00728 \text{ amu} = 1.67262 \times 10^{-24}$ g
Neutron (n^0)	$m_n = 1.00867 \text{ amu} = 1.67493 \times 10^{-24}$ g
Speed of light in a vacuum	$c = 3.00 \times 10^8$ m/s

TABLE A.2					
COMMON SYMBOLS AND ABBREVIATIONS					
α	alpha rays	GWP	global warming potential	mm	millimeter
β	beta rays	H	enthalpy	mol	mole
γ	gamma rays	ΔH_f	heat of formation	mp	melting point
Δ	change in	h	hour	n^0	neutron
$\delta+, \delta-$	partial ionic charge	h	Planck's constant	n	number of moles
λ	wavelength	Hz	hertz	n	principal quantum number
π	pi bond	J	joule		
σ	sigma bond	K	kelvin	P	pressure
ν	frequency	K_a	acid ionization constant	p^+	proton
amu	atomic mass unit	K_b	base ionization constant	Pa	pascal
(aq)	aqueous solution	K_{eq}	equilibrium constant	R	ideal gas constant
atm	atmosphere	K_w	ion product constant for water	S	entropy
bp	boiling point			s	second
°C	degree Celsius	kcal	kilocalorie	(s)	solid
c	speed of light in a vacuum	kg	kilogram	STP	standard temperature and pressure
cm	centimeter	kPa	kilopascal		
E	energy	L	liter		
e^-	electron	(l)	liquid	T	temperature
EFM	empirical formula mass	M	molarity	$t_{1/2}$	half-life
fp	freezing point	m	meter	V	volume
G	Gibbs free energy	m	mass	v	velocity
g	gram	m	molality	Z_{eff}	effective nuclear charge
(g)	gas	mL	milliliter		

SOME PROPERTIES OF THE ELEMENTS

Element	Symbol	Atomic number	Atomic mass	Melting point (°C)	Boiling point (°C)	Density (g/cm³) (gases at STP)	Oxidation numbers
Actinium	Ac	89	(227)	1050	3200	10.07	+3
Aluminum	Al	13	26.98154	660.37	2467	2.6989	+3
Americium	Am	95	243	994	2607	13.67	+3, +4, +5, +6
Antimony	Sb	51	121.75	630.74	1587	6.691	−3, +3, +5
Argon	Ar	18	39.948	−189.2	−185.7	0.0017837	
Arsenic	As	33	74.9216	817	613	5.73	−3, +3, +5
Astatine	At	85	(210)	302	337	—	
Barium	Ba	56	137.33	725	1640	3.5	+2
Berkelium	Bk	97	(247)	986	—	14.78	
Beryllium	Be	4	9.01218	1278	2970	1.848	+2
Bismuth	Bi	83	208.9804	271.3	1560	9.747	+3, +5
Bohrium	Bh	107	(264)	—	—	—	
Boron	B	5	10.81	2075	3675	2.34	+3
Bromine	Br	35	79.904	−7.2	58.78	3.12	−1, +1, +5
Cadmium	Cd	48	112.41	320.9	765	8.65	+2
Calcium	Ca	20	40.08	839	1484	1.55	+2
Californium	Cf	98	(251)	900	—	14	
Carbon	C	6	12.011	3550	4827	2.267	−4, +2, +4
Cerium	Ce	58	140.12	799	3426	6.657	+3, +4
Cesium	Cs	55	132.9054	28.40	669.3	1.873	+1
Chlorine	Cl	17	35.453	−100.98	−34.6	0.003214	−1, +1, +5, +7
Chromium	Cr	24	51.996	1907	2672	7.18	+2, +3, +6
Cobalt	Co	27	58.9332	1495	2870	8.9	+2, +3
Copernicium	Cn	112	(277)	—	—	—	
Copper	Cu	29	63.546	1083.4	2567	8.96	+1, +2
Curium	Cm	96	(247)	1340	—	13.51	+3
Darmstadtium	Ds	110	(269)	—	—	—	
Dubnium	Db	105	(262)	—	—	—	
Dysprosium	Dy	66	162.50	1412	2562	8.550	+3
Einsteinium	Es	99	(252)	—	—	—	
Erbium	Er	68	167.26	159	2863	9.066	+3
Europium	Eu	63	151.96	822	1597	5.243	+2, +3
Fermium	Fm	100	(257)	—	—	—	
Flerovium	Fl	114	(289)	—	—	—	
Fluorine	F	9	18.998403	−219.62	−188.54	0.00181	−1
Francium	Fr	87	(223)	27	677	—	+1
Gadolinium	Gd	64	157.25	1313	3266	7.9004	+3
Gallium	Ga	31	69.72	29.78	2204	5.904	+3
Germanium	Ge	32	72.59	937.4	2830	5.323	+2, +4
Gold	Au	79	196.9665	1064.43	2856	19.3	+1, +3
Hafnium	Hf	72	178.49	2227	4602	13.31	+4
Hassium	Hs	108	(265)	—	—	—	
Helium	He	2	4.00260	−272.2	−268.934	0.0001785	
Holmium	Ho	67	164.9304	1474	2695	8.795	+3
Hydrogen	H	1	1.00794	−259.14	−252.87	0.00008988	−1, +1
Indium	In	49	114.82	156.61	2080	7.31	+1, +3
Iodine	I	53	126.9045	113.5	184.35	4.93	−1, +1, +5, +7
Iridium	Ir	77	192.22	2410	4130	22.42	+3, +4
Iron	Fe	26	55.847	1535	2750	7.874	+2, +3
Krypton	Kr	36	83.80	−156.6	−152.30	0.003733	
Lanthanum	La	57	138.9055	921	3457	6.145	+3
Lawrencium	Lr	103	(262)	—	—	—	+3
Lead	Pb	82	207.2	327.502	1740	11.35	+2, +4
Lithium	Li	3	6.941	180.54	1342	0.534	+1
Livermorium	Lv	116	(293)	—	—	—	
Lutetium	Lu	71	174.967	1663	3395	9.840	+3
Magnesium	Mg	12	24.305	648.8	1107	1.738	+2
Manganese	Mn	25	54.9380	1244	1962	7.32	+2, +3, +4, +7

SOME PROPERTIES OF THE ELEMENTS

Element	Symbol	Atomic number	Atomic mass	Melting point (°C)	Boiling point (°C)	Density (g/cm³) (gases at STP)	Oxidation numbers
Meitnerium	Mt	109	(278)	—	—	—	
Mendelevium	Md	101	257	—	—	—	+2, +3
Mercury	Hg	80	200.59	−38.842	356.58	13.55	+1, +2
Molybdenum	Mo	42	95.94	2617	4612	10.22	+6
Moscovium	Mc	115	(289)	—	—	—	
Neodymium	Nd	60	144.24	1021	3068	6.90	+3
Neon	Ne	10	20.179	−248.67	−246.048	0.0008999	
Neptunium	Np	93	(237)	640	3902	20.25	+3, +4, +5, +6
Nickel	Ni	28	58.69	1453	2732	8.902	+2, +3
Nihonium	Nh	113	(286)	—	—	—	
Niobium	Nb	41	92.9064	2468	4742	8.57	+3, +5
Nitrogen	N	7	14.0067	−209.86	−195.8	0.0012506	−3, +3, +5
Nobelium	No	102	(259)	—	—	—	+2, +3
Oganesson	Og	118	(294)	—	—	—	
Osmium	Os	76	190.2	3045	5027	22.57	+3, +4
Oxygen	O	8	15.9994	−218.4	−182.962	0.001429	−2
Palladium	Pd	46	106.42	1554	2970	12.02	+2, +4
Phosphorus	P	15	30.97376	44.1	280	1.82	−3, +3, +5
Platinum	Pt	78	195.08	1772	3627	21.45	+2, +4
Plutonium	Pu	94	(244)	641	3232	19.84	+3, +4, +5, +6
Polonium	Po	84	(209)	254	962	9.32	+2, +4
Potassium	K	19	39.0982	63.25	760	0.862	+1
Praseodymium	Pr	59	140.9077	931	3512	6.64	+3
Promethium	Pm	61	(145)	1168	2460	7.22	+3
Protactinium	Pa	91	231.0359	1560	4027	15.37	+4, +5
Radium	Ra	88	(226)	700	1140	5.5	+2
Radon	Rn	86	(222)	−71	−61.8	0.00973	
Rhenium	Re	75	186.207	3180	5627	21.02	+4, +6, +7
Rhodium	Rh	45	102.9055	1966	3727	12.41	+3
Roentgenium	Rg	111	(272)	—	—	—	
Rubidium	Rb	37	85.4678	38.89	686	1.532	+1
Ruthenium	Ru	44	101.07	2310	3900	12.41	+3
Rutherfordium	Rf	104	(261)	—	—	—	
Samarium	Sm	62	150.36	1077	1791	7.520	+2, +3
Scandium	Sc	21	44.9559	1541	2831	2.989	+3
Seaborgium	Sg	106	(263)	—	—	—	
Selenium	Se	34	78.96	217	684.9	4.79	−2, +4, +6
Silicon	Si	14	28.0855	1410	2355	2.33	−4, +2, +4
Silver	Ag	47	107.8682	961.93	2212	10.50	+1
Sodium	Na	11	22.98977	97.81	882.9	0.971	+1
Strontium	Sr	38	87.62	769	1381	2.63	+2
Sulfur	S	16	32.06	112.8	444.7	2.07	−2, +4, +6
Tantalum	Ta	73	180.9479	2996	5425	16.654	+5
Technetium	Tc	43	(98)	2172	4877	11.50	+4, +6, +7
Tellurium	Te	52	127.60	449.5	989.8	6.24	−2, +4, +6
Tennessine	Ts	117	(294)	—	—	—	
Terbium	Tb	65	158.9254	1356	3123	8.229	+3
Thallium	Tl	81	204.383	303.5	1457	11.85	+1, +3
Thorium	Th	90	232.0381	1750	4790	11.72	+4
Thulium	Tm	69	168.9342	1545	1947	9.321	+3
Tin	Sn	50	118.69	231.968	2270	7.31	+2, +4
Titanium	Ti	22	47.88	1660	3287	4.54	+2, +3, +4
Tungsten	W	74	183.85	3410	5660	19.3	+6
Uranium	U	92	238.0289	1132.3	3818	18.95	+3, +4, +5, +6
Vanadium	V	23	50.9415	1890	3380	6.11	+2, +3, +4, +5
Xenon	Xe	54	131.29	−111.9	−107.1	0.005887	
Ytterbium	Yb	70	173.04	819	1194	6.965	+2, +3
Yttrium	Y	39	88.9059	1522	3338	4.469	+3
Zinc	Zn	30	65.38	419.58	907	7.133	+2
Zirconium	Zr	40	91.22	1852	4377	6.506	+4

TABLE A.4
ELECTRON CONFIGURATION OF THE ELEMENTS

	Element	Sublevels																		
		1s	2s	2p	3s	3p	3d	4s	4p	4d	4f	5s	5p	5d	5f	6s	6p	6d	7s	7p
1	Hydrogen	1																		
2	Helium	2																		
3	Lithium	2	1																	
4	Beryllium	2	2																	
5	Boron	2	2	1																
6	Carbon	2	2	2																
7	Nitrogen	2	2	3																
8	Oxygen	2	2	4																
9	Fluorine	2	2	5																
10	Neon	2	2	6																
11	Sodium	2	2	6	1															
12	Magnesium	2	2	6	2															
13	Aluminum	2	2	6	2	1														
14	Silicon	2	2	6	2	2														
15	Phosphorus	2	2	6	2	3														
16	Sulfur	2	2	6	2	4														
17	Chlorine	2	2	6	2	5														
18	Argon	2	2	6	2	6														
19	Potassium	2	2	6	2	6		1												
20	Calcium	2	2	6	2	6		2												
21	Scandium	2	2	6	2	6	1	2												
22	Titanium	2	2	6	2	6	2	2												
23	Vanadium	2	2	6	2	6	3	2												
24	Chromium	2	2	6	2	6	5	1												
25	Manganese	2	2	6	2	6	5	2												
26	Iron	2	2	6	2	6	6	2												
27	Cobalt	2	2	6	2	6	7	2												
28	Nickel	2	2	6	2	6	8	2												
29	Copper	2	2	6	2	6	10	1												
30	Zinc	2	2	6	2	6	10	2												
31	Gallium	2	2	6	2	6	10	2	1											
32	Germanium	2	2	6	2	6	10	2	2											
33	Arsenic	2	2	6	2	6	10	2	3											
34	Selenium	2	2	6	2	6	10	2	4											
35	Bromine	2	2	6	2	6	10	2	5											
36	Krypton	2	2	6	2	6	10	2	6											
37	Rubidium	2	2	6	2	6	10	2	6			1								
38	Strontium	2	2	6	2	6	10	2	6			2								
39	Yttrium	2	2	6	2	6	10	2	6	1		2								
40	Zirconium	2	2	6	2	6	10	2	6	2		2								
41	Niobium	2	2	6	2	6	10	2	6	4		1								
42	Molybdenum	2	2	6	2	6	10	2	6	5		1								
43	Technetium	2	2	6	2	6	10	2	6	5		2								
44	Ruthenium	2	2	6	2	6	10	2	6	7		1								
45	Rhodium	2	2	6	2	6	10	2	6	8		1								
46	Palladium	2	2	6	2	6	10	2	6	10										
47	Silver	2	2	6	2	6	10	2	6	10		1								
48	Cadmium	2	2	6	2	6	10	2	6	10		2								
49	Indium	2	2	6	2	6	10	2	6	10		2	1							
50	Tin	2	2	6	2	6	10	2	6	10		2	2							
51	Antimony	2	2	6	2	6	10	2	6	10		2	3							
52	Tellurium	2	2	6	2	6	10	2	6	10		2	4							
53	Iodine	2	2	6	2	6	10	2	6	10		2	5							
54	Xenon	2	2	6	2	6	10	2	6	10		2	6							
55	Cesium	2	2	6	2	6	10	2	6	10		2	6			1				
56	Barium	2	2	6	2	6	10	2	6	10		2	6			2				
57	Lanthanum	2	2	6	2	6	10	2	6	10		2	6	1		2				
58	Cerium	2	2	6	2	6	10	2	6	10	1	2	6	1		2				
59	Praseodymium	2	2	6	2	6	10	2	6	10	3	2	6			2				

ELECTRON CONFIGURATION OF THE ELEMENTS

	Element	Sublevels																		
		1s	2s	2p	3s	3p	3d	4s	4p	4d	4f	5s	5p	5d	5f	6s	6p	6d	7s	7p
60	Neodymium	2	2	6	2	6	10	2	6	10	4	2	6			2				
61	Promethium	2	2	6	2	6	10	2	6	10	5	2	6			2				
62	Samarium	2	2	6	2	6	10	2	6	10	6	2	6			2				
63	Europium	2	2	6	2	6	10	2	6	10	7	2	6			2				
64	Gadolinium	2	2	6	2	6	10	2	6	10	7	2	6	1		2				
65	Terbium	2	2	6	2	6	10	2	6	10	9	2	6			2				
66	Dysprosium	2	2	6	2	6	10	2	6	10	10	2	6			2				
67	Holmium	2	2	6	2	6	10	2	6	10	11	2	6			2				
68	Erbium	2	2	6	2	6	10	2	6	10	12	2	6			2				
69	Thulium	2	2	6	2	6	10	2	6	10	13	2	6			2				
70	Ytterbium	2	2	6	2	6	10	2	6	10	14	2	6			2				
71	Lutetium	2	2	6	2	6	10	2	6	10	14	2	6	1		2				
72	Hafnium	2	2	6	2	6	10	2	6	10	14	2	6	2		2				
73	Tantalum	2	2	6	2	6	10	2	6	10	14	2	6	3		2				
74	Tungsten	2	2	6	2	6	10	2	6	10	14	2	6	4		2				
75	Rhenium	2	2	6	2	6	10	2	6	10	14	2	6	5		2				
76	Osmium	2	2	6	2	6	10	2	6	10	14	2	6	6		2				
77	Iridium	2	2	6	2	6	10	2	6	10	14	2	6	7		2				
78	Platinum	2	2	6	2	6	10	2	6	10	14	2	6	9		1				
79	Gold	2	2	6	2	6	10	2	6	10	14	2	6	10		1				
80	Mercury	2	2	6	2	6	10	2	6	10	14	2	6	10		2				
81	Thallium	2	2	6	2	6	10	2	6	10	14	2	6	10		2	1			
82	Lead	2	2	6	2	6	10	2	6	10	14	2	6	10		2	2			
83	Bismuth	2	2	6	2	6	10	2	6	10	14	2	6	10		2	3			
84	Polonium	2	2	6	2	6	10	2	6	10	14	2	6	10		2	4			
85	Astatine	2	2	6	2	6	10	2	6	10	14	2	6	10		2	5			
86	Radon	2	2	6	2	6	10	2	6	10	14	2	6	10		2	6			
87	Francium	2	2	6	2	6	10	2	6	10	14	2	6	10		2	6		1	
88	Radium	2	2	6	2	6	10	2	6	10	14	2	6	10		2	6		2	
89	Actinium	2	2	6	2	6	10	2	6	10	14	2	6	10		2	6	1	2	
90	Thorium	2	2	6	2	6	10	2	6	10	14	2	6	10		2	6	2	2	
91	Protactinium	2	2	6	2	6	10	2	6	10	14	2	6	10	2	2	6	1	2	
92	Uranium	2	2	6	2	6	10	2	6	10	14	2	6	10	3	2	6	1	2	
93	Neptunium	2	2	6	2	6	10	2	6	10	14	2	6	10	4	2	6	1	2	
94	Plutonium	2	2	6	2	6	10	2	6	10	14	2	6	10	6	2	6		2	
95	Americium	2	2	6	2	6	10	2	6	10	14	2	6	10	7	2	6		2	
96	Curium	2	2	6	2	6	10	2	6	10	14	2	6	10	7	2	6	1	2	
97	Berkelium	2	2	6	2	6	10	2	6	10	14	2	6	10	9	2	6		2	
98	Californium	2	2	6	2	6	10	2	6	10	14	2	6	10	10	2	6		2	
99	Einsteinium	2	2	6	2	6	10	2	6	10	14	2	6	10	11	2	6		2	
100	Fermium	2	2	6	2	6	10	2	6	10	14	2	6	10	12	2	6		2	
101	Mendelevium	2	2	6	2	6	10	2	6	10	14	2	6	10	13	2	6		2	
102	Nobelium	2	2	6	2	6	10	2	6	10	14	2	6	10	14	2	6		2	
103	Lawrencium	2	2	6	2	6	10	2	6	10	14	2	6	10	14	2	6	1	2	
104	Rutherfordium	2	2	6	2	6	10	2	6	10	14	2	6	10	14	2	6	2	2	
105	Dubnium	2	2	6	2	6	10	2	6	10	14	2	6	10	14	2	6	3	2	
106	Seaborgium	2	2	6	2	6	10	2	6	10	14	2	6	10	14	2	6	4	2	
107	Bohrium	2	2	6	2	6	10	2	6	10	14	2	6	10	14	2	6	5	2	
108	Hassium	2	2	6	2	6	10	2	6	10	14	2	6	10	14	2	6	6	2	
109	Meitnerium	2	2	6	2	6	10	2	6	10	14	2	6	10	14	2	6	7	2	
110	Darmstadium	2	2	6	2	6	10	2	6	10	14	2	6	10	14	2	6	9	1	
111	Roentgenium	2	2	6	2	6	10	2	6	10	14	2	6	10	14	2	6	10	1	
112	Copernicium	2	2	6	2	6	10	2	6	10	14	2	6	10	14	2	6	10	2	
113	Nihonium	2	2	6	2	6	10	2	6	10	14	2	6	10	14	2	6	10	2	1
114	Flerovium	2	2	6	2	6	10	2	6	10	14	2	6	10	14	2	6	10	2	2
115	Moscovium	2	2	6	2	6	10	2	6	10	14	2	6	10	14	2	6	10	2	3
116	Livermorium	2	2	6	2	6	10	2	6	10	14	2	6	10	14	2	6	10	2	4
117	Tennessine	2	2	6	2	6	10	2	6	10	14	2	6	10	14	2	6	10	2	5
118	Oganesson	2	2	6	2	6	10	2	6	10	14	2	6	10	14	2	6	10	2	6

TABLE A.5

COMMON POLYATOMIC IONS

Charge	Name	Formula	Charge	Name	Formula
1−	Chlorate	ClO_3^-	2−	Carbonate	CO_3^{2-}
	Chlorite	ClO_2^-		Chromate	CrO_4^{2-}
	Cyanide	CN^-		Dichromate	$Cr_2O_7^{2-}$
	Dihydrogen phosphate	$H_2PO_4^-$		Oxalate	$C_2O_4^{2-}$
	Ethanoate	CH_3COO^-		Peroxide	O_2^{2-}
	Hydroxide	OH^-		Silicate	SiO_3^{2-}
	Hydrogen carbonate	HCO_3^-		Sulfate	SO_4^{2-}
	Hydrogen sulfate	HSO_4^-		Sulfite	SO_3^{2-}
	Hydrogen sulfite	HSO_3^-		Thiosulfate	$S_2O_3^{2-}$
	Hypochlorite	ClO^-			
	Nitrate	NO_3^-	3−	Phosphate	PO_4^{3-}
	Nitrite	NO_2^-		Phosphite	PO_3^{3-}
	Perchlorate	ClO_4^-			
	Permanganate	MnO_4^-	1+	Ammonium	NH_4^+
	Thiocyanate	SCN^-			

TABLE A.6

SOLUBILITIES OF COMPOUNDS AT 25°C

	ethanoate	bromide	carbonate	chlorate	chloride	hydroxide	iodide	nitrate	oxide	perchlorate	phosphate	sulfate	sulfide
aluminum	S	S	X	S	S	I	S	S	I	S	I	S	d
ammonium	S	S	S	S	S	X	S	S	X	S	S	S	S
barium	S	S	I	S	S	S	S	S	sS	S	I	I	d
calcium	S	S	I	S	S	S	S	S	sS	S	I	sS	I
copper(II)	S	S	X	S	S	I	S	S	I	S	I	S	I
iron(II)	S	S	I	S	S	I	S	S	I	S	I	S	I
iron(III)	S	S	X	S	S	I	S	S	I	S	I	sS	d
lithium	S	S	sS	S	S	S	S	S	S	S	sS	S	S
magnesium	S	S	I	S	S	I	S	S	I	S	I	S	d
potassium	S	S	S	S	S	S	S	S	S	S	S	S	S
silver	sS	I	I	S	I	X	I	S	I	S	I	sS	I
sodium	S	S	S	S	S	S	S	S	S	S	S	S	S
strontium	S	S	I	S	S	S	S	S	S	S	I	I	I
zinc	S	S	I	S	S	I	S	S	I	S	I	S	I

Key: S = soluble   d = decomposes in water
        sS = slightly soluble   X = no such compound
         I = insoluble

	TABLE A.7	
SI UNITS AND EQUIVALENTS		
Quantity	**SI unit**	**Common equivalents**
Length	meter (m)	1 meter = 1.0936 yards 1 centimeter = 0.39370 inch 1 inch = 2.54 centimeters 1 mile = 5280 feet = 1.6093 kilometers
Volume	cubic meter (m^3)	1 liter = 10^{-3} m^3 = 1.0567 quarts 1 gallon = 4 quarts = 8 pints = 3.7854 liters 1 quart = 32 fluid ounces = 0.94635 liter
Temperature	kelvin (K)	1 kelvin = 1 degree Celsius $°C = \frac{5}{9}(°F - 32)$ $K = °C + 273.15$
Mass	kilogram (kg)	1 kilogram = 1000 grams = mass weighing 2.2046 pounds 1 amu = 1.6605×10^{-27} kilograms
Time	second (s)	1 hour = 60 minutes 1 hour = 3600 seconds
Energy	joule (J)	1 joule = 1 kg•m^2/s^2 (exact) 1 joule = 0.2390 calorie 1 calorie = 4.184 joules
Pressure	pascal (Pa)	1 atmosphere = 101.3 kilopascals = 760 mm Hg (Torr) = 14.70 pounds per square inch

The experiments in this program have been carefully designed to minimize the risk of injury. However, safety is also your responsibility. The following rules are essential for keeping you safe in the laboratory. The rules address pre-lab preparation, proper laboratory practices, and post-lab procedures.

Pre-Lab Preparation

1. Read the entire procedure before you begin. Listen to all of your teacher's instructions. When in doubt about a procedure, ask your teacher.

2. Do only the assigned experiments. Only do experiments when your teacher is present and has given you permission to work.

3. Know the location and operation of the following safety equipment: fire extinguisher, fire blanket, emergency shower, and eye wash station.

4. Know the location of emergency exits and escape routes. To make it easy to exit quickly, do not block walkways with furniture. Keep your work area orderly and free of personal belongings, such as coats and backpacks.

5. Protect your clothing and hair from chemicals and sources of heat. Tie back long hair and roll up loose sleeves when working in the laboratory. Avoid wearing bulky or loose-fitting clothing. Remove dangling jewelry. Wear closed-toe shoes at all times in the laboratory.

Proper Laboratory Practices

6. Even with well-designed and tested laboratory procedures, an accident may occur while you are working in the lab. Report any accident, no matter how minor, to your teacher.

7. Wear chemical splash goggles at all times when working in the laboratory. These goggles are designed to protect your eyes from injury. While working in the lab, do not rub your eyes, because chemicals are easily transferred from your hands to your eyes.

⚠ If, despite these precautions, a chemical gets in your eye, remove any contact lenses and immediately wash your eye with a continuous stream of lukewarm water for at least 15 minutes.

8. Always use the minimal amounts of chemicals specified for an experiment to reduce danger, waste, and cleanup.

9. Never taste any chemical used in the laboratory, including food products that are the subject of an investigation. Treat all items as though they are contaminated with unknown chemicals that may be toxic. Keep all food and drink that is not part of an experiment out of the laboratory. Do not eat, drink, or chew gum in the laboratory.

⚠ If you accidentally ingest a substance, notify your teacher immediately.

10. Don't use chipped or cracked glassware. Don't handle broken glass. If glassware breaks, tell your teacher and nearby classmates. Discard broken glass as instructed by your teacher.

⚠ If, despite these precautions, you receive a minor cut, allow it to bleed for a short time. Wash the injured area under cold, running water and notify your teacher. More serious cuts or puncture wounds require immediate medical attention.

11. Do not handle hot glassware or equipment. You can prevent burns by being aware that hot and cold equipment can look exactly the same.

⚠ If you are burned, immediately run cold water over the burned area for several minutes until the pain is reduced. Cooling helps the burn heal. Ask a classmate to notify your teacher.

12. Recognize that the danger of an electrical shock is greater in the presence of water. Keep electrical appliances away from sinks and faucets to minimize the risk of electrical shock. Be careful not to spill water or other liquids in the vicinity of an electrical appliance.

⚠ If, despite these precautions, you spill water near an electrical appliance, stand back, notify your teacher, and warn other students in the area.

13. Report any chemical spills immediately to your teacher. Follow your teacher's instructions for cleaning up spills. Warn other students about the identity and location of spilled chemicals.

⚠ If, despite these precautions, a corrosive chemical gets on your skin or clothing, notify your teacher. Then wash the affected area with cold running water for several minutes.

Post-Lab Procedures

14. Dispose of chemicals in a way that protects you, your classmates, and the environment. Always follow your teacher's directions for cleanup and disposal. Clean your small-scale reaction surface by draining the contents onto a paper towel. Then wipe the surface with a damp paper towel and dry the surface completely. Dispose of the paper towels in the waste bin.

15. Wash your hands thoroughly with soap and water before leaving the laboratory.

A Materials Safety Data Sheet (MSDS) for a chemical describes any safety issues. A diagram summarizes risks related to flammability, health, and reactivity. A number scale indicates the level of risk.

0 Low
1 Slight
2 Moderate
3 High
4 Extreme

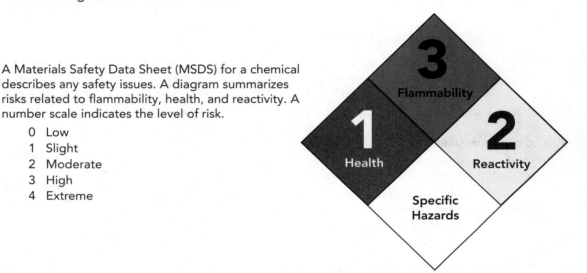

Safety Procedures

Take appropriate precautions when any of the following safety symbols appears in an experiment.

 **Eye Safety** Wear safety goggles.

Clothing Protection Wear a lab coat or apron when using corrosive chemicals or chemicals that can stain clothing.

Skin Protection Wear plastic gloves when using chemicals that can irritate or stain your skin.

Broken Glass Do not use chipped or cracked glassware. Do not heat the bottom of a test tube.

Open Flame Tie back hair and loose clothing. Never reach across a lit burner.

Flammable Substance Do not have a flame near flammable materials.

Corrosive Substance Wear safety goggles, an apron, and gloves when working with corrosive chemicals.

 Poison Don't chew gum, drink, or eat in the laboratory. Never taste a chemical in the laboratory.

 Fume Avoid inhaling substances that can irritate your respiratory system. Use a fume hood whenever possible.

 Thermal Burn Do not touch hot glassware or equipment.

 Electrical Equipment Keep electrical equipment away from water or other liquids.

Sharp Object To avoid a puncture wound, use scissors or other sharp objects only as intended.

 Disposal Dispose of chemicals only as directed.

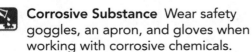 **Hand Washing** Wash your hands thoroughly with soap and water.

INVESTIGATION 9

1. How would decreasing the temperature of gas molecules in a fixed-volume container affect their kinetic energy?

2. Complete the table to show how the pressure and volume of a fixed amount of gas at a constant temperature would change as a result of the given changes in volume and pressure.

	Volume	Pressure
a	The volume of the gas triples.	
b		The pressure of the gas doubles.

3. The pressure-volume, temperature-volume, and temperature-pressure relationships that exist within gases do not exist in liquids or solids. Identify two factors related to gases' particles that allow for these relationships to exist in gases.

4. Gas laws relate the temperature, pressure, and volume of gases. Complete the table by identifying the correct gas law for each description and the relationship between the variables listed.

	Related Variables	Which Law?	Are the Two Variables Directly or Inversely Related?
a	volume and temperature, when pressure is constant		
b	volume and pressure, when temperature is constant		
c	pressure and temperature, when volume is constant		

5. Use the appropriate gas law to determine the unknown quantity in each case for a syringe containing 2.5 mL of air at a pressure of 100.0 kPa and a temperature of 25°C. Assume that the amount of air in the syringe remains constant.
   a. The syringe is heated to 50°C while the pressure is kept constant at 100 kPa. What is the new volume?
   b. The syringe plunger is pulled up to expand the air volume to 3.5 mL while the temperature remains constant at 25°C. What is the new pressure?
   c. The syringe is heated at constant volume until the air pressure inside the syringe reaches 104 kPa. What is the new temperature?

6. Calculate the unknown quantity (temperature, pressure, or volume), assuming that the amount of gas in the container remains constant and the gas is ideal. Where necessary, assume that STP conditions are $T = 273$ K and $P = 100$ kPa.
   a. A flexible container holds 20.0 L of gas at a pressure of 100.0 kPa and a temperature of 30.0°C. The container is then plunged into a tank that has a temperature of −30.0°C and a pressure of 90.0 kPa. What is the new volume of the gas in the container?
   b. A volume of 60.0 L of gas at a pressure of 200.0 kPa triples its volume under STP conditions. What was the initial temperature of the gas?
   c. A volume of gas at temperature 200 K experiences conditions in which its volume doubles and its pressure is reduced to one-quarter of its initial pressure. What is the new temperature of the gas?

7. Use the principles of Avogadro's Law to answer the following questions. In each case, assume STP conditions for the gases.
   a. A 5.0-g sample of an ideal gas occupies a volume of 2.8 L at STP. What is the molar mass of the gas?
   b. Calculate the number of moles of methane (CH_4) needed to occupy the same volume as 16 g of oxygen (O_2) if the temperature and pressure conditions are the same.
   c. A balloon contains 6.00 g of helium (He) gas at STP. What is the volume of the balloon?

8. a. Calculate the density (in g/L) of one mole of each of the following gases at STP:
   (i)   propane (C_3H_8) gas
   (ii) ammonia (NH_3) gas
   (iii) hydrogen (H_2) gas
   b. Describe how the density of a gas would change if each of the following variables were changed. Is the density of the gas inversely or directly related to the variable?
   (i) the pressure on the gas is increased
   (ii) the temperature of the gas is decreased

9. A flexible container holds 21.0 g of ethylene (C_2H_4) gas at STP.
   a. What is the volume of the gas?
   b. What is the density (in g/L) of ethylene gas at STP?
   c. The ethylene gas is cooled at constant pressure until the volume of the container is 14.0 L. What is the temperature of the gas?

10. Use the ideal gas law to determine the unknown quantity in each scenario.
    a. What is the pressure of 3.00 mol of an ideal gas that occupies a volume of 50.0 L at 35.0°C?
    b. What is the temperature of 0.200 mol of an ideal gas that occupies a volume of 483 mL at a pressure of 105 kPa?
    c. An ideal gas occupies a volume of 2.0 kL at STP. How many moles of the gas are there?

11. An oxygen tank contains 500.0 L of O_2 gas at a pressure of 200.0 kPa and a temperature of −15.0°C. Use this information to answer the following questions.
    a. What mass of O_2 gas is present in the tank?
    b. What is the density (in g/L) of the O_2 gas in the tank?
    c. How does the density of O_2 gas in the tank compare to the density of O_2 gas at STP?

12. Arrange the following Period 2 gases, N_2, O_2, and F_2, in order of increasing value of a according to the van der Waals equation.

13. A tank at a pressure of 2.00 atm contains a mixture of three gases: oxygen (O_2), water vapor (H_2O), and neon (Ne).
    a. If the partial pressures of the oxygen and water vapor in the tank are 0.75 atm and 0.36 atm respectively, what is the partial pressure of the neon gas in the tank?
    b. If the tank contained 2.20 moles of oxygen (O_2), 1.10 moles of water vapor (H_2O), and 5.50 moles of neon (Ne), what would be the partial pressure of the neon gas?

14. A balloon at STP contains a mixture of gases made up of 48 g of oxygen (O_2) and 21 g of nitrogen (N_2).
    a. What is the partial pressure (in kPa) of the oxygen in the mixture?
    b. What is the volume of the balloon?

15. For each pair of gases, state which one will effuse faster and by what numerical factor. Assume that the temperature remains constant in each case.
    a. hydrogen (H_2) and ethane (C_2H_6)
    b. oxygen (O_2) and water vapor (H_2O)
    c. argon (Ar) and ammonia gas (NH_3)

16. Provide an explanation for the statement, "Wind is the diffusion of air," with respect to what is meant by diffusion and how wind forms.

17. Atmospheric pressure decreases with increasing altitude. How does this factor affect:
    a. the ratio of oxygen to nitrogen in the air?
    b. the total amount of oxygen in the air?

INVESTIGATION 10

1. What are the two sources of energy for Earth's geological systems?

2. What energy source primarily drives the water cycle? Explain how the force of gravity and this energy source work together to drive the water cycle.

3. Do the following processes store or release carbon in the carbon cycle? What source of energy ultimately drives each process?
   a. Photosynthesis
   b. Rock formation
   c. Volcanic eruption
   d. Burning fossil fuels

4. How do each of the three types of rock form? What is the effect of melting glaciers on rock formation?

5. How does reinforcing and counterbalancing feedback work to keep a system in equilibrium? What is an example of each?

6. What is non-linear feedback? Describe how the collapse of an ice shelf is an example of non-linear feedback.

7. Describe how each of the following are affected by geologic processes and how human activity affects each of these.
   a. Earthquakes
   b. Atmospheric composition

8. What is Earth's energy budget?

9. How does solar radiation influence each of the following?
   a. Evaporation
   b. Atmospheric convection
   c. Atmospheric pressure and wind

10. What is albedo and what role does it play in arctic sea ice feedbacks?

11. Are the following feedback cycles reinforcing or counterbalancing in regard to global warming? Why?
    a. Ocean and carbon dioxide feedbacks
    b. Biomass feedbacks
    c. Methane hydrate feedbacks
    d. Surface radiation feedbacks

12. What has been the trend with solar output throughout the history of Earth?

13. How does each of the following impact atmospheric CO_2 long-term? What is the effect on temperature?
    a. Living organisms
    b. Erosion
    c. Volcanic Activity

14. What is currently happening in Earth's long-term, intermediate-term, and short-term climate, and for how long has it been happening?

15. What are the three orbital parameters, and how do they affect Earth's climate?

16. How do volcanic eruptions affect climate in the short-term?

17. How do changes in solar radiation affect intermediate-term climate?

18. What are the effects of short-term ocean circulation changes like ENSO on the atmosphere?

INVESTIGATION 11

1. Imagine a world where the initial atmospheric concentration of CO_2 is 420.00 ppm and the initial average global temperature is 4.00°C. If CO_2 concentration annually increases 0.7% and average temperature annually increases 0.1%, what is the expected CO_2 concentration and average global temperature in:
   a. 1 year?
   b. 5 years?
   c. 25 years?
   d. 100 years?

2. What is the greenhouse effect in terms of energy absorption and radiation? Why are greenhouse gases called greenhouse gases?

3. What modes of oscillation do the following have? How does this affect energy absorption?
   a. H_2O
   b. CO_2

4. What was sea level like and how did it affect human settlements
   a. 22,000 years ago?
   b. 8,000 years ago?
   c. in 2017?

5. Explain how each of the following types of geologic data is used to track changes in Earth's past climate?
   a. Ice cores
   b. Tree rings
   c. Varves

6. What is the effect of warmer global temperatures on sea level? How would this affect human settlements?

7. What is the difference between the 1917 NASA temperature series and the 2017 temperature series for the following places? What could be a reason for the difference?
   a. Atlantic Ocean near Greenland
   b. Eastern South America
   c. Western North America
   d. Northern Europe

8. What is the effect of increased CO_2 on the temperature of the Arctic compared to other regions of Earth? Why?

9. Since 1960, global GDP per capita has increased from ~$500 to ~$10,500 in 2015, while the average global temperature has increased from ~−0.1°C to ~0.8°C. Explain how these factors are related.

10. How do climate scientists use the ratio of carbon-12 to carbon-13? What does it mean if carbon-13 is lower than expected?

11. Describe how weather models and climate models are similar.

12. Describe how weather models and climate models are different.

13. The Intergovernmental Panel on Climate Change uses several models to predict climate change. How would average global temperatures be likely to respond to the following changes in greenhouse gas emissions?
   a. Greenhouse gas emissions continue to rise indefinitely.
   b. Greenhouse gas emissions continue until 2080, then decrease.
   c. Greenhouse gas emissions peak in 2020, then decrease significantly.

14. What would humanity have to do to achieve the following gas emissions changes?
   a. Greenhouse gas continues to rise indefinitely.
   b. Greenhouse gas emissions continue to rise until 2080, then decrease.
   c. Greenhouse gas emissions peak in 2020, then decrease significantly.

15. Alpine and tidewater glaciers cover 730,000 km^2 of land and are on average 2.0 kilometers thick.
   a. How much water do they hold?
   b. If the glaciers melted at a rate of 5% per year, how long would it take for 50% of the glaciers to melt?
   c. If the glaciers completely melted, how many meters would the level of the oceans rise if they covered 361,900,000 km^2?
   d. What would be the expected effects on people if alpine and tidewater glaciers melted?

16. Solar panels that are 1 m^2 in size produce 260 kWh per year. The average person uses 10,932 kWh per year, but only 2% of that comes from solar. How many more square meters of solar panels are needed per person for 100% solar power? Is this feasible if the surface of Earth is 5.1×10^{14} m^2 and there are 8 billion people who need at least 10 m^2 each for living space?

17. Are each the following methods of addressing climate change more feasible now, in the near future, or far future? Explain why you chose "Now", "Future", or "Far Future."
    a. Changing building codes to require building carbon-neutral buildings
    b. Injecting aerosols into the atmosphere
    c. Promoting electric vehicles and building infrastructure to support them
    d. Capturing and storing carbon dioxide and other carbon compounds

18. One option to address climate change is carbon sequestration. What are the potential concerns for using this method?

INVESTIGATION 12

1. For the reaction $2NO_2(g) \rightarrow 2NO(g) + O_2(g)$, determine the rate of disappearance of NO_2 if its concentration is 0.0055 mol/L at 150 seconds and drops to 0.0048 mol/L at 200 seconds.

2. Explain what is meant when a reaction rate is determined to be a negative value for a chemical during a reaction.

3. Explain how an increase in temperature can affect the rate of a chemical reaction.

4. The following reaction, $A + 2B \rightarrow C$, is run twice. If the concentration of A is cut in half for the second trial, predict what will happen to the rate of the reaction compared to the first trial.

5. Will the addition of a catalyst to a reaction increase, decrease, or have no effect on the rate of the reaction?

6. In your lab, you are asked to react antacid tablets with water to produce carbon dioxide gas, but you are short on time. How could you change the tablet to increase the reaction rate? Why does that work?

7. If the rate of reaction has been calculated to be 2.6×10^{-3} mol/L·s, how long will it take the concentration of a species to drop from 1.68×10^{-3} mol/L to 2.5×10^{-4} mol/L?

8. How does activation energy affect a chemical reaction?

9. Give an "everyday example" of activation energy being overcome.

10. Sketch an energy diagram for an endothermic reaction.

11. Explain what is meant by a one-step and a multi-step reaction.

12. Explain how the addition of a catalyst to a reaction does not violate the law of conservation of mass.

13. Given the following reaction diagram, determine which step in the multi-step reaction is the rate-determining step.

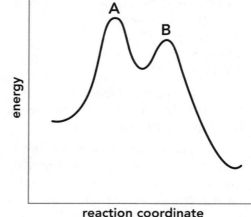

14. What is occurring in a system that has reached equilibrium?

15. Briefly describe the concepts involved in Le Châtelier's principle.

16. For the equilibrium reaction, $2SO_2(g) + O_2(g) \rightleftharpoons 2SO_3(g)$, use Le Châtelier's principle to predict what will happen to the remaining two species for each change made.
    a. remove some SO_2
    b. add O_2
    c. remove SO_3

17. Given that the reaction in #16 is endothermic, what will happen to each chemical if the temperature is raised after it reaches equilibrium?

18. For the reaction in #16, what will happen to each substance if the pressure is decreased on the system?

19. Reference the equation $\Delta G = \Delta H - T\Delta S$. What is the **best** way to adjust the variables ΔH, T, and ΔS to ensure a thermodynamically favorable reaction?

20. Calculate ΔG of the decomposition reaction of phosgene (carbonyl chloride) into carbon monoxide and chlorine gas at 250°C when $\Delta H = -110.5$ kJ and $\Delta S = 136.8$ J/K.

$$COCl_2(g) \rightarrow CO(g) + Cl_2(g)$$

21. During a chemical reaction, the temperature of the system changes from 600 K to 280 K. Also, the total number of reactant molecules is greater than the total number of product molecules. Has entropy increased or decreased in the reaction? Explain your answer.

22. Draw a molecular model that demonstrates the movement of molecules within a container when a reaction is thermodynamically unfavorable. How does entropy and the movement of molecules change in this type of reaction?

INVESTIGATION 13

1. Acids and bases have distinct properties that distinguish them from one another. Label each description as being a property of a base or a property of an acid.
   a. tastes tart or sour
   b. pH above 7.0
   c. makes skin feel slippery or soapy
   d. pH below 7.0

2. Determine the pH of each solution described.
   a. $[H^+] = 0.0015M$
   b. $[H^+] = 3.8 \times 10^{-5}M$
   c. $[H^+] = 4.13 \times 10^{-9}M$

3. Determine the hydrogen ion concentration in each solution from its given pH.
   a. pH = 2.89
   b. pH = 11.50
   c. pH = 7.0

4. Identify whether each species acts as a Brønsted–Lowry acid or base.
   a. NH_3
   b. $C_2O_4^{2-}$
   c. H_2O
   d. $HC_2H_3O_2$

5. Identify whether each substance is a Lewis acid or Lewis base.
   a. NH_3
   b. PBr_3
   c. BCl_3

6. What is the maximum number of hydrogen ions a molecule of citric acid ($H_3C_6H_5O_7$) can form when in an aqueous solution? Explain your answer.

7. Briefly describe the steps to determine the unknown concentration of an acid if you are given a sample of base with a known concentration.

8. What two factors would increase the pH of an acidic solution?

9. Calculate the pH of each solution. Round each answer to two significant figures.
   a. $[H^+] = 1.00 \times 10^{-6}M$
   b. $[OH^-] = 4.00 \times 10^{-3}M$
   c. $[H^+] = 1.14 \times 10^{-2}M$
   d. $[OH^-] = 2.16 \times 10^{-2}M$

10. Name two properties that can be determined from an Arrhenius base that has OH^- ions that do not completely dissociate in a solution.

11. Explain why there is a larger change in pH in strong acids than in weak acids when the acid dissociates in a solution. Explain your answer in terms of the ions they both produce.

12. How many milliliters of $0.35M$ NaOH are needed to neutralize 25.0 mL of $0.40M$ H_2SO_4?

13. What is the concentration of a sodium hydroxide solution if 85.50 mL is required to neutralize 75.25 mL of $0.500M$ hydrochloric acid?

14. Will the equivalence point for a strong acid titrating a weak base be in the acidic region, at the neutral point, or in the basic region? Explain your reasoning.

15. Name the salt that is formed in a neutralization reaction between the following acids and bases.
    a. hydrochloric acid and calcium hydroxide
    b. sulfuric acid and potassium hydroxide
    c. nitric acid and lithium hydroxide
    d. phosphoric acid and sodium hydroxide

16. Describe what happens with respect to the pH of the solution as a small amount of a strong acid is slowly added to a buffered solution.

17. Write equations that show what happens when the following situations occur in a buffer solution.
    a. acid is added to a sulfate (SO_4^{2-}) buffer
    b. base is added to a hydrogen carbonate (HCO_3^-) buffer

18. Describe the types of compounds needed to prepare a buffer solution.

INVESTIGATION 14

1. Many marine organisms are dependent on the production of calcium carbonate ($CaCO_3$) to form their skeletons. Describe how increased atmospheric carbon dioxide levels in Earth's atmosphere are affecting these organisms. Use the chemical equations to formulate your answer.

   $$CO_2 + H_2O \rightleftharpoons H_2CO_3$$

   $$H_2CO_3 \rightleftharpoons H_2O + CO_2$$

   $$H_2CO_3 \rightleftharpoons H^+ + HCO_3^-$$

2. Which of the following is true for pH values in the deeper parts of oceans, in general?
   a. In deep parts of the ocean, the temperature is warm, and the solubility of carbon dioxide is high.
   b. In deep parts of the ocean, the temperature is cold, and the solubility of carbon dioxide is high.
   c. In deep parts of the ocean, the temperature is cold, and there are many hydrogen ions.
   d. In deep parts of the ocean, the temperature is warm, and there are few hydrogen ions.

3. How does climate change impact the salinity of ocean water?

4. What factors are methane hydrate stability dependent on? How might global warming impact the stability zone of offshore methane gas hydrates?

5. According to the Scripps Institution of Oceanography, nearly 9.3 billion tons of carbon were released per year during 2002–2011. Of this, an estimated 26% was absorbed by the ocean. How many tons of carbon dioxide were absorbed into the ocean during this time?

6. Ocean temperatures can vary across different latitudes. Explain why temperatures vary across different latitudes.

7. How will increased temperatures affect the amount of dissolved oxygen in the ocean? What effect will this have on marine life?

8. Global warming causes an increase in temperatures around the world. How does the ocean contribute to equilibration of the rising temperatures from global warming?

9. Explain why algal blooms have such a negative impact on other ocean life. How are these blooms linked to increased CO_2?

10. What are some of the potential impacts of increased CO_2 on the dynamics of the food web? How are predator and prey species affected? Explain your answer.

INVESTIGATION 15

1. Identify which reactant is the oxidizing agent in the following reactions.
   a. $2H_2 + C \rightarrow CH_4$
   b. $Ca + S \rightarrow CaS$
   c. $4Fe + 3O_2 \rightarrow 2Fe_2O_3$
   d. $2Na + Cl_2 \rightarrow 2NaCl$

2. Determine the oxidation number of the following elements in the compounds listed.
   a. O in $Ca(OH)_2$
   b. K in K_3PO_4
   c. Cl in $CuCl_2$
   d. Ca in $Ca(NO_3)_2$

3. The corrosion of iron can be written in two separate equations, as follows:
   $Fe(s) \rightarrow Fe^{2+}(aq) + 2e^-$
   $O_2(g) + 4H^+(aq) + 4e^- \rightarrow 2H_2O(l)$

   Identify this method of writing two separate equations for one chemical reaction, and explain what processes occur at the anode and the cathode. What type of reaction is shown?

4. Categorize each of the following chemical reactions as either a redox reaction or a non-redox reaction. Then, specify what type of redox or non-redox reaction it is.
   a. $CH_4 + O_2 \rightarrow H_2O + CO_2$
   b. $ZnS \rightarrow Zn + S$
   c. $NaOH + HNO_3 \rightarrow NaNO_3 + H_2O$
   d. $Cu + 2AgNO_3 \rightarrow Cu(NO_3)_2 + 2Ag$

5. In a molecular compound, what property determines the oxidizing agent? Explain your answer.

6. Order the following elements by their element symbol from least to greatest reactivity, with the least reactive element listed first and the most reactive element listed last: aluminum, potassium, silver, iron.

7. How can a redox reaction be balanced, other than by using the half-reaction method? Using this alternative method, identify the balanced equation for the following reaction and identify which elements were unbalanced in the initial equation:
   $HNO_3 + H_2S \rightarrow NO + S + H_2O$

8. Use the oxygen rule to determine the oxidation number of the element being oxidized in each of the following redox reactions.
   a. $Mg + O_2 \rightarrow MgO$
   b. $Li + O_2 \rightarrow Li_2O$
   c. $Al + O_2 \rightarrow Al_2O_3$
   d. $Zn + O_2 \rightarrow ZnO$

9. Describe what is demonstrated by a model of a voltaic cell with lead and lead dioxide electrodes, and a potassium sulfate salt bridge. Be sure to describe the charges of each electrode, where oxidation and reduction will take place, and the salt bridge.

10. Categorize each of the following as a property of a voltaic cell, electrolytic cell, or both.
    a. has a thermodynamically favorable redox reaction
    b. converts chemical and electrical energy
    c. anode is negative and cathode is positive
    d. converts electrical energy into chemical energy

11. Using the standard reduction potentials, calculate the standard cell potential for a cell with the following half-reactions:
    $I_2(s) + 2e^- \rightarrow 2I^-(aq)$ $E^\circ_{I^-} = 0.54$ V
    $Al^{3+}(aq) + 3e^- \rightarrow Al(s)$ $E^\circ_{Al^{3+}} = 1.66$ V

12. Explain how a jeweler could use a silver solution to protect the surface of a nickel bracelet. Identify the materials that would serve as the cathode and anode during the process. What type of cell is this? What are the charges of each electrode?

13. Between alkaline, lithium-ion, and lead-acid batteries, what type of battery would be the **best** choice for a battery that is lightweight and has high energy density? What makes this the best choice? Explain your answer.

14. An electrochemical cell in a beaker filled with water and KNO_3 is shown. Identify the type of cell and what gas is being collected in the test tubes. Why is KNO_3 added to the solution? Explain your answer.

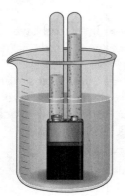

15. Why do many brands use lithium-ion batteries in their power tools, such as a hand-held power drill, rather than lead-acid batteries?

INVESTIGATION 16

1. Why are saturated hydrocarbons, such as methane, preferred as fuels? Be sure to reference the relationship between oxidation number and energy density.

2. What are the differences between an optical isomer and a geometric isomer? How are they similar?

3. Considering cycloalkanes have a stronger dispersion force than alkanes, which has a higher boiling point, cyclobutane or butane? What differences in molecular structures exist between cycloalkanes and alkanes?

4. Identify the correct formula for the hydrocarbon formed when a butane (C_4H_{10}) molecule is lengthened by becoming an octane molecule. How do the boiling points between both molecules compare? Explain your answer.

5. Identify whether each class of hydrocarbon will undergo an addition reaction.
   a. alkanes
   b. alkenes
   c. alkynes
   d. aromatic

6. Identify the functional group and compound types for the following compounds based on their structural formulas:
   a. C_3H_7COOH
   b. $CH_3COOC_2H_5$
   c. CH_3COCH_3
   d. $CH_3CH_2CH_2OH$
   e. $CH_3CH_2OCH_2CH_3$

7. Identify any pair or pairs of structural isomers present in the formulas given.
   (i) $CH_3CHCH_3CHCH_3CH_3$
   (ii) $CH_3C(CH_3)_2CH_3$
   (iii) $CH_3CHCH_3CH_2CH_3$
   (iv) $CH_3CH_2CHCH_3CH_2CH_3$

   Select the correct option(s).
   A. (i) and (ii); (iii) and (iv)
   B. (i) and (iii); (ii) and (iv)
   C. (i) and (iv); (ii) and (iii)
   D. (i), (ii), and (iii)

8. What is the difference between the way addition polymers and condensation polymers are formed?

9. What type of polymer is formed through the chemical reaction shown? Identify the polymer, given the monomer is styrene.

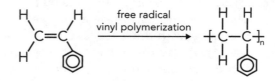

10. Compound A has the formula $CH_3CH_2CH_2CO_2H$. Compound B has the formula $CH_3CH_2CH_2CO_2CH_3$. To what group(s) of organic compounds do compounds A and B likely belong? Which will show greater solubility in water? Explain your answer.

11. Methane undergoes combustion to release energy as shown in the equation. What must be true about the relative energies associated with making and breaking bonds in the reaction? What is another way of understanding the energy released from combustion reactions?

$$CH_4(g) + 2O_2(g) \longrightarrow CO_2(g) + 2H_2O(g)$$

12. How does the human body get energy from glucose? Identify the general steps involved in the process.

13. What functional group(s) are present in all amino acids? What type of reaction do two amino acids undergo to form a peptide?

14. Are carbohydrates soluble in water? Give two reasons explaining why or why not.

15. Explain a difference between the structures of cellulose and starch. How does this impact digestion?

INVESTIGATION 17

1. **A.** Name the process by which an element undergoes natural transformation (transmutation) into another element.

   B. What are the types of particles and/or rays emitted during this process?

2. Considering the mineral uranium, why would deposits of helium be found underground? Explain your answer and show the process using the chemical symbols of the isotopes.

3. What changes occur when an atom of ^{14}C undergoes beta-minus decay to form an atom of ^{14}N in terms of the following:
   a. quarks
   b. particles emitted
   c. atomic number

4. How did scientists predict the year that dinosaurs evolved and became extinct? How were zircons useful in determining this? Be sure to include the isotopes needed for dating these time periods.

5. Use the Curve of Binding Energy to answer the following questions.

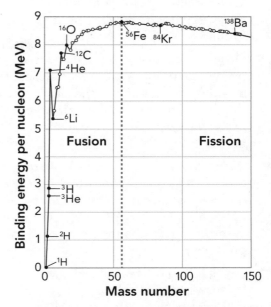

Data Source: National Nuclear Data Center, Brookhaven National Laboratory based on ENSDF and the Nuclear Wallet Cards

   a. Compare the relative strong force per nucleon of Ba-138 and O-16.
   b. What happens to binding energy during fission and fusion?
   c. What will happen to the net mass of Ba-138?

6. The Big Bang theory details different stages in the formation of our universe, as shown.
   (i) Nucleosynthesis stops completely.
   (ii) Orange light wavelengths stretch into Microwave range.
   (iii) Boson particles start to form.
   (iv) Galaxies begin forming.
   (v) The universe is dominated by electrons and positrons.
   Place these events in the correct chronological order, from earliest to latest.

7. The ^4He nuclei of a star fuse with themselves and nuclei that are multiples of alpha elements. Would this star be considered small or large? Explain your answer.

8. A star produces elements through fusion reactions during its lifetime. Which elements are **not** formed by nucleosynthesis? Why? How are they formed?

9. Order the following particles and waves from the particle/wave that is easiest to shield from radiation to the particle/wave that is the most difficult to shield from radiation: beta particles, gamma rays, alpha particles.

10. If a nuclear reactor is being built to produce fission reactions that produce gamma rays, what material should be used for the reactor? Explain your answer in terms of how the ionizing radiation is produced.

11. Evaluate the process of radiation therapy by answering the following questions.
    a. What are two different ways that radiation is administered to people?
    b. During certain types of radiation, radioactive substances that perform alpha decay are injected directly into the body. Why is this more damaging to the body than an X-ray that uses beta decay? Describe your answer in terms of the particles emitted and ionizing radiation.

12. Explain why we currently do not have any nuclear fusion reactors in terms of the temperature, pressure, and radiation that fusion reactions produce. What is the relative amount of energy released in fusion reactions as compared to fission reactions?

INVESTIGATION 18

1. What is the trade-off between Research and Development (R&D) and production in the chemical industry?

2. It has been estimated that the available silver resource is at most 3.1 million tonnes, and the rate of consumption is approximately 28,500 tonnes per year. Assuming a 2% annual increase in the rate of consumption of silver, what is the estimated resource lifetime of silver?

3. Indicate if the following are examples of solutions that will reduce or increase the adverse effects chemical industries have on the environment.
   a. decreasing the use of petroleum as a mineral resource
   b. regulating waste runoff in rivers to decrease the number of algae blooms
   c. increasing the use of petroleum as a mineral resource
   d. removing DDT pesticides

4. Identify whether the following activities are associated with sustainable chemistry or not, and explain why.
   a. using solar power to generate electricity for a nearby town
   b. treating wastewater and reusing it for certain chemical processes
   c. a power plant burning coal to produce energy in London
   d. using chemical processes with larger E-factors for the pharmaceutical industry

5. Recall the formula for calculating the environmental impact factor for a chemical process:
$$\text{E-factor} = \frac{\text{kg of waste}}{\text{kg of product}}$$
   a. What constitutes the waste that is produced by the system?
   b. Does a reaction with a high actual yield *always* have a small E-factor? Explain why or why not.

6. The Claus process is a chemical process used to obtain elemental sulfur from hydrogen sulfide. The reaction consists of two steps:

Step 1: $2H_2S + 3O_2 \rightarrow 2SO_2 + 2H_2O$

Step 2: $4H_2S + 2SO_2 \rightarrow 3S_2 + 4H_2O$

What is the atom economy of the net reaction? Show your work.

7. Describe three ways that catalysts are beneficial for green chemistry.

8. How can real-time analysis prevent the formation of hazardous waste material? Explain the benefits in terms of yields, by-products, and safety.

9. What is the purpose of protecting groups and how do they impact the environment? How can synthetic biology play a role in removing protecting groups in the future?

10. Indicate if each solution listed is one that businesses could implement to ensure greener chemical practices with lower environmental impacts. Explain why or why not.
   a. using chemical processes with high atom economies
   b. factoring in the Triple Bottom Line
   c. reducing the use of solvents
   d. increasing the use of protecting groups

11. Explain the types of renewable energy and biomass by answering the following questions:
   a. Name three types of renewable energy other than energy produced from biomass.
   b. What is biomass, how is it used, and what nonrenewable energy source could it replace? Explain your answer.

12. Sustainable chemistry is a new field with room for future scientific discovery. Explain why the following are important factors in achieving sustainable chemistry:
   a. education
   b. public awareness

GLOSSARY

A

absolute zero: the coldest temperature possible, when all the kinetic motion of the particles in matter stops (15)

activated complex: an unstable cluster of atoms that exists during the transition from reactants to products (169)

activation energy: the minimum energy colliding particles must have in order to react (168)

addition polymer: a polymer formed when unsaturated monomers react to form a polymer (337)

addition reaction: a reaction in which a substance is added at the double or triple bond of an alkene or alkyne (336)

albedo: the proportion of incoming sunlight that reflects off an object's surface (67)

alcohol: an organic compound with a hydroxy (—OH) group (329)

aldehyde: an organic compound in which the carbon of the carbonyl group is joined to at least one hydrogen (331)

alkane: a hydrocarbon with only single covalent bonds (315)

alkene: a hydrocarbon that contains one or more carbon-carbon double covalent bonds (318)

alkyl halide: a halocarbon in which a halogen atom is attached to a hydrocarbon chain (328)

alkyne: a hydrocarbon that contains one or more carbon-carbon triple covalent bonds (318)

alpha (α) decay: when an unstable nucleus emits an alpha particle (363)

amine: an organic compound in which NH_2 is bonded to a carbon group (330)

amino acid: a compound that contains an amino group and a carboxyl group in the same molecule (345)

amino group: the NH_2 functional group in an amine (330)

anode: the electrode at which oxidation occurs (299)

Anthropocene: the current geologic time period, characterized by the impact of human activities on Earth's biomes (138)

anthropogenic: caused or produced by humans (120)

aromatic compound: an organic compound that contains a benzene ring or other ring in which the bonding is like that of benzene; also called an arene (323)

aryl halide: a halocarbon in which the halogen atom is attached to an aromatic hydrocarbon (328)

atom economy: the mass of the desired product divided by the mass of the starting materials multiplied by 100 (419)

auxiliaries: substances used to help with a chemical reaction that do not become part of the final products (422)

Avogadro's law: any two samples of gas containing the same number of particles (atoms or molecules) have the same volume when held at the same pressure and temperature (21)

B

band of stability: the location of stable nuclides on a plot of protons versus neutrons (364)

beta (β) decay: a type of radioactivity involving the conversion between neutrons and protons with the emission of a beta particle (362)

Boyle's law: when the temperature and number of particles in a gas are held constant, the volume varies inversely with the pressure (11)

branched-chain alkane: an alkane that contains at least one carbon atom bonded to three other carbon atoms (315)

buffer: a solution in which the pH remains relatively constant when small amounts of acid or base are added; can be either a solution of a weak acid and the salt of a weak acid (conjugate base) or a solution of a weak base and the salt of a weak base (conjugate acid) (222)

buffer capacity: a measure of the amount of acid or base that may be added to a buffer system before a significant change in pH occurs (225)

buffer range: a measure of the overall pH range in which a buffer system is effective at maintaining a relatively constant pH (225)

by-product: a product of a chemical reaction that is not the targeted product (406)

C

calcification: the use of carbon from dissolved carbon dioxide to build the shells of marine organisms out of calcium carbonate (260)

Calorie: unit used in the United States to measure the energy content of food; equivalent to one kilocalorie (1000 calories) (340)

carbohydrates: monomers and polymers of aldehydes and ketones that have numerous hydroxy groups attached (341)

carbon compensation depth: the depth at which calcium carbonate shells of organisms dissolve into calcium ions and bicarbonate ions (241)

carbon reservoirs: components of the Earth system that store carbon (238)

carbonyl group: a functional group with the general structure C=O (331)

carboxyl group: the combination of carbonyl and hydroxy groups (332)

carboxylic acid: an organic compound with a carbonyl group and a hydroxy group (332)

catalyst: a substance that increases reaction rates by providing a lower energy path for the reaction without being used up during the reaction (171)

cathode: the electrode at which reduction occurs (299)

cellular respiration: the complex process through which glucose is converted into energy (344)

cellulose: a polymer made up of glucose monomers that is the main structural component of plant cell walls (342)

Charles's law: when the volume of a fixed mass of gas at constant pressure is directly proportional to its temperature (13)

chemical equilibrium: a state of balance in which the rates of the forward and reverse reactions are equal (175)

chromosomes: large, tightly-packed DNA molecules that contain all or part of the information needed for the construction of an organism (353)

climate forcings: factors driving climate; includes an increase in incoming sunlight (due to changes in the sun's activity), a decrease in how much sunlight gets reflected from the surface back out into space, and an increase in how much of that energy is kept by greenhouse gases (66)

collision theory: a theory that states that bonds are broken when molecules collide with enough energy to break bonds in reactants and with the correct orientation to form bonds that make products (163)

combined gas law: the combination of Boyle's law, Charles's law, and Gay-Lussac's law that describes the relationship between the pressure, volume, and temperature of a fixed amount of gas (19)

Community Earth System Model (CESM): a powerful Earth System Model that issues predictions based on data provided by climate scientists from all over the world (125)

compressibility: the measure of how much the volume of matter decreases under a certain amount of pressure (6)

condensation polymer: a polymer formed when two monomers are joined with the loss of a small molecule such as water (338)

condensed structural formula: a chemical formula that leaves out some bonds and/or atoms, resulting in a simpler representation (316)

conjugate acid: the particle formed when a base gains a hydrogen ion (196)

conjugate acid-base pair: two substances that are related by the loss or gain of a single hydrogen ion (196)

conjugate base: the particle that remains when an acid has donated a hydrogen ion (196)

coral bleaching: a phenomenon that occurs when stressed coral loses its photosynthetic algae, removing the coral's food source and color (266)

Coriolis effect: the apparent curved path that an object takes when it moves in a straight line across a rotating object perpendicular to the axis of rotation (248)

counterbalancing feedback: feedback that resists or reduces a change; also called a "negative" feedback (51)

crossover temperature: the unique temperature at which ΔG is zero for every process that has one favorable and one unfavorable factor; those factors being entropy and enthalpy (188)

cyclic hydrocarbon: a compound that contains a hydrocarbon ring (322)

D

Dalton's law: when volume and temperature are constant, the total pressure exerted by a mixture of gases is equal to the sum of the partial pressures of the component gases (32)

deep ocean currents: masses of ocean water below the ocean surface that flow steadily in a particular direction (249)

degree of saturation: the ratio of hydrogen atoms to carbon atoms (319)

denaturation: any process that disrupts or destroys the secondary, tertiary, and quaternary structures of a protein (348)

deoxyribonucleic acid: a nucleic acid that stores the information needed to make proteins and governs the reproduction and growth of new cells and new organisms; also called DNA (353)

dewpoint: the temperature at which the air is saturated with water vapor (39)

diffusion: the tendency of molecules to move toward areas of lower concentration until the concentration is uniform (34)

disaccharide: a sugar that forms from the condensation reaction of two monosaccharides (341)

E

E-factor: the mass of waste generated divided by the mass of the targeted product; also called the environmental impact factor (418)

Earth System Model (ESM): a computer model that uses a set of equations to calculate interactions between various parameters (such as pressure, temperature, mass, water vapor amount, and momentum) in specific geographic locations (124)

effusion: when a gas escapes through a tiny hole in its container (35)

El Niño/Southern Oscillation (ENSO): the cyclical circulation pattern in the tropical Pacific that results in periodic variation between below-normal and above-normal sea surface temperatures and dry and wet conditions (254)

electric potential: the electric potential energy divided by the charge; electric potential is measured in units of volts, or joules/coulomb (297)

electrochemical cell: any device that converts chemical energy into electrical energy or vice-versa (298)

electrochemical process: any conversion between chemical potential energy and electrical energy (298)

electrode: a conductor in a circuit that carries electrons (299)

electrolysis: a process by which electrical energy is used to bring about a chemical change (305)

electrolytic cell: an electrochemical cell that causes a chemical change through the application of electrical energy (304)

electron capture: when a nucleus absorbs an electron from its innermost electron shell (363)

electroplating: the deposition of a thin layer of metal on an object in an electrolytic cell (307)

energy budget: describes where energy at Earth's surface comes from and where it goes; driven by incoming solar radiation (55)

entropy: a measure of the disorder of a system—the opposite of the order of the system (183)

equilibrium position: the relative concentrations of the reactants and products at equilibrium (175)

equivalence point: the point in a titration where the number of moles of hydrogen ions equals the number of moles of hydroxide ions (218)

ester: an organic compound with a carbonyl group and an —OR group from an alcohol (332)

ether: an organic compound in which oxygen is bonded to two carbon groups (330)

ether group: the O functional group in an ether (330)

evapotranspiration: the combination of evaporation from bodies of water and transpiration from the leaves of plants (58)

extensive (property): a property of a substance that changes based on the scale, or size, of the substance; volume and number of moles are extensive properties (29)

F

fatty acids: carboxylic acids with long side chains of 12 to 24 carbons (349)

feedback: when an affected system responds to and applies a change back on another system (51)

feedstocks: the raw materials that are fed into an industrial process for conversion into something different (407)

fissile: able to undergo nuclear fission (379)

free energy: the overall energy change for a process (181)

fuel cell: a type of voltaic cell in which a fuel undergoes oxidation and from which electrical energy can be continuously obtained (307)

functional group: a specific arrangement of atoms in an organic compound that is capable of characteristic chemical reactions (327)

G

Gay-Lussac's law: when the pressure of a fixed mass of gas at constant volume is proportional to its temperature (17)

geometric isomers: a type of stereoisomer, also called *cis-trans* isomers, that have atoms joined in the same order, but the spatial orientations of the groups differ (321)

glacier ice: yearly snows that slowly become compacted, building up a record of climate that extends across time (107)

global warming potential (GWP): a measure of the heat-trapping capacity of a greenhouse gas over a given period of time, compared to that of a similar amount of CO_2 (101)

glycogen: large, branched polymers of glucose polysaccharides used by our bodies to store energy (343)

Graham's law of effusion: the rate of effusion of a gas is inversely proportional to the square root of the gas's molar mass (35)

green chemistry: the design of chemical products and processes to reduce or eliminate the use and generation of hazardous substances (415)

greenhouse effect: the cycle of energy absorbed by Earth's surface being reradiated upward as infrared energy, some of which is absorbed by gases in the atmosphere and then reradiated back toward the surface (55)

greenhouse gas: a gas that absorbs infrared radiation (101)

H

half-cell: one part of a voltaic cell in which either oxidation or reduction takes place (298)

half-life: the amount of time it takes for half of a radioactive isotope to decay (365)

half-reaction: just the oxidation or reduction component of a redox reaction; determined from the change in oxidation number of the substances (286)

half-reaction method: a method of balancing a redox reaction by first balancing its separate half-reaction equations and then combining them into a balanced redox equation (294)

halocarbon: an organic compound that contains at least one covalently bonded halogen atom (328)

halogen group: the halogen atom or atoms attached to the hydrocarbon in a halocarbon (328)

hydration reaction: a type of addition reaction in which water is added to an alkene, resulting in the formation of an alcohol (336)

hydrocarbon: a compound composed of hydrogen and carbon (313)

hydrogenation reaction: a type of addition reaction in which hydrogen is added to a C=C double bond to produce an alkane with single bonds (336)

hydronium ion: H_3O^+; the positive ion formed when a water molecule gains a hydrogen ion (195)

hydroxy group: the —OH functional group in alcohols (329)

I

ideal gas: a hypothetical gas that exactly obeys the kinetic model of gases (23)

ideal gas law: the relationship among number of moles (n), pressure (P), volume (V), and temperature (T) for any ideal gas; the quantity $(P \times V)/(T \times n)$ is a constant (R) for any ideal gas and has a value of 8.31 (L•kPa)/(K•mol) (23)

intensive (property): a property of a substance that does not change based on the scale, or size, of the substance; pressure and temperature are intensive properties (29)

Intergovernmental Panel on Climate Change (IPCC): a scientific body dedicated to assessing the science of climate change (125)

ionizing radiation: radiation with the ability to knock electrons off of atoms to produce ions that can be damaging to living organisms (387)

ion-product constant for water (K_w): the product of the hydrogen-ion concentration and the hydroxide-ion concentration in water or aqueous solutions; equal to 1×10^{-14} at 25°C (198)

isobaric process: a closed-system process for which the pressure is held constant (26)

isomers: compounds that have the same molecular formula but different molecular structures (320)

isothermal process: a closed-system process for which the temperature is held constant (26)

isovolumetric process: also called an isochoric process, is a closed-system process for which the pressure is held constant (26)

K

ketone: an organic compound in which the carbon of the carbonyl group is joined to two other carbon atoms (331)

kilocalorie: unit used to show energy content of food; equivalent to a Calorie in the United States (340)

L

Le Châtelier's principle: when a chemical system at equilibrium experiences a stress, it changes in a way that relieves the stress (176)

Lewis acid: any substance that can accept a pair of electrons to form a covalent bond (197)

Lewis base: any substance that can donate a pair of electrons to form a covalent bond (197)

lipids: fats, oils, and other water-insoluble compounds (349)

Little Ice Age: a period that lasted about 500 years and had several periods of colder temperatures that correlate with periods of decreased solar activity and sunlight (114)

M

macronutrients: nutrients that must be consumed in large amounts (340)

mass defect: the difference in the mass of an atom and the total mass of its nucleons and electrons (373)

metamorphism: primarily a chemical process in which increasing temperature and pressure alter the shape and composition of minerals (50)

methane hydrates: frozen combinations of methane and water (244)

micronutrients: nutrients that are required in small amounts and that regulate body chemistry (340)

mineral reserves: the estimated amounts of mineral resources that are fairly certain and can be currently mined for profit (409)

mineral resources: the estimated amounts of minerals in Earth's crust that have the potential to be extracted for profit now or in the future (409)

monomers: the smaller hydrocarbon molecules that combine to form a polymer (337)

monosaccharides: the simplest type of carbohydrate molecules; also called simple sugars (341)

N

neutral solution: an aqueous solution in which the concentrations of hydrogen ions and hydroxide ions are equal; solution with a pH of 7.0 (198)

neutralization reaction: a reaction in which an acid and a base react in an aqueous solution to produce a salt and water (212)

nuclear binding energy: the minimum energy required to break apart an atomic nucleus into its component nucleons (373)

nuclear breeding: the process of producing fissile isotopes by bombarding non-fissile isotopes with neutrons (393)

nuclear fission: the splitting of a nucleus into smaller fragments, with the release of neutrons and a large amount of energy (379)

nuclear fusion: the process of combining nuclei to produce a nucleus of greater mass (380)

nucleic acids: nitrogen-containing polymers found in the nuclei of cells (352)

nucleosynthesis: the process of making new elements within a star's core (383)

nucleotides: the monomers that make up DNA and RNA polymers (352)

nutrients: substances required by our bodies to survive (340)

O

ocean deoxygenation: the expansion of low-oxygen zones in the ocean as a consequence of rising temperatures (253)

ocean surface currents: areas of ocean water that flow steadily in a particular direction close to the ocean's surface (246)

optical isomers: pairs of isomers that are mirror images and not superimposable; also called enantiomers (321)

organic compound: a chemical compound that contains carbon (312)

oxidation: the loss of an electron by a reactant in a chemical reaction (276)

oxidation number: a positive or negative number assigned to a species to indicate its degree of oxidation or reduction; also called the oxidation state (279)

oxidation-number-change method: a method of balancing a redox chemical equation by comparing the increase and decrease in oxidation numbers (292)

oxidation potential: a measure of a half-reaction's tendency to occur as an oxidation, or a loss of electrons (300)

oxidizing agent: a reactant in a redox reaction that gains one or more electrons (276)

P

partial pressure: the contribution each gas makes to the total atmospheric pressure (31)

peptide: any combination of amino acids in which the amino group of one is united with the carboxyl group of another (346)

peptide bond: the bond between the amino group of one amino acid with the carboxyl group of another in a peptide (346)

phospholipids: lipids that contain phosphate groups (350)

PMI: the mass of raw materials used in a chemical process divided by the mass of the targeted products; also called the process mass intensity (418)

polymer: a large molecule formed by the covalent bonding of repeating smaller molecules (337)

polypeptide: long strings of peptides caused by condensation polymerization (346)

polysaccharides: polymers produced by the linkage of many monosaccharide monomers (342)

precipitation: the product of condensation of water vapor that falls toward Earth's surface due to gravity (63)

primary structure: a long, straight chain of amino acids (347)

protein: a peptide polymer containing more than 100 amino acids (346)

Q

quaternary structure: a macromolecule of multiple proteins combined and tangled together due to intermolecular forces (347)

R

radiation: the emission of electromagnetic energy or high-energy particles (387)

radioactivity: the process by which nuclei emit particles and rays (358)

radiometric age dating: a method of estimating the age of a material by comparing the relative amounts of a radioactive isotope and its daughter isotope in the material (368)

rate: the ratio between two related quantities expressed in different units (160)

reaction intermediate: a product of one step in a multistep reaction and a reactant in the next step (170)

reaction rate: the rate of a chemical reaction; the speed at which reactants become products (161)

redox reaction: any chemical reaction that involves transferring electrons from one atom to another; also called an oxidation-reduction reaction (276)

reducing agent: a reactant in a redox reaction that gives up one or more electrons (276)

reduction: the gain of an electron by a reactant in a chemical reaction (276)

reduction potential: a measure of a half-reaction's tendency to occur as a reduction, or a gain of electrons (300)

reinforcing feedback: feedback that amplifies a change; also called a "positive" feedback (51)

relative humidity: a measure of the percentage of water vapor in the air compared to the maximum amount the air can hold at that particular temperature (39, 62)

reversible reactions: reactions in which the product molecules can react to form the original reactant molecules (174)

rock cycle: the process that describes the changes and cycling of geologic material through Earth's systems; describes the processes that form the three main types of rock: igneous, metamorphic, and sedimentary (49)

S

salinity: the amount of dissolved salts in a solution like water (234)

salt hydrolysis: a process in which the cations or anions of a dissociated salt accept hydrogen ions from water or donate ions to water (215)

saturated compound: an organic compound that contains the maximum number of hydrogen atoms per carbon atom (319)

saturated vapor pressure: the maximum pressure of water vapor in air (39)

second law of thermodynamics: the entropy of an isolated system never decreases (184)

secondary structures: the helices and sheet-like structures of proteins due to hydrogen bonding between nearby amino acids (347)

specific gas constant ($R_{specific}$): the gas constant divided by molar mass (29)

standard cell potential: the measured cell potential when the ion concentrations in the half-cells are $1M$ and at a temperature of 25°C and a pressure of 100 kPa (301)

standard reduction potential: the reduction potential of a half-cell measured with respect to a standard hydrogen electrode (300)

starches: polysaccharide polymers consisting of glucose monomers linked in long chains that are the major storage form of glucose in plants (342)

stereoisomers: molecules in which the atoms are joined in the same order, but the positions of the atoms in space are different (321)

straight-chain alkane: an alkane that can have any number of carbon atoms, one after another (315)

strong acid: an acid that completely ionizes in aqueous solution to form hydronium ions (203)

strong base: a base that completely ionizes in solution to produce hydroxide ions (203)

strong nuclear force: the attractive force that holds quarks together to form protons and neutrons, and holds neutrons and protons together within atomic nuclei (361)

structural formula: a graphical representation of a molecule's shape, with lines used to show chemical bonding (313)

structural isomers: also called constitutional isomers, compounds that have the same molecular formula, but the atoms are joined together in different orders (320)

substituent: an atom or group of atoms that takes the place of a hydrogen atom on a parent hydrocarbon molecule (315)

substitution reaction: a common organic reaction in which an atom or group of atoms replaces another atom or group (335)

T

tertiary structures: intricate structures formed from the folding of entire chains of amino acids due to side interactions between amino acids far from each other (347)

thermocline: the transition zone between the warm upper and cold lower layers of the ocean; thicker in tropical regions and almost non-existent in polar regions (252)

thermodynamically favorable process: a process that produces free energy; also called a spontaneous process (181)

thermodynamically unfavorable process: a process that does not produce free energy; also called a nonspontaneous process (181)

tipping point: the moment when an old equilibrium of a system cannot be restored by the usual feedback mechanisms (52)

titration: the process used to determine the concentration of a solution (often an acid or base) in which small increments of a measured amount of a solution of known concentration are added to a solution with known volume but unknown concentration until an indicator signals the end point (218)

titration curve: a graph of solution pH versus the volume of standard solution added during a titration; used to determine the equivalence point for a titration (218)

total alkalinity: the sum of excess ions in water that could absorb hydrogen ions (235)

toxicity: the risk of damage to living organisms through the effects of a substance on individual organs or bodily systems (420)

transmutation: the conversion of an atom of one element into an atom of another element (358)

triglyceride: formed when three fatty acids undergo a condensation reaction with glycerol, a compound with three hydroxy groups; also called triesters of glycerol (349)

triple bottom line: an accounting framework used by companies that practice green chemistry to measure their performance based on social, environmental, and economic factors (432)

tropical cyclones: large, rapidly rotating storm systems with high winds, a low-pressure center ("eye"), and spiraling arms of thunderstorms (64)

U

unsaturated compound: an organic compound with the presence of double or triple bonds, reducing the number of hydrogen atoms in the compound (319)

V

van der Waals equation: a modification of the ideal gas law that takes into account both gas particle size and intermolecular forces of attraction between gas particles (28)

varves: annual layers of sedimentation, observed in lakes, that are characterized by larger particles deposited by spring storms, separated by finer particles that accumulate during the rest of the year (111)

voltaic cell: an electrochemical cell used to convert chemical energy into electrical energy (298)

W

waste: any material that is unwanted and must be disposed of (407)

weak acid: an acid that ionizes only partially in solution to produce hydronium ions (204)

weak base: a base that ionizes only partially in water to produce hydroxide ions because the formation of reactants is favored (206)

weak nuclear force: the force through which certain fundamental particles interact resulting in some forms of radioactive decay (362)

INDEX

Bohr atomic model,
  Vol 1: 24–26
counting, Vol 1: 176
effective nuclear charge,
  Vol 1: 53–54, 56
and elements, Vol 1: 13
energy levels in, Vol 1: 24, 26
isotopes, Vol 1: 16
mass and properties,
  Vol 1: 18–21
mass number, Vol 1: 15–16
nucleus, Vol 1: 12, 35
quantum mechanical model,
  Vol 1: 28–29
shell model, Vol 1: 29
size of, Vol 1: 56–59
types of, Vol 1: 13–14
See also **Chemical bonding;
  Electrons; Neutrons;
  Protons**
Auxiliaries, Vol 2: **422**
Average atomic mass, Vol 1: **18**
  see also **Atomic mass**
Avogadro, Amedeo, Vol 2: **21**
Avogadro's hypothesis,
  Vol 1: **187**
Avogadro's law, Vol 2: **21**
Avogadro's number, Vol 1: **176**

B

Band of stability, Vol 2: **364**
Basalt, Vol 2: 81
Bases. *See* **Acids and bases**
Basicity, Vol 2: 235
Batteries, Vol 2: 306
Becquerels (Bq), Vol 2: **389**
Beta decay, Vol 2: **362**–363
Big Bang theory,
  Vol 2: 376–377
Binary compound, Vol 1: **99**
Binding energy, Vol 2: 146,
  373–375
Biodiversity, Vol 2: 80
Biogeochemical cycles,
  Vol 2: 45
Biogeochemistry, Vol 2: 45
Biomass feedbacks, Vol 2: 70
Biosphere, Vol 2: 138
Black Death, Vol 2: 113
Black-body curves, Vol 2: 73
Bohr, Niels, Vol 1: 24
Bohr atomic model,
  Vol 1: 24–26
Boiling point
  and atomic radius, Vol 1: 127
  and hydrogen bonding,
    Vol 1: 151

and intermolecular forces,
  Vol 1: 127
metals, Vol 1: 79
molecular substances,
  Vol 1: 95
and vapor pressure,
  Vol 1: 130–131
Bond enthalpy, Vol 1: **285**–286
Bonding. *See* **Chemical
  bonding**
Boron, Vol 1: 83
Bosons, Vol 2: 360, 376
Boyle's law, Vol 2: **11**–12
Branched-chain alkanes,
  Vol 2: **315**
Bromine, Vol 1: 18, 94
Brønsted, Johannes, Vol 2: 196
**Brønsted-Lowry model of
  acids and bases,** Vol 2: 196
Buffer capacity, Vol 2: **225**
Buffer range, Vol 2: **225**
Buffer solutions, Vol 2: 223–224
Buffers, Vol 2: **222**–225
By-products, Vol 2: **406**

C

Calcification, Vol 2: **260**–261
Calcite, Vol 2: 263, 268
Calorie, Vol 2: **340**
Carbohydrates, Vol 2: **341**–344
Carbon, anthropogenic,
  Vol 2: 115–122, 127
Carbon bonding, Vol 2: 312
**Carbon capture and
  sequestration (CCS),**
  Vol 2: 149
Carbon cycle, Vol 2: 44–48
Carbon dioxide, Vol 2: 69–70
  atmospheric, Vol 2: 79–80,
    116, 119–121, 230
  in carbonated beverages,
    Vol 1: 166
  and erosion, Vol 2: 82
  mass of, Vol 1: 180
  molecules, Vol 1: 90
  and ocean pH, Vol 2:
    230–231, 236, 262–263
  ocean-atmosphere carbon
    dioxide exchange, Vol 2:
    238–241
  phase diagram of, Vol 1: 134
  and radiation absorption,
    Vol 2: 104
  and temperature, Vol 2: 115
  and volcanic activity, Vol 2: 81
Carbon hybrid orbitals,
  Vol 1: 81

Carbon isotopes, Vol 2: 119
Carbon nanotubes, Vol 1: 139
Carbon reservoirs, Vol 2: 48,
  238–239
Carbon sink, Vol 2: 238
Carbon-12, Vol 1: 17
Carbon-14 age dating,
  Vol 2: 90, 369–370
**Carbonate compensation
  depth,** Vol 2: 240–**241,**
  268–269
Carbonic acid, Vol 2: 82
Carbonyl group, Vol 2: **331**
Carboxyl group, Vol 2: **332**
Carboxylic acids, Vol 2: **332**
Catalysts, Vol 1: 218;
  Vol 2: **171**–172, 426
Cathodes, Vol 2: **299**
Cations, Vol 1: **58,** 62, 69, 97
Cellular respiration, Vol 2: **344**
Cellulose, Vol 2: **342**
Change in enthalpy, Vol 1: **284**
Changes of state, Vol 1: 304
Charles, Jacques, Vol 2: 13, 15
Charles's law, Vol 2: **13**–14
Chemical bonding,
  Vol 1: 66–96
  binding energy, Vol 2: 374
  and boiling point, Vol 1: 127,
    151
  bond energies, Vol 1: 223
  bond enthalpy, Vol 1:
    285–286
  carbon bonding, Vol 2: 312
  and collision theory, Vol 2: 163
  covalent bonds, Vol 1: 81–85,
    87, 94–95, 141
  and electronegativity,
    Vol 1: 86–87
  hydrogen bonds, Vol 1: 93,
    119, 148, 151, 153
  ionic bonds, Vol 1: 68–76, 87,
    99–100
  and melting point, Vol 1: 132
  metallic bonds, Vol 1: 77–80
  peptide bonds, Vol 2: 346
  and solubility, Vol 1: 244–245
  and valence electrons,
    Vol 1: 68
Chemical energy, Vol 1: **9**
Chemical equations, Vol 1:
  252–277
  balanced, Vol 1: 220–222,
    252–255, 257
  coefficients of, Vol 1: 221

and famines, Vol 2: 139

glacial melting, Vol 2: 52, 136–137

and greenhouse gases, Vol 2: 101, 116, 121, 128, 143

Ice Ages, Vol 2: 107–108, 113–114

and infectious diseases, Vol 2: 140

measures of, Vol 2: 107, 110, 111

and migration, Vol 2: 141–142

and population growth, Vol 2: 118

precipitation projections, Vol 2: 129

regional, Vol 2: 117, 129

and renewable energies, Vol 2: 145–146

and sea levels, Vol 2: 108–109, 130, 137

and social justice, Vol 2: 152

and temperatures, Vol 2: 110–112, 117, 126, 128–129

Climate forcings, Vol 2: **66**

Cloud forcing, Vol 2: 68

Clouds, Vol 2: 62

Coal, Vol 2: 120

Coastal flooding, Vol 2: 137

Coefficients (of chemical equations), Vol 1: **221**

Collision theory, Vol 1: **225,** 282; Vol 2: 163

Colloidal systems, Vol 1: 169

Colloids, Vol 1: **168**–169

Colors, Vol 1: 22

Combination reactions, Vol 1: 227**–228,** 230, 238; Vol 2: 290

Combined gas law, Vol 2: **19**–20

Combustion. *See* Energy

Combustion reactions, Vol 1: 227, **236**–237, 239; Vol 2: 291

Common gases, Vol 1: 113

Community Earth System Model (CESM), Vol 2: **125**–126

Complete ionic equations, Vol 1: **242**–243

Compounds. *See* Molecular compounds

Compounds, ionic and molecular, Vol 2: 277, 280

Compressibility, Vol 2: **6**

Computer tomography (CT) scan, Vol 2: 396

Concentrated solutions, Vol 1: **203**

Concentration (of reactant), Vol 2: 161, 164, 177

Concentration (of solution), Vol 1: **203**–206

Condensation, Vol 1: **126,** 128–129, 302; Vol 2: 62

Condensation polymers, Vol 2: **338**

Condensed structural formula, Vol 2: **316**

Conduction

electrolyte, Vol 1: 156–157

ionic compounds, Vol 1: 75

in metals, Vol 1: 143

Conjugate acid-base pair, Vol 2: **196**

Conjugate acids, Vol 2: **196**

Conjugate bases, Vol 2: **196**

Conservation of energy, law of, Vol 1: 223, 283

Conservation of mass, law of, Vol 1: 220, 256

Constant composition, law of, Vol 1: 194

Constant pressure, Vol 2: 16

Contrast media, Vol 2: 397

Consumerism, Vol 2: 410

Continental distribution, Vol 2: 83

Convection, atmospheric, Vol 2: 59

Convective zone of sun, Vol 2: 77

Copper sulfate, Vol 1: 158

Coral bleaching, Vol 2: **266**–267

Corals, fossil, Vol 2: 111

Core electrons, Vol 1: 38, 50, 53

Core of sun, Vol 2: 77

Coriolis effect, Vol 2: **248,** 257

Cosmic rays, Vol 2: 391

Coulomb's law, Vol 1: 52, 59, 73

Counterbalancing feedbacks, Vol 2: **51,** 72

Covalent bonds, Vol 1: **81**–85, 94–95

atomic orbitals in, Vol 1: 81

bonding/lone pairs, Vol 1: 82–83

electron dot structures, Vol 1: 83

electron sharing in, Vol 1: 82–84, 141

and electronegativity, Vol 1: 87

polar/nonpolar, Vol 1: 87

types of, Vol 1: 84

Covalent network solids, Vol 1: 120–**121,** 139

Crosscutting Concepts

Cause and Effect, Vol 1: 9, 71, 88, 144; Vol 2: 21, 57, 59, 60, 82, 83, 101, 139, 141, 146, 150, 159, 166, 167, 176, 208, 213, 224, 229, 237

Energy and Matter, Vol 1: 5, 25, 73, 95, 215, 255, 256, 281, 284, 290, 307; Vol 2: 5, 46, 63, 99, 103, 105, 118, 119, 149, 190, 229, 247, 259, 275, 284, 295, 301, 311, 357, 362, 372, 380, 386, 390, 394, 395, 403

Patterns, Vol 1: 26, 36, 39, 43, 45, 49, 59, 62, 63, 67, 69, 82, 86, 93, 98, 104, 113, 162, 254, 304; Vol 2: 28, 48, 58, 62, 99, 134, 163, 169, 180, 211, 233, 245, 250, 255, 313

Scale, Proportion, and Quantity, Vol 1: 12, 13, 153, 173, 179, 180, 258; Vol 2: 211, 251, 374, 384

Stability and Change, Vol 1: 133; Vol 2: 43, 75, 77, 110, 127, 130, 136, 159, 175, 179, 231, 237, 241, 245, 249, 263, 266, 357, 367, 416

Structure and Function, Vol 1: 78, 79, 111, 123, 155, 198, 251; Vol 2: 148, 320, 336, 352, 422, 425

Systems and System Models, Vol 1: 10, 159, 164, 279; Vol 2: 45, 124, 125, 137, 184, 296, 416, 438

Crossover temperature, Vol 2: **188**–189

Crystal lattices, Vol 1: **72**–74, 122–123

Crystalline packing structures, Vol 1: 144

Nucleosynthesis, Vol 2: 377, **383**–384
Nucleotides, Vol 2: **352**
Nucleus, Vol 1: **12**, 35, 53–54
Nutrients, Vol 2: **340**

O

Ocean deoxygenation, Vol 2: **253**
Ocean surface currents, Vol 2: **246**–247
Oceans, Vol 2: 228–269
    acidification, Vol 2: 228, 230–231, 240, 260–265
    alkalinity of, Vol 2: 235
    average sea surface pH, Vol 2: 232, 236
    biologic and solubility carbon pumps, Vol 2: 242–243
    calcification in, Vol 2: 260–261
    carbonate compensation depth, Vol 2: 240–241, 268–269
    coral bleaching, Vol 2: 266–267
    Coriolis effect, Vol 2: 248, 257
    currents in, Vol 2: 83–84, 88, 234, 242, 246–250
    deoxygenation of, Vol 2: 253
    depth variations in pH, Vol 2: 233
    El Niño/La Niña, Vol 2: 254–257
    feedbacks, Vol 2: 69, 245
    heat reservoirs in, Vol 2: 250
    marine ecosystems, Vol 2: 264–265
    marine shell dissolution in, Vol 2: 262–263
    ocean-atmosphere carbon dioxide exchange, Vol 2: 238–239
    oscillations in, Vol 2: 258–259
    pH levels in, Vol 2: 230–233, 262–263, 266
    plastics in, Vol 2: 265
    salinity of, Vol 2: 234
    sea surface salinity/alkalinity, Vol 2: 234–235
    sea-level rise, Vol 2: 93, 108–109
    temperatures, Vol 2: 112, 258–259, 266
    thermoclines, Vol 2: 252
Octet rule, Vol 1: **68**–69
One-step chemical reactions, Vol 2: 170

Optical isomers, Vol 2: **321**
Orbital parameters of Earth, Vol 2: 86–87
Organic chemistry, Vol 2: 311, 335–336
Organic compounds, Vol 2: **312**, 327–336
    alcohols, Vol 2: 329
    aldehydes and ketones, Vol 2: 331
    carboxylic acids and esters, Vol 2: 332
    ethers and amines, Vol 2: 330
    functional groups, Vol 2: 327, 333–334
    halocarbons, Vol 2: 328
    identifying, Vol 2: 333–334
Osmium, Vol 1: 37
Oxidation, Vol 2: **276**–277, 291
Oxidation numbers, Vol 2: **279**–283
Oxidation-number-change method, Vol 2: **292**–293
Oxidation potential, Vol 2: **300**
Oxidation-reduction reactions, Vol 2: 275–277, 284–295
Oxidizing agents, Vol 2: **276**–278
Oxygen, Vol 1: 16, 164
Ozone, Vol 2: 103

P

Partial pressure, Vol 2: **31**
Particle accelerators, Vol 2: 378
Pascal, Vol 1: 115
Peptide bonds, Vol 2: **346**
Peptides, Vol 2: **346**
Percent by mass (of solution), Vol 1: **210**
Percent by volume (of solution), Vol 1: **210**–211
Percent composition (of compound), Vol 1: **192**–197
    from chemical formulas, Vol 1: 194–195
    as conversion factor, Vol 1: 196
    from mass data, Vol 1: 193
Percent success, Vol 1: 274
Percent yield, Vol 1: **275**, 277
Performance-Based Assessment, Vol 1: 41, 65, 107, 171, 213, 249, 279, 307; Vol 2: 97, 155, 191, 227, 271

Period (periodic table), Vol 1: **46**
Periodic law, Vol 1: **46**
Periodic table, Vol 1: **14**, 36, 43–63
    atomic numbers in, Vol 1: 46
    atomic radius, Vol 1: 56–57
    blocks of, Vol 1: 50
    common gases, Vol 1: 113
    development of, Vol 1: 44–45
    electron affinity, Vol 1: 61
    and electron configurations, Vol 1: 50–52
    and electronegativity, Vol 1: 86
    element properties, Vol 1: 63
    groups and periods, Vol 1: 46
    ion size and charge, Vol 1: 58, 62
    ionic compounds in, Vol 1: 137
    ionization energy, Vol 1: 59–60
    main group elements, Vol 1: 48
    metals, nonmetals, and metalloids, Vol 1: 47
    and molar mass, Vol 1: 179
    molecular compounds in, Vol 1: 137
    noble gas configurations, Vol 1: 38
    overview, Vol 1: 44–48
    as predictive model, Vol 1: 50–51
    regions of, Vol 1: 48
    trends in, Vol 1: 63
Petroleum, Vol 2: 120, 409
pH
    and buffers, Vol 2: 222–225
    calculating, Vol 2: 199–201
    factors affecting, Vol 2: 210, 216–217
    and ions, Vol 2: 216–217
    ocean levels of, Vol 2: 230–233, 262–263, 266
    of weak acids and bases, Vol 2: 208–210
pH curves, Vol 2: 219
Phanerozoic climate change, Vol 2: 78
Phase changes, Vol 1: **125**–126, 299–301, 303
Phase diagrams, Vol 1: **134**
Phospholipids, Vol 2: **350**–351
Photosphere of sun, Vol 2: 77
Photosynthesis, Vol 2: 47

Phytoplankton, Vol 2: 243, 252
Pinning, Vol 1: 146
Planetary atmospheres,
Vol 2: 72
Plankton, Vol 2: 238, 243, 252
PMI, Vol 2: **418**
Point defects, Vol 1: **145**
Polar cells, Vol 2: 61
Polar compounds, Vol 1: 154
Polar covalent bonds, Vol 1: **87**
Polar molecules, Vol 1: 88–89,
91, 148
Pollution, Vol 2: 54
Polyatomic ions, Vol 1: **98**, 101
Polymers, Vol 2: **337–338**
Polypeptides, Vol 2: **346**
Polysaccharides, Vol 2: **342**
Population growth, Vol 2: 118,
410
**Positron emission tomography
(PET) scan,** Vol 2: 397
Positrons, Vol 2: 360
Potential energy, Vol 1: **9**
See also **Chemical
potential energy**
Pounds per square inch (psi),
Vol 1: 115
Precession of Earth, Vol 2: 86
Precipitates, Vol 1: 234, 242,
245–246
Precipitation, Vol 2: **63**, 129,
131, 133–135
Pressure
in atmosphere, Vol 1: 115;
Vol 2: 31, 57, 60
and boiling points,
Vol 1: 130–131
Boyle's law, Vol 2: 11–12
and chemical equilibrium,
Vol 2: 178
combined gas law,
Vol 2: 19–20
constant, Vol 2: 16
of gases, Vol 2: 7–9, 31–33
and solubility, Vol 1: 166;
Vol 2: 241
and temperature, Vol 2: 9,
16–18
units of, Vol 1: 115–116
**Primary structure (of peptide
chains),** Vol 2: **347**
**Products (of chemical
reactions),** Vol 1: **216**
Protecting groups, Vol 2: 425
Proteins, Vol 2: **346**–348
Protons, Vol 1: **12**, 16
atomic number, Vol 1: 13
mass number, Vol 1: 15

Proxy data, Vol 2: 78
Psi (pounds per square inch),
Vol 1: 115

Q
Quantum, Vol 1: **24**
Quantum mechanical model,
Vol 1: **28**–29
Quarks, Vol 2: 359–360
**Quaternary structure (of
peptide chains),** Vol 2: **347**

R
Radiation, Vol 2: **387**–399
absorption and reradiation,
Vol 2: 102–106
black-body, Vol 2: 73
cosmic rays, Vol 2: 391
detecting, Vol 2: 390
electromagnetic, Vol 2: 44,
66, 72–73, 102
exposure, Vol 2: 388–389,
398
and gene mutation,
Vol 2: 399–400
infrared, Vol 2: 101, 103–106
ionizing, Vol 2: 387–389, 398
measurement, Vol 2: 389
and medicine, Vol 2: 396–397
solar, Vol 2: 44, 55, 89
Radiative zone of sun,
Vol 2: 77
Radioactivity, Vol 2: **358**–367
alpha decay, Vol 2: 363
beta decay, Vol 2: 362–363
decay chains, Vol 2: 367
electron capture, Vol 2: 363
half-lives, Vol 2: 365–366
measurement units, Vol 2: 389
nuclear waste, Vol 2: 394
Standard Model, Vol 2:
359–360
transmutation, Vol 2: 358, 378
Radiometric dating,
Vol 2: **368**–372
carbon-14, Vol 2: 90, 369–370
rocks and fossils,
Vol 2: 371–372
Rainfall, Vol 2: 63, 129, 131,
133–135
Rate (of change), Vol 2: **160**
Reactants, Vol 1: **216**
See also **Chemical reactions**
Reaction intermediates,
Vol 2: **170**

Reaction rates, Vol 1: **225;**
Vol 2: 161–166
calculating, Vol 2: 161–162
and catalysts, Vol 2: 171–172
and collision theory,
Vol 2: 163
and concentration, Vol 2: 161,
164
and enzymes, Vol 2: 172
and equilibrium, Vol 2: 159
expressing, Vol 2: 160
and favorability, Vol 2: 182
and particle size, Vol 2: 166
rate-determining step,
Vol 2: 170
and temperature, Vol 1: 225;
Vol 2: 165, 168
See also **Chemical reactions**
Real gases, Vol 2: 27–28
Red tides, Vol 2: 265
Redox reactions, Vol 2: **276–**
277, 284–295
balancing, Vol 2: 292–295
combination and
decomposition reactions,
Vol 2: 290
combustion reactions,
Vol 2: 291
half-reactions, Vol 2: 286,
294–295
and non-redox reactions,
Vol 2: 284–285
single-replacement reactions,
Vol 2: 288–289
Reducing agents,
Vol 2: **276**–278
Reduction, Vol 2: **276**–277, 291
Reduction potential,
Vol 2: **300**
Regional climate change,
Vol 2: 117, 129
Reinforcing feedbacks,
Vol 2: **51**
Relative humidity, Vol 2: **39,**
62
Renewable energies,
Vol 2: 145–146
Renewable feedstocks,
Vol 2: 424, 431, 433
**Representative Concentration
Pathways (RCPs),**
Vol 2: 127
Representative particles,
Vol 1: **176,** 178
**Research and development
(R&D),** Vol 2: 405
Residence time, Vol 2: 45

Respiration, Vol 2: 58
Reversible reactions,
   Vol 2: **174**–175
Ribonucleic acid (RNA),
   Vol 2: 352
Rock cycle, Vol 2: **49**–50
Rotation, Vol 1: **117**

S

Salinity, Vol 2: **234,** 249
Salt hydrolysis, Vol 2: **215**–217
Salt solutions, Vol 2: 215–217
Salts, Vol 2: 194
Saturated compounds,
   Vol 2: **319**
Saturated solutions, Vol 1: **162**
Saturated vapor pressure,
   Vol 2: **39**
Schrödinger, Erwin, Vol 1: 28
Science and Engineering
   Practices
   Analyze Data, Vol 1: 18, 23,
      41, 126, 132, 140, 152, 188,
      225, 271, 278, 287; Vol 2:
      11, 17, 32, 67, 71, 74, 78,
      80, 88, 94, 108, 109, 111,
      112, 113, 126, 128, 129,
      131, 135, 140, 193, 216,
      239, 256, 257, 297, 305,
      319, 323, 370
   Apply Mathematical
      Concepts, Vol 1: 253, 261,
      263, 265, 267, 272, 273,
      276, 277
   Apply Scientific Reasoning,
      Vol 2: 227, 271
   Argue from Evidence,
      Vol 1: 117, 187, 215, 236,
      241; Vol 2: 102, 144, 147,
      286, 304, 342, 351
   Ask Questions, Vol 1: 129;
      Vol 2: 275, 347, 353
   Calculate, Vol 2: 153, 162,
      201, 214, 220, 253
   Carry Out Investigations,
      Vol 1: 146, 204; Vol 2: 54
   Communicate Information,
      Vol 1: 16, 218, 288;
      Vol 2: 47, 339
   Compare Models, Vol 1: 77
   Construct Explanations,
      Vol 1: 5, 8, 27, 40, 41, 43,
      46, 47, 67, 72, 76, 80, 100,
      114, 121, 135, 138, 148,
      150, 151, 169, 182, 221,
      224, 240, 244, 246, 251,
      275, 294, 305, 306; Vol 2:

40, 52, 72, 79, 81, 92, 117,
   161, 165, 170, 182, 187,
   191, 197, 217, 221, 234,
   252, 270, 280, 291, 296,
   318, 326, 329, 330, 331,
   343, 346, 350, 368, 372,
   377, 386, 389, 397, 398,
   406, 414, 420, 423, 426,
   430, 433
Construct Models, Vol 2: 69,
   337
Define Problems, Vol 1: 147,
   171, 203, 248, 274;
   Vol 2: 155
Design Experiments,
   Vol 1: 249
Design Solutions, Vol 1: 147,
   160, 170, 191, 209, 211,
   297; Vol 2: 7, 68, 70, 152,
   177, 225, 265, 289, 391,
   403, 418, 435
Develop Models, Vol 1: 7, 17,
   52, 55, 57, 60, 61, 89, 106,
   112, 119, 124, 143, 154,
   166, 176, 207, 217, 220,
   226, 230, 231, 233, 235,
   237, 242, 243, 259, 262,
   264, 281, 283, 293, 302;
   Vol 2: 5, 8, 16, 30, 35, 43,
   51, 56, 61, 65, 73, 87, 104,
   116, 164, 171, 202, 268,
   277, 299, 300, 308, 314,
   316, 328, 339, 348, 354,
   365
Engage in Argument,
   Vol 1: 65, 215, 236, 241;
   Vol 2: 54, 65, 75, 84, 96,
   102, 106, 114, 122, 132,
   142, 144, 147, 154, 259,
   400, 407
Evaluate Claims, Vol 1: 96
Evaluate Information,
   Vol 1: 140, 157, 202; Vol 2:
   10, 18, 38, 47, 290, 311
Evaluate Models, Vol 1: 11,
   21; Vol 2: 243
Evaluate Solutions, Vol 2: 405,
   409, 424, 434
Explain Phenomena,
   Vol 2: 235
Identify Limitations of
   Models, Vol 1: 6, 107, 213
Identify Unknowns, Vol 1: 173
Interpret Data, Vol 1: 127,
   131, 132, 134, 163, 175,
   191, 200, 208, 225, 228,
   229, 245, 270, 278; Vol 2: 9,

11, 13, 15, 17, 32, 67, 71,
   74, 78, 80, 88, 94, 108, 109,
   111, 112, 113, 126, 128,
   129, 131, 135, 140, 190,
   219, 256, 315, 319, 325,
   370, 429
Interpret Evidence, Vol 2: 215
Interpret Graphs, Vol 2: 261
Obtain Information, Vol 1:
   202, 218; Vol 2: 10, 18, 38,
   47, 193, 290, 311, 339
Plan Investigations, Vol 1: 75,
   111, 142, 165, 193, 196,
   212, 300; Vol 2: 6, 26, 54,
   173, 324
Refine Your Plan, Vol 2: 271
Refine Your Solutions,
   Vol 1: 64
Revise Explanations, Vol 1: 32
Support Explanations with
   Evidence, Vol 1: 55;
   Vol 2: 52
Synthesize Information,
   Vol 2: 438
Use Computational Thinking,
   Vol 1: 18, 266; Vol 2: 19, 93,
   121, 138
Use Mathematical Thinking,
   Vol 2: 22, 185
Use Mathematics, Vol 1: 15,
   87, 175, 177, 181, 185, 186,
   189, 193, 194, 195, 197,
   199, 201, 205, 206, 223,
   252, 257, 260, 268, 279,
   285, 292, 298; Vol 2: 25, 90,
   93, 110, 121, 138, 198, 200,
   205, 207, 218, 267, 344,
   366, 413, 419
Use Models, Vol 1: 29, 31,
   46, 48, 51, 52, 58, 60, 61,
   99, 103, 137, 219, 222, 234,
   239, 247, 269, 282, 286; Vol
   2: 27, 29, 43, 51, 56, 61, 65,
   69, 73, 87, 97, 104, 116,
   178, 197, 226, 243, 248,
   269, 282, 287, 308, 316,
   332, 335, 345, 360, 379,
   382, 393
Science Literacy Skills
   Apply Concepts, Vol 1: 35,
      38; Vol 2: 195, 428
   Compare, Vol 1: 19;
      Vol 2: 307
   Compare and Contrast, Vol 1:
      21, 90
   Connect to Society,
      Vol 2: 155, 227

Sun
fluctuations, Vol 2: 85, 87, 89–90
structure of, Vol 2: 77
surface radiation, Vol 2: 72

Sunspots, Vol 2: 89

Supernovas, Vol 2: 384–386

Supersaturated solutions, Vol 1: **165**

Surface area, Vol 2: 166

Surface radiation feedbacks, Vol 2: 72

Surface temperature of Earth, Vol 2: 73, 85, 90–91, 236, 256

Surface tension, Vol 1: **149**–150

Surfactants, Vol 1: **150**

Surroundings, Vol 1: **10, 283**

Suspensions, Vol 1: **168**–169

Sustainability, Vol 2: 151, 433–436
energy practices, Vol 2: 434
resource management, Vol 2: 433

Synthesis reactions, Vol 1: 228

Systems, Vol 1: **10, 283;** Vol 2: 44
See also **Earth system; Feedbacks**

T

Temperature, Vol 1: 283
absolute zero, Vol 2: 15
in atmosphere, Vol 2: 57
and carbon dioxide, Vol 2: 115
Charles's law, Vol 2: 13–14
and chemical equilibrium, Vol 2: 179
and climate change, Vol 2: 110–112, 117, 126, 128–129
combined gas law, Vol 2: 19–20
condensation and evaporation, Vol 1: 129
crossover, Vol 2: 188–189
and density, Vol 2: 249
of Earth's surface, Vol 2: 73, 85, 90–91, 117, 236, 256
and entropy, Vol 2: 184
and free energy, Vol 2: 188
and gas pressure, Vol 1: 114

ocean variations of, Vol 2: 112, 258–259, 266
and phase changes, Vol 1: 125–126
and precipitation, Vol 2: 63
and pressure, Vol 2: 9, 16–18
and reaction rates, Vol 1: 225; Vol 2: 165, 168
and solubility, Vol 1: 162–163; Vol 2: 240, 253
and vapor pressure, Vol 1: 130–131
and volume, Vol 2: 15
and water vapor, Vol 2: 62
See also **Conduction; Radiation**

Tertiary structures (of peptide chains), Vol 2: **347**

Tetrahedral structure, Vol 1: 139

Theoretical yield, Vol 1: **275**–276

Thermal conductivity, Vol 1: **143**

Thermal energy, Vol 1: **9**

Thermochemical equations, Vol 1: **288**

Thermochemistry, Vol 1: 281

Thermoclines, Vol 2: **252**, 257

Thermodynamically favorable process, Vol 2: **181**–183, 185–188

Thermodynamically unfavorable process, Vol 2: **181**–183, 185

Tipping point, Vol 2: **52**

Titration curves, Vol 2: **218**–219

Titrations, Vol 2: **218**–220

Total alkalinity (TA), Vol 2: **235**

Toxicity, Vol 2: **420**–421

Trade winds, Vol 2: 59

Transformations. *See* **Thermochemistry**

Translation, Vol 1: **117**

Transmutation, Vol 2: **358**, 378

Transpiration, Vol 2: 58

Transportation energy use, Vol 2: 147

Tree rings, Vol 2: 111

Triglycerides, Vol 2: **349**, Vol 2: 351

Triple Bottom Line, Vol 2: **432**

Triple covalent bonds, Vol 1: **84**

Triple point, Vol 1: 134

Triprotic acids, Vol 2: 195

Tropical cyclones, Vol 2: **64**

U

Ultrasound, Vol 2: 396

Unit cells, Vol 1: 74, 123

Universe, origin of, Vol 2: 376–377

Unsaturated compounds, Vol 2: **319**

V

Valence electrons, Vol 1: **38**–39, 50, 53, 68

van der Waals forces, Vol 1: **91**–92

van der Waals equation, Vol 2: **28**

Vapor pressure, Vol 1: **130**–131

Vaporization, Vol 1: **126**, 302–305

Varves, Vol 2: **111**

Vibration, Vol 1: **117**

Volatility, Vol 1: **94**

Volcanoes, Vol 2: 49–50
and carbon dioxide, Vol 2: 81
and climate, Vol 2: 91–92
large eruptions, Vol 2: 92

Voltaic cells, Vol 2: **298**–307

Volume, Vol 1: 174
Boyle's law, Vol 2: 11–12
Charles's law, Vol 2: 13–14
combined gas law, Vol 2: 19–20
and gas pressure, Vol 2: 8
and temperature, Vol 2: 15

Volume-volume calculations, Vol 1: 264–265

VSEPR theory, Vol 1: **88**

W

Walker circulation, Vol 2: 254

Warner, John, Vol 2: 415

Waste, Vol 2: **407**, 412, 435

Water
aqueous solutions, Vol 1: 154–156
density of, Vol 1: 152
in Earth systems, Vol 2: 45
and electrolytes, Vol 1: 156–157
freezing, Vol 2: 187
hydrates, Vol 1: 158–159

hydrogen bonding in,
Vol 1: 93, 148, 151, 153
as ice, Vol 1: 152–153
ion-product constant for,
Vol 2: 198
molecular vibration modes,
Vol 2: 102
percent composition of,
Vol 1: 194
phase diagram for, Vol 1: 134
self-ionization of, Vol 2: 198
surface tension of, Vol 1:
149–150
Water cycle, Vol 2: 46, 58
Water of hydration, Vol 1: 158
Water reservoirs, Vol 2: 45
Water vapor, Vol 2: 62, 103
Wavelengths of light,
Vol 1: 22–23

Weak acids, Vol 2: **204**–205,
209
Weak bases, Vol 2: **206**–208
Weak nuclear force, Vol 2: **362**
Weather
and climate, Vol 2: 42–43,
117, 123
colliding air masses, Vol 2: 65
extreme, Vol 2: 131, 135
models, Vol 2: 123
precipitation, Vol 2: 63
and pressure differences,
Vol 2: 60
severe, Vol 2: 64
Weathering, Vol 2: 50, 82
White dwarfs, Vol 2: 384–385
Wildfires, Vol 2: 139

Winds
and atmospheric pressure,
Vol 2: 60
as diffusion of air,
Vol 2: 37–38
as energy source,
Vol 2: 145–146, 153
Word equations, Vol 1: 216–
217, 220
Work hardening, Vol 1: 146

X

X-rays, Vol 2: 396

Y

Young's modulus, Vol 1: 144

CREDITS

PHOTOGRAPHY

Photo locators denoted as follows: Top (T), Center (C), Bottom (B), Left (L), Right (R), Background (Bkgd)

Cover: Sebastian Janicki/Shutterstock; (Bkgd): Sylverarts Vectors/Shutterstock

FRONT MATTER

ii: Sebastian Janicki/Shutterstock; **iii** TC: Up Late Creative; **iii** B: Kai Kiefer; **iv:** Tanya Katovich; **vi** T: Paolo Lo Pinto/RealyEasyStar/Alamy Stock Photo; **vi** TC: Mint Images RF/Getty Images; **vi** C: Eddtoro/Shutterstock; **vi** BC: Hendrik Holler/Look-Foto/Getty Images; **vi** B: Nalidsa/Shutterstock

STORYLINES

002: Eddtoro/Shutterstock; **003** TL: NASA Image Collection/Alamy Stock Photo; **003** TC: Justin Sullivan/Getty Images; **003** TR: Tom Radford/Alamy Stock Photo; **156:** Hendrik Holler/Look-Foto/Getty Images; **157** L: Joe Ravi/Shutterstock; **157** TR: David Fleetham/Alamy Stock Photo; **157** C: Heinz Linke/Westend61 GmbH/Alamy Stock Photo; **272:** Nalidsa/Shutterstock; **273** TL: Syda Productions/Shutterstock; **273** TCL: Extreme Media/E+/Getty Images; **273** TCR: JPL-Caltech/MSSS/NASA; **273** TR: Pascal Goetgheluck/Science Source

INVESTIGATION 9

004: NASA Image Collection/Alamy Stock Photo; **010:** NASA Image Collection/Alamy Stock Photo; **013:** Matt Meadows/Photolibrary/Getty Images; **022:** NASA Image Collection/Alamy Stock Photo; **025:** Aleksei Lazukov/Shutterstock; **029:** Cq photo juy/Shutterstock; **030:** NASA Image Collection/Alamy Stock Photo; **040:** NASA Image Collection/Alamy Stock Photo

INVESTIGATION 10

042: Justin Sullivan/Getty Images; **049:** Barcroft Media/Getty Images; **054:** Justin Sullivan/Getty Images; **055:** Dennis Hallinan/Alamy Stock Photo; **058:** Uladzimir Navumenka/Shutterstock; **064:** National Oceanic and Atmospheric Administration; **065:** Justin Sullivan/Getty Images; **066:** Mattias Klum/National Geographic Image Collection/Getty Images; **071:** DOE Photo/Alamy Stock Photo; **072T:** Pailin Pinrarainon/123RF; **072C:** Timothy Hodgkinson/Alamy Stock Photo; **072B:** Tristan3D/Alamy Stock Photo; **075T:** Roy Langstaff/Alamy Stock Photo; **075B:** Justin Sullivan/Getty Images; **084:** Justin Sullivan/Getty Images; **089:** Goddard Space Flight Center/SDO/AIA/HMI/NASA; **091:** Design Pics Inc/Alamy Stock Photo; **096:** Justin Sullivan/Getty Images

INVESTIGATION 11

098: Tom Radford/Alamy Stock Photo; **105:** MODTRAN® is a registered trademark owned by the United States Government as represented by the Secretary of the Air Force. Chart provided courtesy of Spectral Sciences, Inc.; **106:** Tom Radford/Alamy Stock Photo; **107:** Ragnar Th Sigurdsson/Arctic Images/Alamy Stock Photo; **111:** Matthijs Wetterauw/Shutterstock; **114:** Tom Radford/Alamy Stock Photo; **117:** NASA; **118:** Thomas La Mela/Shutterstock; **122:** Tom Radford/Alamy Stock Photo; **125:** Gary Strand/UCAR-NCAR; **126:** Figure 10.1 from, and Figure 10.1 (b) adapted from Bindoff, N.L., P.A. Stott, K.M. AchutaRao, M.R. Allen, N. Gillett, D. Gutzler, K. Hansingo, G. Hegerl, Y. Hu, S. Jain, I.I. Mokhov, J. Overland, J. Perlwitz, R. Sebbari and X. Zhang, 2013: Detection and Attribution of Climate Change: from Global to Regional. In: *Climate Change 2013: The Physical Science Basis. Contribution of Working Group I to the Fifth Assessment Report of the Intergovernmental Panel on Climate Change* [Stocker, T.F., D. Qin, G.-K. Plattner, M. Tignor, S.K. Allen, J. Boschung, A. Nauels, Y. Xia, V. Bex and P.M. Midgley (eds.)]. Cambridge University Press, Cambridge, United Kingdom and New York, NY, USA.; **127:** Figure TS.19 from Stocker, T.F., D. Qin, G.-K. Plattner, L.V. Alexander, S.K. Allen, N.L. Bindoff, F.-M. Bréon, J.A. Church, U. Cubasch, S. Emori, P. Forster, P. Friedlingstein, N. Gillett, J.M. Gregory, D.L. Hartmann, E. Jansen, B. Kirtman, R. Knutti, K. Krishna Kumar, P. Lemke, J. Marotzke, V. Masson-Delmotte, G.A. Meehl, I.I. Mokhov, S. Piao, V. Ramaswamy, D. Randall, M. Rhein, M. Rojas, C. Sabine, D. Shindell, L.D. Talley, D.G. Vaughan and S.-P. Xie, 2013: Technical Summary. In: *Climate Change 2013: The Physical Science Basis. Contribution of Working Group I to the Fifth Assessment Report of the Intergovernmental Panel on Climate Change* [Stocker, T.F., D. Qin, G.-K. Plattner, M. Tignor, S.K. Allen, J. Boschung, A. Nauels, Y. Xia, V. Bex and P.M. Midgley (eds.)]. Cambridge University Press, Cambridge, United Kingdom and New York, NY, USA.; **129:** Box 2.2, Figure 1 from IPCC, 2014: *Climate Change 2014: Synthesis Report. Contribution of Working Groups I, II and III to the Fifth Assessment Report of the Intergovernmental Panel on Climate Change* [Core Writing Team, Pachauri, R.K. and Meyer, L.A. (eds.)]. IPCC, Geneva, Switzerland.; **130:** Figure 13.27 from Church, J.A., P.U. Clark, A. Cazenave, J.M. Gregory, S. Jevrejeva, A. Levermann, M.A. Merrifield, G.A. Milne, R.S. Nerem, P.D. Nunn, A.J. Payne, W.T. Pfeffer, D. Stammer and A.S. Unnikrishnan, 2013: Sea Level Change. In: *Climate Change 2013: The Physical Science Basis. Contribution of Working Group I to the Fifth Assessment Report of the Intergovernmental Panel on Climate Change* [Stocker, T.F., D. Qin, G.-K. Plattner, M. Tignor, S.K. Allen, J. Boschung, A. Nauels, Y. Xia, V. Bex and P.M. Midgley (eds.)]. Cambridge University Press, Cambridge, United Kingdom and New York, NY, USA.; **131:** Figure 12.26 (b) and (c) from Collins, M., R. Knutti, J. Arblaster, J.-L. Dufresne, T. Fichefet, P. Friedlingstein, X. Gao, W.J. Gutowski, T. Johns, G. Krinner, M. Shongwe, C. Tebaldi, A.J. Weaver and M. Wehner, 2013: Long-term Climate Change: Projections, Commitments and Irreversibility. In: *Climate Change 2013: The Physical Science Basis. Contribution of Working Group I to the Fifth Assessment Report of the Intergovernmental Panel on Climate Change* [Stocker, T.F., D. Qin, G.-K. Plattner, M. Tignor, S.K. Allen, J. Boschung, A. Nauels, Y. Xia, V. Bex and P.M. Midgley (eds.)]. Cambridge University Press, Cambridge, United Kingdom and New York, NY, USA; **132:** Tom Radford/Alamy Stock Photo; **133:** Scott London/Alamy Stock Photo; **136:** USGS/Science Source; **140:** Steven Ellingson/Shutterstock; **142:** Tom Radford/Alamy Stock Photo; **147:** You Touch Pix of EuToch/Shutterstock; **148:** Ivan Smuk/123RF; **150:** Arnd Wiegmann/Reuters; **152:** Bill Barksdale/Design Pics Inc/Alamy Stock Photo; **154:** Tom Radford/Alamy Stock Photo; **155:** Eddtoro/Shutterstock

INVESTIGATION 12

158: Joe Ravi/Shutterstock; **160:** Aleksandr Belugin/Alamy Stock Photo; **164:** Andrew Lambert Photography/Science Source; **165:** Andrew Lambert Photography/Science Source; **166L:** IU Liquid and water photo/Shutterstock; **166R:** SPL/Science Source; **167:** Joe Ravi/Shutterstock; **173:** Joe Ravi/Shutterstock; **175:** Martin Castrogiovanni/Shutterstock; **179:** Turtle Rock Scientific/Science Source; **180:** Joe Ravi/Shutterstock; **181:** John Harper/Photographer's Choice

RF/Getty Images; **185L:** Mariusz Szczygiel/Shutterstock; **185R:** Thomas Barrat/Shutterstock; **187:** Liuyangzi Hu/EyeEm/Getty Images; **190:** Joe Ravi/Shutterstock

INVESTIGATION 13

192: Heinz Linke/Westend61 GmbH/Alamy Stock Photo; **202:** Heinz Linke/Westend61 GmbH/Alamy Stock Photo; **207:** Hero Images Inc./Alamy Stock Photo; **208:** Elena Schweitzer/Shutterstock; **211:** Heinz Linke/Westend61 GmbH/Alamy Stock Photo; **212:** Universal Images Group Editorial/Getty Images; **215:** Mariusz S. Jurgielewicz/Shutterstock; **221:** Heinz Linke/Westend61 GmbH/Alamy Stock Photo; **222:** Adriaticfoto/Shutterstock; **226:** Heinz Linke/Westend61 GmbH/Alamy Stock Photo

INVESTIGATION 14

228: David Fleetham/Alamy Stock Photo; **228(Inset):** Helmut Corneli/Alamy Stock Photo; **235:** Rana A. Fine/Debra Willey/Charles Thompson/Marit Jentoft-Nilsen/JPL/NASA; **237:** David Fleetham/Alamy Stock Photo; **238:** The Natural History Museum/Alamy Stock Photo; **240:** Gresei/Shutterstock; **245:** David Fleetham/Alamy Stock Photo; **247:** Goddard Space Flight Center Scientific Visualization Studio/NASA; **250:** Timo Bremer/Lawrence Livermore National Laboratory; **259:** David Fleetham/Alamy Stock Photo; **263:** David Liittschwager/National Geographic Creative; **264:** Carrie Vonderhaar/Ocean Futures Society/National Geographic Image Collection/Getty Images; **265:** Merten Snijders/Lonely Planet Images/Getty Images; **270:** David Fleetham/Alamy Stock Photo; **271:** Hendrik Holler/Look-Foto/Getty Images

INVESTIGATION 15

274: Syda Productions/Shutterstock; **282:** Savvas Learning Services LLC.; **284L:** Declan Fleming/Alamy Stock Photo; **284R:** Turtle Rock Scientific/Science Source; **287:** Syda Productions/Shutterstock; **291:** Nickolay Khoroshkov/Shutterstock; **292:** Agencja Fotograficzna Caro/Alamy Stock Photo; **294:** Helen Sessions/Alamy Stock Photo; **296:** Syda Productions/Shutterstock; **307L:** Aflo Co. Ltd./Alamy Stock Photo; **307R:** Jeff J. Daly/Fundamental photographs, NYC; **308:** Syda Productions/Shutterstock

INVESTIGATION 16

310: Extreme Media/E+/Getty Images; **312:** Andrew Richard Hara/Ena Media Hawaii/Getty Images; **313T:** Ppart/Shutterstock; **313B:** Yegor Larin/Shutterstock; **316:** showcake/Shutterstock; **322:** Vladimir Zhoga/Shutterstock; **323:** Amero/Shutterstock; **326:** Extreme Media/E+/Getty Images; **329L:** ThamKC/Shutterstock; **329R:** Heller/Shutterstock; **331L:** Akos Nagy/Shutterstock; **331R:** Angela Hampton Picture Library/Alamy Stock Photo; **336L:** New Africa/Shutterstock; **336R:** Diane39/iStock/Getty Images; **337:** Rawpixel.com/Shutterstock; **338:** Eightstock/Shutterstock; **339:** Extreme Media/E+/Getty Images; **340:** Livertoon/Shutterstock; **341L:** Monticello/Shutterstock; **341C:** Kovaleva_Ka/Shutterstock; **341R:** Chones/Shutterstock; **343:** Halfpoint/Shutterstock; **348:** Mikhaylovskiy/Shutterstock; **350:** Ye.Maltsev/Shutterstock; **351L:** New Africa/Shutterstock; **351R:** Yeti studio/Shutterstock; **354:** Extreme Media/E+/Getty Images

INVESTIGATION 17

356: JPL-Caltech/MSSS/NASA; **358:** Irakli Keshelashvili/500px/Getty Images; **368:** World History Archive/Age Fotostock; **371L:** John Valley, University of Wisconsin-Madison; **371R:** Sabena Jane Blackbird/Alamy Stock Photo; **372T:** The Natural

History Museum/Alamy Stock Photo; **372B:** JPL-Caltech/MSSS/NASA; **373:** Billion Photos/Shutterstock; **378:** Fabrice Coffrini/AFP/Getty Images; **385:** Night Sky Network/NASA; **386:** JPL-Caltech/MSSS/NASA; **395:** Gerard Julien/AFP/Getty Images; **396L:** Scott Camazine/Alamy Stock Photo; **396R:** Cultura Creative Ltd/Alamy Stock Photo; **397:** BelezaPoy/Shutterstock; **398:** Mark Kostich/E+/Getty Images; **399:** Classic Image/Alamy Stock Photo; **400:** JPL-Caltech/MSSS/NASA

INVESTIGATION 18
402: Pascal Goetgheluck/Science Source; **409:** Magnifier/Shutterstock; **410:** 1000 Words/Shutterstock; **414:** Bettmann/Getty Images; **416:** Pascal Goetgheluck/Science Source; **417:** Jennifer Stone/123RF; **419:** Science Stock Photography/Science Source; **420:** SPL/Science Source; **421:** Uwe Moser/Alamy Stock Photo; **427:** Peter Essick / Cavan/Alamy Stock Photo; **430:** Pascal Goetgheluck/Science Source; **431:** Sheila Terry/Science Source; 431(Bkgd): Hjochen/Shutterstock; **433:** Gopixa/123RF; **436:** JohnnyGreig/E+/Getty Images; **438:** Pascal Goetgheluck/Science Source; **439:** Nalidsa/Shutterstock

TEXT ACKNOWLEDGEMENTS
134: Data from: Karl, T. R., J. T. Melillo, and T. C. Peterson, Eds., 2009: "Global Climate Change Impacts in the United States. **142:** Data from: Hisiang et al., "Quantifying the influence of climate on Human Conflict". *Science*, Vol 341, Issue 6151, September13, 2013. **242:** Data Based on report from *Science magazine.org,* 10 June 2005 Vol 308. **243:** Data from: Knevolden (1988). **249:** Data from: Schmitz, William J., "On the world ocean circulation. Volume II, the Pacific and Indian Oceans/a global update". **268:** Data from *Science*, 2004. **388:** NCRP Report 160. Reprinted with permission of the National Council on Radiation Protection and Measurements, http://NCRPonline.org

Notes

Notes

Notes

Notes

Notes

Notes

Notes

Notes

Notes

Notes

Notes

Notes

Copyright © Savvas Learning Company LLC. All Rights Reserved.

†The atomic masses in parentheses refer to the longest lived or most important isotope of radioactive elements.

Main-Group Elements

- ■C Solid
- ●Br Liquid
- ●He Gas
- ×Tc Not applicable; not found in nature

Element classification
- □ Alkali metals
- ▣ Alkaline earth metals
- ▣ Other metals
- ◆ Metalloids
- △ Nonmetals
- ▽ Halogens
- ⊕ Noble gases

Transition Elements
- ▽ Transition metals
- △ Inner transition metals

Phase at STP

13 — Atomic number
26.982 — Atomic mass†
■Al — Element symbol
[Ne]3s²3p¹ — Electron configuration
Aluminum — Element name
◇ — Element classification

Elements 104–118 are the transactinide elements.

Lanthanide series

Actinide series

Group	1 / 1A	2 / 2A	3 / 3B	4 / 4B	5 / 5B	6 / 6B	7 / 7B	8	9 / 8B	10	11 / 1B	12 / 2B	13 / 3A	14 / 4A	15 / 5A	16 / 6A	17 / 7A	18 / 8A

Period 1: H (1, 1.008), He (2, 4.003)

Period 2: Li (3, 6.94), Be (4, 9.012), B (5, 10.81), C (6, 12.011), N (7, 14.007), O (8, 15.999), F (9, 18.998), Ne (10, 20.180)

Period 3: Na (11, 22.990), Mg (12, 24.305), Al (13, 26.982), Si (14, 28.085), P (15, 30.974), S (16, 32.06), Cl (17, 35.45), Ar (18, 39.948)

Period 4: K (19, 39.098), Ca (20, 40.078), Sc (21, 44.956), Ti (22, 47.867), V (23, 50.942), Cr (24, 51.996), Mn (25, 54.938), Fe (26, 55.845), Co (27, 58.933), Ni (28, 58.693), Cu (29, 63.546), Zn (30, 65.38), Ga (31, 69.723), Ge (32, 72.630), As (33, 74.922), Se (34, 78.971), Br (35, 79.904), Kr (36, 83.798)

Period 5: Rb (37, 85.468), Sr (38, 87.62), Y (39, 88.906), Zr (40, 91.224), Nb (41, 92.906), Mo (42, 95.95), Tc (43, (98)), Ru (44, 101.07), Rh (45, 102.906), Pd (46, 106.42), Ag (47, 107.868), Cd (48, 112.414), In (49, 114.818), Sn (50, 118.710), Sb (51, 121.760), Te (52, 127.60), I (53, 126.904), Xe (54, 131.293)

Period 6: Cs (55, 132.905), Ba (56, 137.327), Lu (71, 174.967), Hf (72, 178.49), Ta (73, 180.948), W (74, 183.84), Re (75, 186.207), Os (76, 190.23), Ir (77, 192.217), Pt (78, 195.084), Au (79, 196.967), Hg (80, 200.592), Tl (81, 204.38), Pb (82, 207.2), Bi (83, 208.980), Po (84, (209)), At (85, (210)), Rn (86, (222))

Period 7: Fr (87, (223)), Ra (88, (226)), Lr (103, (262)), Rf (104, (267)), Db (105, (268)), Sg (106, (269)), Bh (107, (270)), Hs (108, (269)), Mt (109, (278)), Ds (110, (281)), Rg (111, (280)), Cn (112, (285)), Nh (113, (286)), Fl (114, (289)), Mc (115, (289)), Lv (116, (289)), Ts (117, (294)), Og (118, (294))

Lanthanide series: La (57, 138.905), Ce (58, 140.116), Pr (59, 140.908), Nd (60, 144.242), Pm (61, (145)), Sm (62, 150.36), Eu (63, 151.964), Gd (64, 157.25), Tb (65, 158.925), Dy (66, 162.500), Ho (67, 164.930), Er (68, 167.259), Tm (69, 168.934), Yb (70, 173.045)

Actinide series: Ac (89, (227)), Th (90, 232.038), Pa (91, 231.036), U (92, 238.029), Np (93, (237)), Pu (94, (244)), Am (95, (243)), Cm (96, (247)), Bk (97, (247)), Cf (98, (251)), Es (99, (252)), Fm (100, (257)), Md (101, (258)), No (102, (259))